LESSONS IN

Seismic Computing

A MEMORIAL TO THE AUTHOR

MORRIS MILLER SLOTNICK

Edited
by
RICHARD A. GEYER

Published by
THE SOCIETY OF EXPLORATION GEOPHYSICISTS
Lawrence Y. Faust, Editor
1959

Society of Exploration Geophysicists
P.O. Box 3098
Tulsa, Oklahoma 74135

© 1959
BY
Society of Exploration Geophysicists

————

All Rights Reserved

————

Published 1959
Second Printing 1970

COMPOSED AND PRINTED BY
GEORGE BANTA COMPANY, INC.
MENASHA, WISCONSIN

EDITOR'S FOREWORD

The decision of the Humble Oil & Refining Company, with the concurrence of Mrs. M. M. Slotnick, to permit this series of lessons in seismic computation to be published is a most fortunate one for the geophysical profession. A comprehensive presentation of the fundamentals of seismic computation and interpretation is now available to all. The combination of its broad scope, degree of detail, and clarity of style results in this Memorial Volume's filling the dual role of a textbook as well as an authoritative reference.

The history of the origin and objectives of this series of lessons is described in some detail in the Preface. There is no need to elaborate except to emphasize that the original manuscript has been faithfully adhered to, but for the few minor editorial changes that are always necessary in transforming a manuscript to book format. The reader is therefore able to gain a better insight into the author's unique pedagogical philosophy. This is important because he had the rare gift of combining in his teaching not only the successful presentation of subject matter, but, simultaneously, something of infinitely greater value—a way of life. A few carefully selected paragraphs from an address the author was invited to give at the Colorado School of Mines on Engineers' Day in 1950 are included in this Foreword. The purpose of these quotations is to illustrate some of his basic ideas of the role of seismic interpretation in exploration geophysics.

"The interpretation of seismic data is tantamount to a 'translation,' if you will, of a set of *physical data*, obtained by *physical means*, into terms which are essential for the geological understanding of the subsurface. To say that such a set of data has but one solution—as, by the way, is sometimes claimed—cannot possibly be true, since one of the most important items implicit in the interpretation—namely, the 'velocity'—does not persist as 'constant' even to the desired limits of accuracy. The degree of latitude or variation between one possible interpretation of the data in an area and another may at times be sizeable. In such events, is it not clear that those on whom the responsibility of planning ahead from this stage should know something of the circumscribing limitations, but better yet, place their confidence in well-trained geophysicists?

"The responsibility of the geophysicist rests in interpreting the data, making sections, drawing conclusions of a physical-geometric nature. He has no indication whatever as to geologic age of a reflecting horizon from his data. That is why cooperation is necessary and why that cooperation pays the greatest dividends. The geologist and the geophysicist translate to each other the significance of their results. And after that is done, the geologist can go ahead with more intelligence and understanding. . . ."

"The geophysicist obtains and deals with physical data, and his interpretations should be delimited to that area of endeavor until he dons a geological mantle. He should know, and be honest in transmitting, the value and limits to this conclusion. Then and only then does he do his full duty."

The Editor would like to acknowledge his appreciation and indebtedness to all those, both individually and collectively, who have given so generously of their time and efforts culminating in the publication of this Memorial Volume. In particular, to D. P. Carlton for preparing the Preface, and to the members of the Society of Exploration Geophysicists' Publication Committee, including Cecil H. Green, Chairman, Sigmund I. Hammer, H. B. Peacock, Sidney Schafer, and Robert J. Watson, as well as the Editor of *Geophysics*, Lawrence Y. Faust; and to Colin C. Campbell Business Manager of the Society. In addition, the excellent cooperation of H. L. Farris, Editorial Assistant of the Society and Mrs. Helen V. Barker in the preparation of the index and help in proofreading is gratefully acknowledged.

RICHARD A. GEYER

Houston, Texas
October 13, 1958

PREFACE

The Society of Exploration Geophysicists is proud to publish this Memorial Volume honoring the late Dr. Morris Miller Slotnick. Dr. Slotnick was an outstanding figure in the geophysical field and during his career was the author of numerous papers dealing with geophysical interpretation. Some of the computing procedures which he developed have been used extensively. He was Editor of *Geophysics* in 1937 and 1938, and, in this capacity, contributed much to the improvement of the technical stature of the journal.

The title of the book is "Lessons in Seismic Computing." It deals entirely with seismic computing, and its contents consist of an orderly sequence of lessons arranged just as they were used in the classroom.

Even though Dr. Slotnick was well known to many members of the Society, it seems fitting to review briefly his background of education and experience.

He received the degree of Doctor of Philosophy in mathematics from Harvard University in 1926. This was followed by a year of post doctoral studies atHamburg, Germany, as the recipient of a Harvard Traveling Research Fellowship. Then came a year at Princeton as a National Research Fellow, a year as a mathematics instructor at Harvard, and then a year as an assistant professor of mathematics at Grinnell College.

In September of 1930, he was employed by the Humble Oil & Refining Company as a research mathematician and assigned to the Geophysics Research Group in Humble's Geophysics Department. He continued in this work, becoming Chief Mathematician for Humble in 1949. In 1954, he left Humble to become a Consultant in Geophysics at the Standard Vacuum Oil Company, a position which he held until his death May 7, 1956.

With his excellent training in pure mathematics, his experience in teaching, for which he had a flair, Dr. Slotnick was unusually well equipped to study the theoretical and practical phases of the mathematical problems which arose in geophysical exploration. He wrote numerous papers on seismology for Humble's use, and over a period of years several of them have appeared in *Geophysics*.

Very early in his career at Humble he sought to improve computing techniques by teaching and preparing manuals of instruction.

His reputation grew among his colleagues, and his ability in mathematical analysis was sought and used by members of Humble's Petroleum Engineering, Accounting, Tax, and Sales organizations. Many were the students who came to him for help in mathematics, and he gave it to them freely.

Early in 1949 Dr. Slotnick began a series of talks on seismic computing to a group of Humble's Geophysics Department. The response and interest were most gratifying; so much so, that it was decided that these talks or lessons should be published and distributed to all interested personnel.

At the time the decision was announced, Dr. Slotnick wrote: "There are at the present six lessons distributed or being processed. The total number to be written is indefinite as is also the frequency with which they will be written. At the present time, it is simply proposed to continue as time, need, and the mood permit, in the hopes that in the fullness of time, as complete a course of study as possible will have been covered.

"The level of mathematical abilities varies greatly among our personnel. We shall strive to meet as many as we can on some common ground. There will be some lessons which at times will render the 'mathematically weak' reader at a loss. He is not to be discouraged for we shall try to overcome such situations by many numerical practice examples and by hewing to the line of practical results."

As to the purpose of these lessons, I again quote Dr. Slotnick. "The series of lessons in the theory behind the day-to-day techniques used in seismic interpretations which are being compiled, has a two-fold purpose. In the first place, there have been many requests from our computers for such lessons in order to satisfy an understandable desire for a more complete knowledge of their scientific activity. More important perhaps is that such an understanding is becoming increasingly mandatory for the seismic computer. The trend of interpretation demands, which for so many years has had the savor of the 'qualitative' rather than the 'quantitative' simply because the quest has been for the 'larger structures,' indicates that we must try to use a sharper pencil wherever the data are amenable. We hope that these lessons will furnish that sharper pencil."

The text of the memorial volume might have been revised to conform more nearly to a textbook pattern, but it was decided to leave it as nearly as possible as it was arranged by Dr. Slotnick. As it is published, this book contains forty-four lessons on seismology. The subject matter, the numerical practice examples, the figures, plates and tables are arranged in the order in which they were presented in the lectures and in the printed copies that were distributed.

The last lesson, lesson number forty-four, was completed and distributed in August, 1952, and in Dr. Slotnick's cover letter of August 22, 1952, he restates that, "The purpose of the lessons has been to furnish the seismic computer with a broad understanding of seismic paths, the properties of which form the basis of most of the necessary numerical calculations."

Before Dr. Slotnick left the Humble Company, the possibility of publishing these lessons was discussed, but no action was taken for he expressed an intention of writing a series of lessons on gravity interpretations. After his death, the question of publication was again raised. The paper was submitted to the Publication Committee of the Society of Exploration Geophysics who examined the text and agreed to publish it as a Memorial Volume to Dr. Slotnick. It was necessary to get clearance from the Humble Oil & Refining Company and permission to publish from Mrs. M. M. Slotnick. Both very graciously gave their consent and the geophysical profession is thereby indebted to them.

In view of the enthusiasm for the lessons among those who have used them, it seems reasonable that they will eventually become a standard reference in the libraries of those who would strive for a more complete understanding of the science of seismology.

D. P. CARLTON

Houston, Texas
October 13, 1958

CONTENTS
(Part I)

(Part II)

LESSONS
IN
SEISMIC COMPUTING

PART I

Lesson No. 1

SEISMIC INTERPRETATION THEORY

EMERGENCE ANGLES

Of fundamental importance in the discussion of seismic interpretation theory and technique is the concept of the *emergence angle* of a seismic wave.

As a seismic wave emerges to the surface of the earth, its direction of approach is not necessarily vertical; that is to say, the wave front need not be horizontal. A moving wave front, at any particular instant is the totality of points, at that instant, which are in the same cycle and phase of cycle in the propagation. This implies that the travel-times from the source, wherever it is, to each of the points of the wave front are the same.

For our purposes we may reduce the concept to a two-dimensional situation and look at a section of the wave fronts as they emerge to the surface, somewhat as indicated in Figure 1. The various positions of sections of a wave front, at times t_1, t_2, t_3, t_4, etc., as the wave travels toward the surface, are indicated by WW and the trace of the surface of the earth by SS.

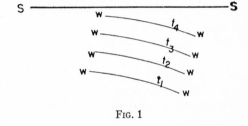

FIG. 1

Closely allied to these wave fronts is the concept of wave paths. These wave paths are curves, or straight lines, which represent the direction of travel of the waves. Thus, these paths are curves which intersect the wave fronts at right angles. A series of wave fronts with the related wave paths is shown in Figure 2.

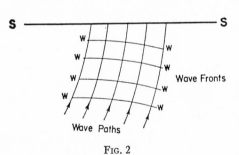

FIG. 2

In the discussion which follows, it is sometimes more convenient to speak of wave fronts and, at others, of wave paths. It is thus very important to grasp the concepts of both and of their interrelationship.

Definition 1. The angle between a straight line wave path, or the tangent to the wave path, if it is curved, emerging at the earth's surface and the perpendicular (that is, *normal*) to the earth's surface is called the *emergence angle of the wave*.

This is illustrated in Figure 3. The ray RP is emerging at the surface SS at the point P. We therefore draw PN perpendicular to SS at P, and the angle i, between the tangent PT to the path and PN, is the *emergence angle* of the wave.

Ex. 1: Draw a wave path whose emergence angle is 10°, 85°, 0°, 90°.

3

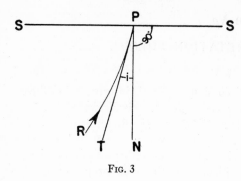

FIG. 3

Ex. 2: Indicate small portions of the related wave fronts of the wave paths in the preceding exercise.

In Figure 4, we indicate two wave paths R_1P_1 and R_2P_2 emerging at SS, the surface of the earth. In general, if P_1 and P_2 are not too far apart and the paths R_1P_1 and R_2P_2 close to the surface, then R_1P_1 and R_2P_2 will be substantially two parallel straight lines, somewhat as shown in the figure. These wave paths will then have the same emergence angle i. The line W_1W_2 here represents a position of the corresponding wave front which later, when W_1 reaches P_1, assumes the position P_1W.

The relationship between the wave paths and wave fronts is such that the lines W_1W_2 and P_1W are perpendicular to the wave paths R_1P_1 and R_2P_2. In particular $\angle P_1WP_2$ is a right angle. Thus, since

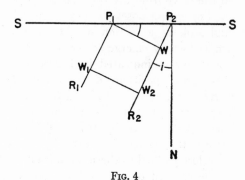

FIG. 4

$$\angle P_1P_2N = 90°$$

and

$$\angle R_2P_2N = i,$$

therefore

$$\angle P_1P_2R_2 = 90° - i.$$

Since

$$\angle P_1WP_2 = 90°,$$

therefore

$$\angle P_2P_1W = i.$$

In other words, the angle of a *wave front* (P_1W in Figure 4) with the surface is the same as the angle of emergence of the wave.

Consider the instant of the wave front in the position P_1W, at which instant R_1P_1 is emerging at the surface. The point W still has the distance WP_2 to travel to the surface. We shall indicate the time necessary for this by Δt. If the velocity of propagation in this medium is v, then, obviously,

$$WP_2 = v\Delta t.$$

The distance P_1P_2 will be indicated by Δx. We show all of this in Figure 5, which has been taken from Figure 4, $P_1WP_2 = 90°$. We note at once that, since the sine of an angle in a right triangle is the ratio of the side opposite that angle to the hypotenuse,

$$\sin i = \frac{WP_2}{P_1P_2};$$

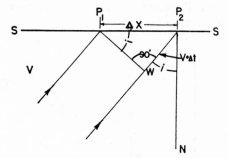

that is,

$$\sin i = \frac{v\Delta t}{\Delta x};$$

or, as we prefer to write it,

$$\sin i = v\Delta t/\Delta x.$$

FIG. 5

This relation is of fundamental importance and its significance should be fully discussed and understood before proceeding.

Ex. 3: A wave emerging to the surface in a medium in which the velocity is 5,400 ft/sec shows a *difference* in time of 0.092 sec at points 960 ft apart. What is its emergence angle? Draw the picture to scale.

Ex. 4: A wave is known to emerge at an angle of 31°15′ to the surface in a medium in which the velocity is 7,200 ft/sec. What will be the difference in time observed in the neighborhood of this emerging wave at two points 520 ft apart? Draw the picture to scale.

Lesson No. 2

TIME-DISTANCE PLOTS

The plot of travel-time of a seismic event against horizontal distance is called the *time-distance* curve of that event. It will be assumed that the concept of this type of plotting is understood; but if this is not the case, the reader is strongly advised to master it before going on. In fact, we strongly recommend that all matters in these lessons be the subjects of group discussion until the ideas are firmly in hand.

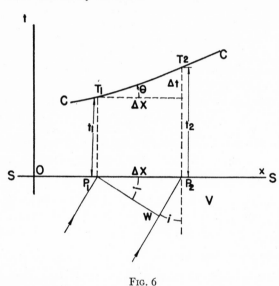

FIG. 6

Let us return to Figure 5, which we repeat in the lower part of Figure 6. We put an x-axis on the surface of the earth SS and construct a t-(time-) axis perpendicular thereto at some convenient point O, usually the "shot-point." Let the travel-time of a wave front to P_1 be t_1 and let it be so plotted, at the point T_1. As we have assumed, the travel-time of the same event to P_2, another point on the same wave front, was longer, by an amount Δt. This travel time is $t_2 = t_1 + \Delta t$ and it is indicated by the point T_2. In general, the *time-distance* curve for the event will be represented by a curve (or straight line) such as CC, of which T_1 and T_2 are two points. If Δx, the distance between the observing points P_1 and P_2, is not too large, the portion of the *time-distance* curve CC under consideration, namely T_1T_2, will be closely approximated by a straight line, if it is not actually so.

Ex. 5: Assuming that the *time-distance* curves for the situations in Ex. 3 and Ex. 4 are straight lines and the earlier travel-times in both cases are each 1.035 sec, draw the associated *time-distance* curves.

Before continuing, we must now introduce some definitions and ideas which can be found in any elementary book on the Calculus and which we must employ in what follows. (See Griffin, *Introduction to Mathematical Analysis*.)

Definition: The angle, measured counter-clockwise, which a straight line, drawn on an (x, y)-coordinate system, makes with the *positive* x-axis, is the *slope angle* of that line.

In Figure 7, the angle θ is the slope angle for each of the lines shown.

6

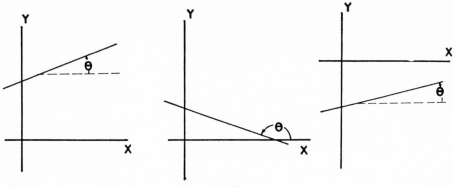

It should be noted that the slope angle of a straight line lies between 0° and 180°.

In particular, a horizontal line has its slope angle equal to 0°. A *vertical* line has its slope angle 90°.

Ex. 6: Draw a line through the point (−1, 6) with its slope angle equal to 45°; equal to 135°.

Ex. 7: What is the slope angle of the line through:

> the points (3, 4) and (−3, −2)?
> the points (4, 3) and (−6, 3)?
> the points (−2, −5) and (−2, 9)?
> the points (5, 0) and (0, 5)?

Definition: The *trigonometric tangent* of the slope angle of a line is the *slope* of that line.

In each of the cases shown in Figure 7, the slope of each line is tan θ.

It is to be noted that if the slope angle θ of a line lies between 0° and 90°, the *slope* is *positive*; if between 90° and 180°, the *slope* is *negative*. In particular, the slope of a horizontal line is 0, since tan 0°=0, and a vertical line has no slope, since tan 90° does not exist.

Ex. 8: What are the slopes of the lines mentioned in the Example 7?

Ex. 9: What can you say about a line if you are told it has slope 1; −1; −1.732? Can you draw these lines or is more information necessary?

Definition: The *slope* of a *curve at a point on it* is the *slope* of the tangent line to the curve at that point.

In the sketch of Figure 8, the slopes of the curve at points A, B, and C are equal respectively to the slopes of the tangents to the curve at those points, as shown. The slope of the curve at A is positive; at B it is negative; and at C it is zero.

We return now to Figure 6. If Δx, the distance between the observing points

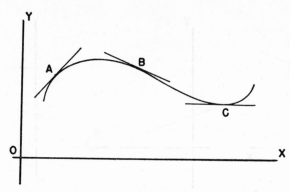

Fɪɢ. 8

P_1 and P_2, is not too large, the piece of the *time-distance* curve CC over that length, that is, T_1T_2, is substantially a straight line. By definition, then, θ is the slope angle of the line T_1T_2 and the slope of that line is

$$\tan \theta = \Delta t/\Delta x.$$

This is an important relation. The slope of the *time-distance* curve of a seismic event over a small distance is equal to the ratio

$$\Delta t/\Delta x.$$

Actually, too, as will be obvious to those who recall the concept of the derivative of a function, the slope of the *time-distance* curve at a point is dt/dx, which is defined

$$dt/dx = \lim_{\Delta x \to 0} \Delta t/\Delta x.$$

If the *time-distance* curve is a portion of a straight line, the two quantities

$$dt/dx \quad \text{and} \quad \Delta t/\Delta x$$

will be equal.

The derivative, dt/dx will occur so often and will play such a central role that very often we shall use a separate letter, p, for the quantity. That is,

$$p = dt/dx = \lim_{\Delta x \to 0} \Delta t/\Delta x.$$

For practical numerical work we usually use $\Delta t/\Delta x$ as will become evident; and thus $p \cong \Delta t/\Delta x$ (read: p is *approximately* equal to $\Delta t/\Delta x$)

Definition: The *reciprocal* of $\Delta t/\Delta x$, that is,

$$1/(\Delta t/\Delta x) = \Delta x/\Delta t$$

is often referred to as the *apparent velocity* of the seismic event, for reasons that will later become evident, particularly in refraction interpretation. This is *not to be confused* with the velocity v of the medium.

Consider, now, the relation on page 5:

$$\sin i = v\Delta t/\Delta x,$$

which expresses the sine of the emergence angle of a wave in terms of the velocity of the medium v and the ratio $\Delta t/\Delta x$. This last term we now recognize as the slope of the *time-distance* curve in the neighborhood of the observing points.

We are now ready to look at this relation from various points of view.

First, the result may be written

$$\sin i = v/(\Delta x/\Delta t).$$

Note that the denominator here is the *apparent velocity* on the *time-distance* curve. In other words, the *sine of the emergence angle of a wave is the ratio of the velocity of the medium to the apparent velocity as shown on the time-distance curve.*

Secondly, since

$$\left| \sin i \right| \leq 1$$

(the sine of an angle is numerically at most equal to unity), the slope of the *time-distance* curve, $\Delta t/\Delta x$, must be less than $1/v$.* Thus the so-called "Δt" of a seismic event has a maximum possible value over a given spread.

Thirdly, the preceding paragraph may be restated thus: The *apparent velocity* as shown on a *time-distance* curve is always greater than or equal to the velocity of the medium below the surface (weathered-layer).

Finally, if we replace $\Delta t/\Delta x$ by its new appellation p, then

$$\sin i = pv.$$

A *time-distance* curve represents t in seconds plotted against x in linear units, usually feet. Consequently, a *time-distance* curve which "rises" uniformly to a total of 0.170 sec ($\Delta t = 0.170$) in 850 ft ($\Delta x = 850$) has, as its slope

$$p = \Delta t/\Delta x = 0.170/850 = 0.0002 \text{ sec/ft.}$$

The apparent velocity indicated by this slope on the *time-distance* curve is

$$\Delta x/\Delta t = 850/0.170 = 5{,}000 \text{ ft/sec.}$$

Ex. 10: What are the slopes of the *time-distance* curves plotted in Ex. 5 and what are the indicated *apparent velocities?*

Ex. 11: A seismic wave recorded at two points on the surface shows an *apparent velocity* of 7,600 ft/sec and the medium below the surface has a seismic velocity of 5,400 ft/sec. At what angle is the wave emerging; that is, what is its emergence angle? Draw the situation of the wave path and as much of its *time-distance* curve as is obtainable from these data. What will be the recorded Δt if the pickup spacing is 250 ft? What is the value of p for this situation?

---

* Since $\sin i = v\Delta t/\Delta x$ and $\sin i \leq 1$, therefore $v\Delta t/\Delta x \leq 1$. This means that $\Delta t/\Delta x \leq 1/v$.

Lesson No. 3

ELEMENTARY CONCEPTS OF THE REFLECTION PROBLEM

In this lesson we shall discuss some of the basic ideas which form the structure of the theory of interpretation of reflection seismology. If the eye of an observer, E in Figure 9, looks into a mirror, MM, in order to see the reflection of a point object O, he will see the reflection at the imaginary point O', which is called the *image* point of O. This image point O' is obtained in this manner: From O drop a perpendicular OP to the plane of the mirror MM. Then, extend this perpendicular to O' so that $OP = PO'$.

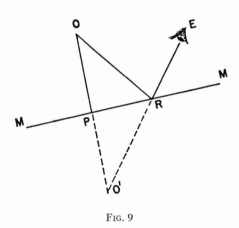

Fig. 9

Actually, although the observer at E looks towards this image point O', the light waves travel from O to the mirror MM and from there they are reflected to E. To obtain the *path* of the light wave from O to E, we join O' to E by a straight line which will intersect MM in a point R. The point R is then the reflecting point and the light wave path is the path ORE.

A *most important* result of this construction is that

$$\measuredangle PRO = \measuredangle MRE.$$

The proof of this fact is rather easy. Since OO' was drawn perpendicular to MM

$$\measuredangle OPR = \measuredangle O'PR = 90°.$$

Also

$$OP = O'P \text{ (by construction)}$$

and

$$PR = PR.$$

Thus, the two right triangles OPR and $O'PR$ are *congruent* (exactly equal, part by part). Hence,

$$\measuredangle PRO = \measuredangle PRO'.$$

But

$$\measuredangle PRO' = \measuredangle MRE \text{ (vertical angles).}$$

Therefore

$$\angle PRO = \angle MRE. \quad Q.E.D.$$

In practice, for reasons which will later become apparent, we deal quite often with two other angles connected with Figure 9. In Figure 10 we repeat Figure 9 and add the normal (perpendicular) RN to MM at R.

Definition: $\angle ORN$ (indicated by α in
Figure 10) is called the
angle of incidence of the
wave path ORE.
$\angle NRE$ (indicated by β in
Figure 10) is called the
angle of reflection of the
wave path ORE.

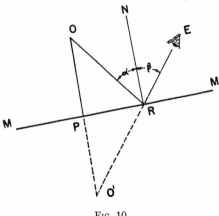

Fɪɢ. 10

Ex. 12: Show that the *angle of incidence* (α) is equal to the *angle of reflection* (β).

The result in Ex. 12, too, is one of great importance, that is, when a ray is reflected, the angle of incidence is equal to the angle of reflection.

Ex. 13: An observer's eye, E, is 10 ft from a vertical mirror MM (see Figure 11). Indicate where he would seem to see an object, O, 3 ft higher than his eye and 5 ft from the mirror. Draw the wave paths involved and compute, by trigonometry and then check by a protractor, the value of the angles of incidence and reflection.

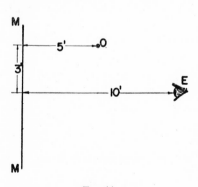

Fɪɢ. 11

Ex. 14: What is the length of the shortest vertical mirror in which a standing 6 ft man can see his entire length? Hint: Let the man's eye be E and his toe O. Draw the situation and use only the part of the mirror necessary for these end points.

We return to Figure 9. Another fundamental concept associated with the broken wave path ORE is this: Of all the paths, from O to the mirror MM and then to E the reflecting path ORE is the *shortest*.

To prove this, we proceed as follows. Obviously, any path consisting of two straight line sections OS and SE, where S is *any* point of MM, is shorter in length than any curved lines joining O to S and S to E, since each of the straight line sections is shorter than any other paths joining its end-points. Thus, the first conclusion is that the shortest path from O to a point of MM and then to E must consist

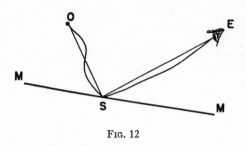

FIG. 12

of two straight lines, somewhat as OS and SE. We, therefore, need to show only, in Figure 13, that

$$OS + SE > OR + RE,$$

if R is determined in the manner of Figure 9. In fact, let S be any point of MM, other than R. Then, since $O'RE$ is a straight line, joining O' and E, $O'S+SE>O'R+RE$.

B

$$O'S = OS,$$

and

$$O'R = OR.$$

This follows from the facts that MM and OO' are at right angles, by construction, and P is the midpoint of OO' for the same reason. If, then, in the preceding inequality we make the substitutions indicated, it will read

$$OS + SE > OR + RE.$$

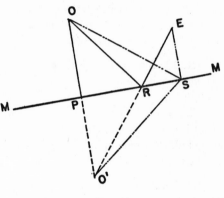

FIG. 13

Remembering that S was *any* point of MM other than R, this inequality in effect says that $OR+RE$ (that is, the wave path ORE) is the shortest path from O to the mirror to E.

Finally, one further remark. The *image point* of a point object with respect to the mirror is in no way affected by the position of the observer. In other words, an object and a reflecting plane determine a definite image point, regardless of the position of any observer or observers.

Lesson No. 4

THE ELEMENTARY SEISMIC REFLECTION PROBLEM. I

We are now in a position to direct our attention specifically to seismology. Let *SS* again represent the trace of the plane surface of the earth. Until we are in a position to deal with low-velocity, uphole, elevation and other corrections, we shall assume ideal conditions, among which will be the supposition that the medium immediately below the surface is one for which the velocity is *v*, *a constant*, in all directions. The shot-point, too, is assumed to be at the surface.

Immediately succeeding the shot-point explosion, seismic waves are excited which, by virtue of our assumptions, spread out equally in all directions in the earth. Consider the successive positions of the foremost wave front. It has the form of an expanding hemisphere concentric with the shot-point, whose radius is increasing at a rate equal to the velocity *v*.

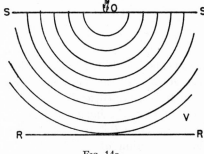

FIG. 14a

We are interested in the vertical plane section indicated in Figure 14a. The positions of the expanding wave front in this section are circles, concentric with *O*, the

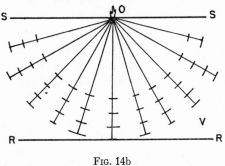

FIG. 14b

shot-point. Associated with these circles are the corresponding wave paths, which, in this case are the straight lines radiating from *O*, as shown in Figure 14b. The circles—or wave fronts—continue to expand with time in the medium until the leading one strikes a barrier, a reflecting surface, *RR*. This surface, *RR*, is for the present assumed parallel to *SS*. At that instant, *some* of the energy is reflected back to the surface from the first point of contact, *P*, of the leading wave front with *RR*. Then, continuously with time, energy is reflected back to the surface from points $P_1, Q_1, P_2, Q_2, \cdots$ on both sides of *P*, as shown in Figure 15a.

The wave front after reflections from *RR* assumes the forms shown in Figure 15a. They are circles concentric with the image point *O'* of *O* in *RR*. This will be proven below. It will be to our advantage to deal with wave paths, the forms of which, in our case, are indicated in Figure 15b. From the shot-point *O*, wave-paths radiate in all directions, and each eventually strikes the reflecting surface *RR*. At the surface, some—not all, of course—of the energy is reflected back to

13

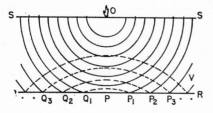

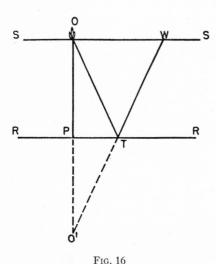

Fig. 15a

the surface *SS* as shown. That is to say, the series of paths drawn from O: $\cdots OQ_3$, $OQ_2, OQ_1, OP, OP_1, OP_2, OP_3, \cdots$, indicate schematically the wave paths from O radiat-in all directions. At the points $\cdots Q_3, Q_2,$ $Q_1, P, P_1, P_2, P_3, \cdots$ they are reflected back to the surface arriving, respectively, at the points $\cdots V_3, V_2, V_1, O, W_1, W_2,$ $W_s, \cdots$.

To draw the picture with more accuracy we proceed in the manner discussed previously. From O, draw a perpendicular OP to the reflecting plane RR. Then extend this to the image point O', obtained by making $O'P = OP$. The ray which emanates

from O and is reflected at RR so that it emerges to the surface at any given point W is obtained, as discussed before. Join O', the image point of O with respect to RR, to W. Let T be the intersection of $O'W$ with RR. The reflecting point on RR will be T, and the path desired is OTW.

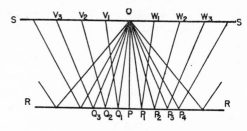

Fig. 15b

Ex. 15: A horizontal reflecting interface is 2,000 ft below the surface. Draw the reflecting paths from a shot-point on the surface

(a) back to the shot-point, O;
(b) to a point on the surface 500 ft from O;
(c) to a point on the surface 1,000 ft from O;
(d) to a point on the surface 2,000 ft from O.

How long is each of these paths?

Ex. 16: If a horizontal reflecting interface is h ft below the surface, what will be the length of the reflected path from a shot-point O to a point on the surface x ft away.

Fig. 16

We return for a moment to wave fronts. Emerging from O we had, as a result of the explosion, an expanding *circular* (in the plane section under consideration) wave front. We said that upon reflection at RR in this case, the wave front is still circular in form; however, the center of the reflected wave front is the image point O'. This follows from the fact that the reflected portion of the wave paths radiate from O'. Accordingly, the wave fronts, being at right angles to the paths, must be the curves which are at right angles to lines radiating from the point O'. Such curves are, of course, circles.

In discussing the reflected wave paths thus far, we have talked only of the *lengths* of the paths. This should be apparent in Exs. 15 and 16. We now introduce the concept of the time involved for the re-flecting waves to travel from the shot-point to the reflecting plane and back to the surface. We shall start with a numerical problem. Consider the situation of Ex. 15. Here the reflecting bed RR was given as 2,000 ft below the surface SS. (See Figure 17.) Let us assume that the velocity of the medium lying between SS and RR is 6,000 ft/sec. If a receiving point W on the surface is 1,000 ft from O, the length of the path OTW is equal to the length (straight line) $O'TW$. This last line, however, is the hy-potenuse of the right triangle $O'OW$; thus,

$$\overline{O'W}^2 = \overline{OO'}^2 + \overline{OW}^2.$$

Now,

$$\overline{OO'} = 2\overline{OP} = 4{,}000 \text{ ft and } \overline{OW} = 1{,}000 \text{ ft;}$$

thus,

$$\overline{O'W}^2 = \overline{4{,}000}^2 + \overline{1{,}000}^2 = 17 \times 10^6$$

and

$$O'W = 4{,}123 \text{ ft.}$$

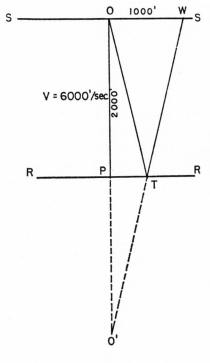

Fig. 17

Thus, the length of the path OTW equals 4,123 ft. Since this was traversed at a veloc-ity of 6,000 ft/sec, the time of travel is

$$4{,}123/6{,}000 = 0.687 \text{ sec.}$$

Ex. 17: Compute the travel times in the preceding problem of the waves from O, reflected RR back to the surface at distances of 0 ft, 500 ft, 1,000 ft, 1,500 ft, 2,000 ft, 2,500 ft, $\cdots$ from O.

Ex. 18: At O, perpendicular to SS, erect a time scale and plot the travel times of Ex. 17 on the coordinate system with SS as a base. *This* represents the *time-distance* curve of the reflected wave.

Ex. 19: What effect will there be on the travel times of the reflection to points on the *other* side of O than the side chosen in Ex. 15? Construct the *time-distance* curve for the problem on *both sides* of O.

Lesson No. 5

THE ELEMENTARY SEISMIC REFLECTION PROBLEM. II

In this lesson we shall deal step by step with a specific numerical case, in order to understand better the more general results in later work. We shall consider that between the surface of the earth, SS, and a plane horizontal reflecting bed, RR, whose depth is $h=6,000$ ft, the medium is *homogeneous* and *isotropic*, insofar as seismic propagation is concerned, and that the speed—or velocity—is $v=7,500$ ft/sec. The reader is requested to draw all the pertinent relations to scale and go through with the detailed developments which follow. The exercises will pertain to the figures and results obtained.

In Figure 18, the situation described is drawn to scale and a t-axis (time-axis) is drawn through the shot-point O. The trace of the surface SS is used as an x-axis oriented positively to the right.

The image point O' of O with respect to the reflector RR is obtained by extending the perpendicular from O to RR ($OP=6,000$ ft) an equal length below RR. The distance OO' is, then, $2h=12,000$ ft.

The reflection from O to RR and back to O will have travelled $2\ OP=12,000$ ft. At 7,500 ft/sec, the travel-time is $12,000/7,500$ ft $=1.600$ sec. Accordingly, on the t-axis, the point 1.600 is a point on the *time-distance* curve. (Note that in order to save space the time-axis in the drawing does *not* start from 0 sec.)

Consider the travel-time of the reflection from O to RR and to P_1 on the surface, 1,000 ft from O. The length of the reflected path is $OR_1P_1=O'P_1$. To obtain the length of $O'P_1$ we note that it is the hypotenuse of the right triangle P_1OO' and thus

$$O'P_1 = (\overline{OP_1}^2 + \overline{OO'}^2)^{1/2},$$
$$= 1,000(145)^{1/2},$$
$$= 12,042 \text{ ft.}$$

This is the length of the reflected path OR_1P_1. At 7,500 ft/sec, the travel-time will be 1.606 sec and is so plotted above P_1.

Continue to P_2. The length of the reflected path here is

$$O'P_2 = (\overline{OP_2}^2 + \overline{OO'}^2)^{1/2},$$
$$= 1,000(148)^{1/2},$$
$$= 12,166 \text{ ft.}$$

The travel-time above P_2 is then plotted as

$$12,166/7,500 = 1.622 \text{ sec.}$$

For P_3 the reflected path is in length found to be 12,369 ft and the travel-time of the reflection to P_3 is therefore 1.649 sec.

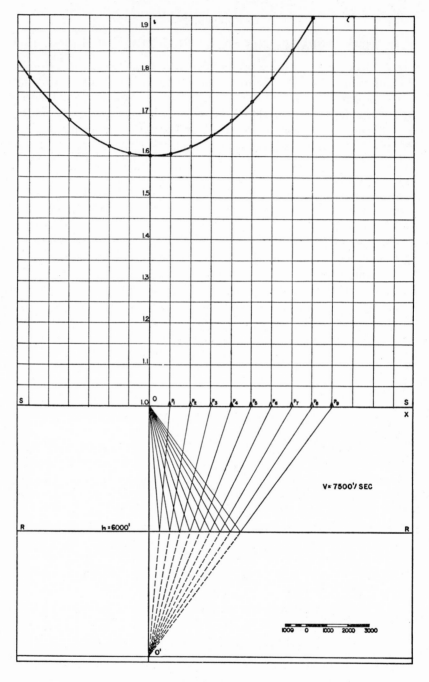

Fig. 18

In this fashion we can construct the following table:

Receiving Point	Horizontal Distance from O (ft)	Reflected Path Length (ft)	Reflection Travel-Time (sec)
O	0	12,000	1.600
P_1	1,000	12,042	1.606
P_2	2,000	12,166	1.622
P_3	3,000	12,369	1.649
P_4	4,000	12,649	1.686
P_5	5,000	13,000	1.733
P_6	6,000	13,416	1.789
P_7	7,000	13,892	1.852
P_8	8,000	14,422	1.923

Some of the reflected paths and the *time-distance* curves are shown in Figure 18.

It should be evident that the part of the *time-distance* curve to the left of the *t*-axis is the same, point for point, as the part to the right of that axis. We say that the *time-distance* curve, in this case, is *symmetrical* with respect to the *t*-axis.

Ex. 20: Construct the *time-distance* curve, as discussed above, using a depth of 8,000 ft to the reflecting horizon with the velocity the same, *i.e.*, 7,500 ft/sec.

Ex. 21: Construct the *time-distance* curve for a reflecting horizon at a depth of 6,000 ft and the velocity in the medium 10,000 ft/sec.

Ex. 22: Construct the *time-distance* curve for a reflecting horizon at a depth of 8,000 ft and the velocity in the medium 10,000 ft/sec.

Let us now see how the properties of this *time-distance* curve illustrate the concepts discussed in the early lessons.

The part of Figure 18 in which the travel-times to P_3 and P_4 were found to be respectively 1.649 and 1.686 sec is isolated to form Figure 19. The distance from P_3 to P_4 is 1,000 ft. Let us take this for our Δx; *i.e.*,

$$\Delta x = 1,000.$$

The corresponding difference in time is

$$1.686 - 1.649 = 0.037 \text{ sec};$$

i.e.,

$$\Delta t = 0.037.$$

The slope of the *time-distance* curve at the point midway between P_3 and P_4 is, then, very close to being

$$\Delta t / \Delta x = 0.037/1,000.$$

The *emergence angle i* of the ray emerging at this midway point should therefore be obtained (see Lesson No. 1, page 5, and Lesson No. 2, page 9) by the

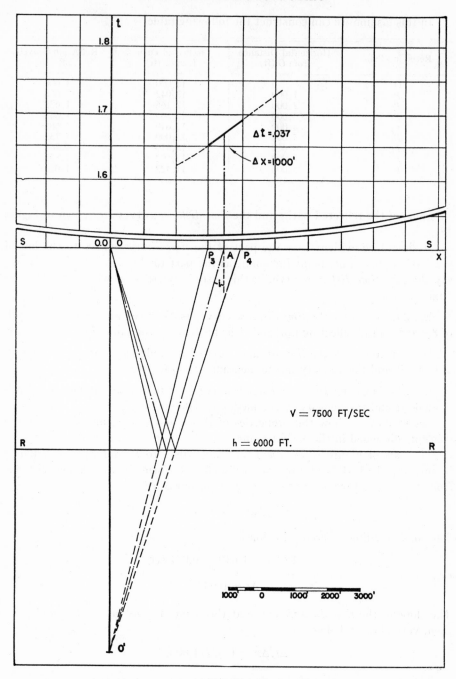

FIG. 19

relation

$$\sin i = v\,(0.037)/1{,}000$$
$$= (7{,}500)\,(0.037)/1{,}000 = 0.278.$$

Thus,

$$i = 16°9'.$$

The reader should first determine by use of a protractor that the emergence angle at P_3 is slightly less than this amount and that at P_4 it is slightly greater. For the midway point between P_3 and P_4 it should be close to this value. Let us check this in another way.

Let the midway point between P_3 and P_4 be indicated by A so that OA $=3{,}500$ ft. The reflected path from O to RR to A, is, of course, in length equal to $O'A$, and this is

$$(\overline{OA}^2 + \overline{OO'}^2)^{1/2} = 1{,}000\,(3.5^2 + 12^2)^{1/2},$$
$$= 1{,}000\,(156.25)^{1/2},$$
$$= 12{,}500 \text{ ft.}$$

The emergence angle i under consideration is equal to $\angle OO'A$, as is obvious from the figure. Thus

$$\sin \angle OO'A = \sin i = OA/O'A = 3{,}500/12{,}500 = 0.280,$$

and

$$i = 16°16'.$$

This checks well with our last value; for it must be remembered that the original value was obtained by assuming the *time-distance* curve was a straight line between P_3 and P_4. The difference obtained is a measure of the amount by which the true *time-distance* curve over the interval P_3P_4 differs from a straight line.

As we move farther and farther out to the right on the x-axis, it is evident that the emergence angle, i, becomes closer and closer to 90°, the sine of which is 1. Since we always have the relation

$$\sin i = v\,(\Delta t/\Delta x),$$

this means that, as $i \to 90°$ (read, as i approaches 90°),

$$\sin i \to 1;$$

that is,

$$v\,(\Delta t/\Delta x) = 7{,}500\,(\Delta t/\Delta x) \to 1.$$

This, in turn, means that

$$\Delta t/\Delta x \to 1/7{,}500;$$

or, better, that

$$\Delta x/\Delta t \to 7{,}500.$$

This is an important result. It shows that the *apparent velocity* as obtained from the reflection *time-distance* curve *cannot* be *less* than the velocity of the medium, 7,500 ft/sec.

It is well to note the implication of this result. It sets limits to the possible values for $\Delta t/\Delta x$ for seismic events. For example, for a spread of $\Delta x = 1{,}000$ ft, since

$$\Delta t/\Delta x < 1/7{,}500$$
$$\Delta t < \Delta x/7{,}500 = 1{,}000/7{,}500;$$

i.e.,

$$\Delta t < 0.133,$$

for any spread of 1,000 ft in line with the shot-point.

Ex. 23: Follow the discussion above for the case of Ex. 22, obtaining the emergence angle at 4,500 ft from the shot-point.

ANALYTIC TREATMENT OF ELEMENTARY REFLECTION PROBLEM

In the preceding lesson we paved the way for solving the general problem by a lengthy numerical example.

We are now in a position to look into this general problem. Let the depth of the horizontal reflecting plane RR be h below the surface SS. If O designates, as usual, the position of the shot-point on SS, the image of O in RR is the point O', where OO' is perpendicular to RR and, in length, equal to $2h$.

Let P be the position of any receiving point, *i.e.*, of a pickup, at a distance x from O, so that $OP = x$.

The length of the reflection path from O to P, *i.e.*, the length of OQP, is equal to $O'P$. This distance is traversed with a speed of v (ft/sec) in a time of t (sec). Its length is therefore vt (ft).

Since $OP = x$, $OO' = 2h$, $O'P = vt$, and $\angle POO'$ is a right angle, we have

$$(vt)^2 = x^2 + (2h)^2;$$

i.e.,

$$v^2t^2 = x^2 + 4h^2.$$

If we write this last equation in the form

$$t = (x^2 + 4h^2)^{1/2}/v$$

we have the travel-time t, in seconds, of the reflection from, depth of h feet to a distance x feet from O with a velocity v ft/sec, expressed *explicitly*.

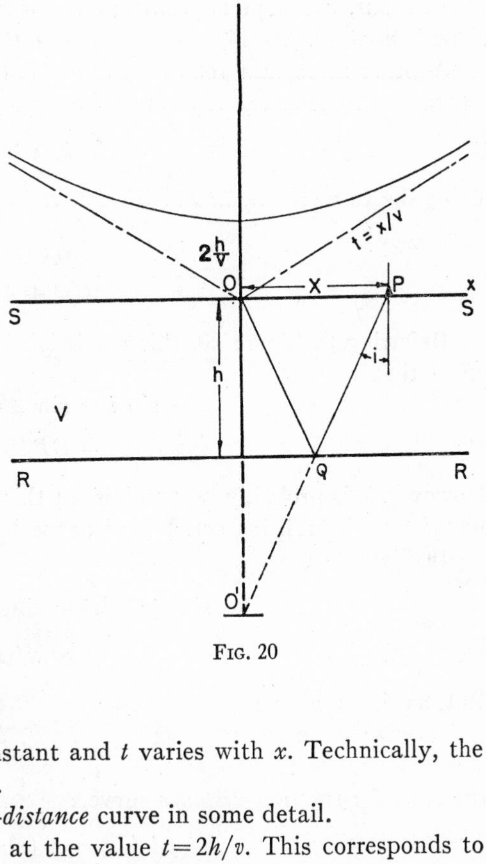

Fig. 20

In this equation, h and v are constant and t varies with x. Technically, the curve so defined is called a hyperbola.

We proceed to examine this *time-distance* curve in some detail.

The curve cuts the t-axis ($x=0$) at the value $t = 2h/v$. This corresponds to the travel-time of the vertical reflection: from O back to O.

The curve also is symmetrical in the t-axis; *i.e.*, the curve to the right of the t-axis is the mirrored image of itself to the left of the t-axis.

As x increases in either direction, the travel-time t increases. It will be of interest and importance to examine the "manner" of this increase in more detail.

23

By methods of analysis, we know that from the relation which expresses the travel-time of the reflection in terms of the distance x; namely,

$$t = (x^2 + 4h^2)^{1/2}/v$$

we can obtain by differentiation the result

$$dt/dx = x/v(x^2 + 4h^2)^{1/2}.$$

This result represents the *slope* of the *time-distance* curve at any point x.

For example, at $x=0$, the slope dt/dx is zero, which means that the curve cuts the t-axis ($x=0$) with a horizontal tangent. Again, when $x>0$, i.e., to the right of the t-axis, the slope is *positive*; and for $x<0$, i.e., to the left of the t-axis, the slope is *negative*. All this checks with the *time-distance* curve as shown.

Another important relation to note is that if, at a distance x from O, the emergence angle of the ray is indicated by i, then, as has been shown

$$\sin i = v \, dt/dx.$$

Using the value for dt/dx which we have found above, we find that

$$\sin i = v \left[x/v \, (x^2 + 4h^2)^{1/2} \right],$$
$$= x/(x^2 + 4h^2)^{1/2}.$$

Referring to Figure 20, this result is not surprising at first, since it states in effect that

$$\sin i = \sin \angle OO'P$$
$$= OP/O'P.$$

However, it is probably best to look at this result in another manner in order to understand its full import. Let us argue in this way:

In Figure 20,

$$\sin \angle OO'P = \sin i = OP/O'P$$
$$= x/(x^2 + 4h^2)^{1/2}$$

But, as shown above

$$\sin i = v \, dt/dx$$

therefore for the *time-distance* curve,

$$v\,dt/dx = x/(x^2 + 4h^2)^{1/2}$$

i.e.,

$$dt/dx = x/v(x^2 + 4h^2)^{1/2}.$$

We have been able to get the *derivative* (*i.e.*, the slope) of our *time-distance* curve from seismic evidence, instead of by differentiating.

Let us, again, return to the preceding expression for dt/dx. We can rewrite it as

$$dt/dx = \pm\, 1/v(1 + 4h^2/x^2)^{1/2}.$$

Written in this form, it is evident that, as x gets larger and larger in magnitude, positively or negatively, the slope, dt/dx, approaches $1/v$. Put another way, the *apparent velocity* of the *time-distance* curve approaches the velocity of the medium as we move farther and farther in distance from the shot-point. At the same time, the emergence angle i is approaching 90°.

Now consider the wave which radiates from O along the surface SS with velocity v. The *time-distance* curve for this wave is obviously a straight line through O with an apparent velocity of v; *i.e.*, with a slope of $1/v$. Its equation is, then,

$$t = x/v.$$

We shall show that as x increases indefinitely, the difference in time between the *time-distance* curve of the reflected waves and this *time-distance* curve approaches zero.

This difference in time is

$$[(x^2 + 4h^2)^{1/2}/v] - x/v = (1/v)\,[(x^2 + 4h^2)^{1/2} - x],$$

$$= (1/v)\,[(x^2 + 4h^2)^{1/2} - x][(x^2 + 4h^2)^{1/2} + x]/[(x^2 + 4h^2)^{1/2} + x],$$

$$= (1/v)\,\{4h^2/[(x^2 + 4h^2)^{1/2} + x]\}.$$

As x gets larger and larger indefinitely and in "either direction," this is seen to approach zero.

We have thus shown that, as x increases indefinitely, the *time-distance* curve approaches the two straight lines $t = \pm x/v$, shown dotted in Figure 20. (These lines are called the *asymptotes* to the hyperbola.)

This lesson carries no exercises. It is felt that a full appreciation of its substance with a clear understanding of the full implications of its mathematical content is of great importance and will be of immeasurable help in the matters which will follow. As an exercise, then, it is suggested that the lesson be reread and that an attempt be made to rewrite it in your own words.

TO READERS OF THE LESSONS:

The series of lessons in the theory behind the day-to-day techniques used in seismic interpretations which are being compiled has a two-fold purpose. In the first place, there have been many requests from our computers for such lessons in order to satisfy an understandable desire for a more complete knowledge of their scientific activity. More important, perhaps, is that such an understanding is becoming increasingly mandatory for the seismic computer. The trend of interpretation demands, which for so many years has had the savor of the "qualitative" rather than the "quantitative" simply because the quest has been for the "larger structures," indicates that we must try to use a sharper pencil—wherever the data are amenable. We hope that these lessons will furnish that sharper pencil.

For a long time, plans of all types were considered for accomplishing the purposes we have mentioned. Early in the spring of 1949, at the insistent request of Mr. C. H. Carlisle and his "bird dogs," a series of weekly talks was given at the Houston Office on this subject. The response was gratifyingly successful. At a later meeting in September, the geophysical supervisory personnel recommended strongly that these talks be put together in a series of lessons and distributed to all interested personnel.

There are at present six lessons distributed or being processed. The total number to be written is indefinite, as is also the frequency with which they will be written. At the present time it is simply proposed to continue them as time, need, and the mood permit in the hopes that in the fullness of time as complete a course of study as possible will have been covered.

The level of mathematical abilities and attainments varies greatly among our personnel. We shall strive to meet as many as we can on some common ground. There will be some lessons which at times will render the "mathematically-weak" reader at a loss. He is not to be discouraged; for we shall try to overcome such situations by many numerical practice examples and by hewing to the line of practical end results.

The success and perhaps continuation of the series will hinge largely upon the response evoked from the readers. Such comments, criticisms, and recommendations as may arise are earnestly desired and we want to encourage the reader to submit these, orally or written, directly to the undersigned "malefactor," M. M. Slotnick. At the same time we want to suggest group discussions of these lessons, particularly when members of the supervisory computing staff are present.

Again, comments and criticisms, both adverse or encouraging, will be gladly welcomed. Do you have any?

M. M. SLOTNICK
November 9, 1949

Lesson No. 7

TIME-DEPTH CHARTS

The most universally accepted method of converting travel-times of re-flected events to subsurface depths is that embodying the use of the so-called time-depth charts. After a set of reflection records have been studied for travel-times and what we might term "correlatability," and after corrections for weath-ering and low-velocity layer have been applied, the resulting travel-times of the reflections are interpreted in terms of depth by means of such charts.

As a result of what we have learned in our preceding lessons, we are now in a position to discuss the simplest form of these time-depth charts, which is also the most useful and important. If we *assume* that the reflection has come from a horizontal bed at a depth h with a uniform velocity v, the travel-time t is given, as we have seen, by the relation

$$v^2 t^2 = x^2 + 4h^2,$$

in which x is the distance from the shot-point to the receiving point.

In practice, the assumption is made, in fact, that an "average" velocity (to be discussed later) exists, which is "uniform enough" for our purposes to a depth h. If such an assumption is valid, and if we rewrite the last equation in the form

$$h = (1/2)\,(v^2 t^2 - x^2)^{1/2}$$

we have the basis of the time-depth charts.

We proceed to show precisely how the method works in practice.

Let us assume that for reflections whose travel-times lie between $t=1.75$ and 2.10 sec the "average" velocity is 9,570 ft/sec. (Later, in the course of these lessons, we shall show how such "average" velocities are obtained. For the present we merely mention that various methods exist, *e.g.*, well-velocity sur-veys, refraction information, reflection Δt-methods, etc.) With such information available we could, of course, compute the depth h in ft for any t in sec. For example, suppose that at 1,000 ft from the shot-point ($x=1,000$), a reflection ar-rives at 1.912 sec. The depth, then, is

$$\begin{aligned}
h &= (1/2)\,[(9{,}570)^2\,(1.912)^2 - (1{,}000)^2]^{1/2}, \\
&= (1/2)\,(10^3)\,[(9.570 \times 1.912)^2 - (1)^2]^{1/2}, \\
&= (1/2)\,(10^3)\,[(18.30)^2 - (1)^2]^{1/2}, \\
&= (1/2)\,(10^3)\,[334.9 - 1]^{1/2}, \\
&= (1/2)\,(10^3)\,[333.9]^{1/2}, \\
&= (1/2)\,18{,}270, \\
&= 9{,}135 \text{ ft.}
\end{aligned}$$

27

Ex. 24: From what depth will a reflection arrive if the travel-time to a point 1,500 ft from the shot-point is 1.821 sec and the medium propagates the seismic wave at a velocity of 9,570 ft/sec?

Ex. 25: If a reflection arrives in 2.124 sec at a distance 2,000 ft from the shot-point from a depth of 8,250 ft, what is the velocity of propagation?

Ex. 26: A "vertical" reflection ($x=0$) comes from a depth of 7,520 ft in a travel-time of 1.765 sec. What is the average velocity?

Ex. 27: In the exercise of the text above, it was found that a reflection from a depth of 9,135 ft travelled 1.912 sec in a medium in which the velocity is 9,570 ft to arrive at the surface 1,000 ft from the shot-point. Compute the travel-time of this reflection to a point 2,000 ft from the shot-point. What is the Δt for this $\Delta x = 1,000$ ft (the horizontal distance between $x=1,000$ and $x=2,000$)? What is the emergence angle at $x=1,500$ ft assuming a straight-line *time-distance* curve?

It is obvious that to build time-depth charts for travel-times t taken at intervals of 0.001 sec and for various x's in the manner shown in the text would be a very burdensome task indeed. Fortunately, this is not necessary, and we shall show how this could actually be done with reasonable speed in practice.

The work is arranged in a form, a portion of which, for $1.75 \leq t \leq 2.10$ (read lying in the interval from and including 1.75 to and including 2.10), is shown in Figure 21, for $x = 1,000$ ft. A chart of this form is made for each x under consideration. In Figure 22, we show a smaller portion of a chart for $x = 2,000$ ft.

$v = 9,570$ ft/sec $x = 1,000$ ft

	0	1	2	3	4	5	6	7	8	9
1.80										
1.81										
1.82										
1.83										
1.84										
1.85										
1.86										
1.87										
1.88										
1.89										
1.90	9,078	9,083	9,088	9,092	9,097	9,102	9,107	9,112	9,116	9,121
1.91	9,126	9,131	9,136	9,140	9,145	9,150	9,155	9,160	9,164	9,169
1.92	9,174	9,179	9,184	9,188	9,193	9,198	9,203	9,208	9,212	9,217
1.93	9,222	9,227	9,232	9,236	9,241	9,246	9,251	9,256	9,260	9,265
1.94	9,270	9,275	9,280	9,284	9,289	9,294	9,299	9,304	9,308	9,313
1.95	9,318									
1.96										
1.97										
1.98										
1.99										
2.00										
2.01										
2.02										
2.03										
2.04										
2.05										

Fig. 21

For $x=1,000$ (Figure 21), we compute h for $t=1.75$, 1.80, 1.85, etc., in this manner:

$$v = 9,570, \qquad x = 1,000, \qquad h = (1/2)(v^2t^2 - x^2)^{1/2}$$

t	vt	v^2t^2	$v^2t^2-x^2$	$(v^2t^2-x^2)^{1/2}$	h
1.75	16,748	280.48×10^6	279.48×10^6	16.718×10^3	8,359
1.80	17,226	296.74×10^6	295.74×10^6	17.197×10^3	8,598
1.85	17,704	313.45×10^6	312.45×10^6	17.676×10^3	8,838
1.90	18,183	330.62×10^6	329.62×10^6	18.155×10^3	9,078
1.95	18,662	348.25×10^6	347.25×10^6	18.635×10^3	9,318
2.00	19,140	366.34×10^6	365.34×10^6	19.114×10^3	9,557
2.05	19,618	384.89×10^6	383.89×10^6	19.593×10^3	9,796
2.10	20,097	403.89×10^6	402.89×10^6	20.072×10^3	10,036

We note that for $t=1.90$, $h=9,078$; and for $t=1.95$, $h=9,318$. Thus, for this interval of 0.050, there is a difference of 240 ft in h. For our purposes, it is close enough to distribute this amount evenly; namely, 4.8 ft for each 0.001 second. In this manner, the interval of $t=1.90$ to 1.95 was filled out in Figure 21.

$v=9,570$ ft/sec $x=2,000$ ft

	0	1	2	3	4	5	6	7	8	9
1.90	9,037									
1.91										
1.92										
1.93										
1.94										
1.95	9,277									
1.96										
1.97										
1.98										
1.99										
2.00	9,518									

Fig. 22

Ex. 28: Fill in the values for h for $1.95 \leq t \leq 2.00$ in Figure 21.

Ex. 29: Fill in the values for h for $1.90 \leq t \leq 2.00$ in Figure 22.

These charts may be used for other purposes as well. We cite one important use:

For $x=1,000$ ft (Figure 21), the travel-time of a reflection from a depth of $h=9,140$ ft is seen to be 1.913 sec.

For $x=2,000$ ft (Figure 22), the travel-time of a reflection from the same depth ($h=9,140$ ft) is 1.921 sec. We may then conclude that at $x=1,500$ (halfway point) the "normal" Δt for $\Delta x=1,000$, for a horizontal reflecting surface is $\Delta t=1.921-1.913=0.008$ sec, if the travel-time at $x=1,500$ is 1.917 sec, which in turn, corresponds to a depth of 9,140 ft.

Ex. 30: Let $v=8,700$ ft/sec and $h=6,950$ ft. Find the travel-time for $x=1,250$ ft and $x=1,500$ ft. Thus find

$$\Delta t/\Delta x.$$

Check this value against the derivative

$$dt/dx = x/v^2 t$$

for the midway point, $x = 1,375$ ft. What is the emergence angle?

Later, we shall show other more elaborate time-depth charts, their formation and use.

Lesson No. 8

VELOCITY DETERMINATION FROM REFLECTION DATA

We continue with the assumptions that we have used heretofore concerning reflection data, namely, that the reflecting bed is a horizontal plane, that the medium intervening between that plane and the horizontal plane of the earth is homogeneous and isotropic to seismic wave propagation, and that all necessary corrections to the data have been applied. We thus have resultant travel-times for the reflected waves which depend only on the distance of the pickups from the shot-point (regardless of azimuth of the pickup points, since the reflecting plane is assumed parallel to the plane of the earth).

In the equation governing this situation:

$$v^2 t^2 = x^2 + 4h^2,$$

consider the various items:

t, the travel-time, is a measured quantity;

x, the distance between shot-point and pickup point is a measured quantity;

h, the thickness of the medium—or, as it is more commonly described, the depth to the reflecting horizon—is a quantity we desire to determine;

v, the velocity of propagation, is either assumed from other information or means, or is also to be determined.

There is still another relation at least equally as important as the preceding equation, if not more so. This is the so-called derivative equation, which is

$$dt/dx = x/v^2 t = x/v(x^2 + 4h^2)^{1/2}.$$

This, we shall write for practical purposes and for the purposes of this discussion in the form

$$\Delta t/\Delta x = x/v(x^2 + 4h^2)^{1/2}.$$

In introducing this new equation, the only new items involved are:

Δt, the difference in travel-time of a reflected wave for pickups which are in line with the shot-point separated by a distance Δx, and so that their midpoint is at a distance x from the shot-point.

With these two equations and with the assumptions made, it will be evident that—at least theoretically—we can determine both unknowns, h and v, from only *two* pickups in line with the shot-point, *not* too far removed* from each other and both on the same side of the shot-point. Suppose, in fact, that two

---

* That is, so that the travel-times of the first, last, and intervening point lie essentially on a straight line.

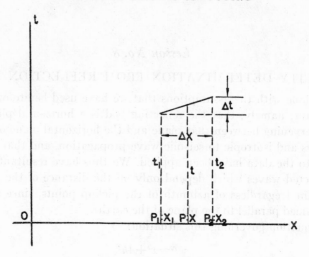

Fig. 23

pickups are at P_1 and P_2 at distances x_1 and x_2 respectively from the shot-point, as shown in Figure 23. Let the distance of their midpoint P and O be x. As usual, we indicate the distance between P_1 and P_2 by Δx;

$$x = (x_1 + x_2)/2, \qquad \Delta x = x_2 - x_1.$$

We shall indicate the travel-time of a reflected wave originating from O to P_1 and P_2 by t_1 and t_2 respectively.

If Δx is small enough, the part of the *time-distance* curve lying between P_1 and P_2 will be substantially a straight line. Thus, the travel-time of the reflection to the midpoint P will be t where

$$t = (t_1 + t_2)/2.$$

As usual, too, we introduce the quantity

$$\Delta t = t_2 - t_1.$$

Before continuing with the discussion, and, as a basis for a numerical discussion, the reader is asked to complete:

Ex. 31: Let $x_1 = 3,000$ ft; $x_2 = 4,000$ ft. Draw a figure using the letters for corresponding points as discussed in the text. What is the value of x? What is the value of Δx?

Ex. 32: Let $t_1 = 1.649$ sec and $t_2 = 1.686$ sec. On the figure for Ex. 31, draw a time-scale and draw the given section of the *time-distance* curve. What is the value of t as described in the text? To what distance from O does this value of t correspond? What is the value of Δt?

The illustrated situation of Exs. 31 and 32 will be called Figure 24 and is so shown. It is well to note that all the data required to complete the items discussed can be obtained from an in-line reflection seismograph set up. Thus, in the two fundamental equations,

$$v^2t^2 = x^2 + 4h^2$$

$$dt/dx \cong \Delta t/\Delta x = x/v^2t,$$

we have enough information with which we can solve for the two unknowns, v and h, from the data from the two pickups suitably spaced.

For those readers who enjoy such matters, it will be an interesting and profitable chore to set up means and methods for so doing. For our purposes we shall content ourselves in showing a graphical means whereby the desired ends may often be attained. After having done so, we shall conclude by pointing out that the indicated method—or for that matter, the theoretical one—may sometimes *not* yield correct, or even sensible, results, and the reasons therefor.

Let us first recall that in the present problem we are assuming that the reflecting bed is horizontal. The simplest, and usually the best, means of validating such an assumption is by shooting a reflection spread on both sides of the shot-hole. If the data are the same—that is, travel-times are the same for equal distances—this assumption is probably quite justified.

Because of this assumption, the image point O' of O with respect to the reflecting plane is *vertically under O*.

For Figure 24, $\Delta t = 0.037$ and $\Delta x = 1,000$ ft. To determine the emergence angle i for the wave at midpoint P, we must have the velocity v. Suppose we make a *first guess* for v, which we shall call v_1, of 6,000 ft/sec; *i.e.*, $v_1 = 6,000$ ft/sec. Let the corresponding value of i be i_1 so that

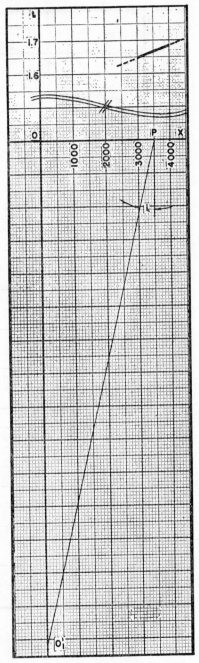

Fig. 24

$$\sin i_1 = v_1 (\Delta t/\Delta x)$$

$$(6,000)\ 0.037/1000 = 0.222.$$

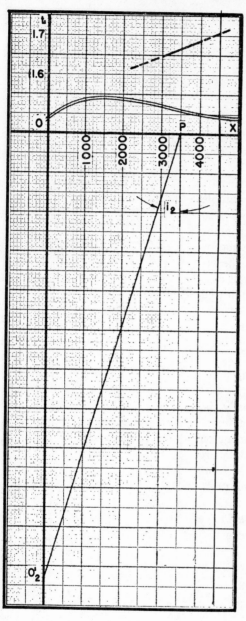

FIG. 25

From a natural table of sines, we find that $i_1 = 12°50'$.

We draw the path with this emergence angle as carefully as possible as shown in the lower half of Figure 24, and extend this to intersect the vertical through O at the point O_1'.

If this guess of v_1 as 6,000 ft/sec is the correct one, then two things must follow:

(1) The distance $O_1'P$ must equal v_1t; *i.e.*, $(6,000)(1.668) = 10,008$; *i.e.*, 10,000 ft.

(2) The reflecting plane will be that whose trace is through the midpoint of $O_1'O$ and parallel to surface OP.

By scaling $O_1'P$ in Figure 24, we note that its length is *not* 10,000 ft. In fact, it is equal to 3,500/0.222, or almost 16,000 ft. Hence, condition (1) above is violated and the guess of $v_1 = 6,000$ ft/sec is *not* a valid one.

Let us then try $v_2 = 8,000$ ft/sec as a second guess.

Ex. 33: Construct Figure 25 as shown in which the velocity assumed is 8,000 ft/sec. Show that $\sin i_2 = 0.296$ and $i_2 = 17°15'$. In this way, the image point O_2' for this assumed velocity is obtained. What is the length of $O_2'P$? How long should it be if the assumed velocity were the correct one?

In Figure 26 we have combined the results of the two guesses, $v_1 = 6,000$ ft/sec and
$v_2 = 8,000$ ft/sec. In the first case, $O_1'P$ was
measured as 3,500/0.222 ft, or about 15,800
ft, and should have been $(6,000)(1.667)$
$=10,000$ ft. In the second case, $O_2'P$ was
measured as 3,500/0.296, or about 11,900
ft, and should have been $(8,000)(1.668)$
$=13,344$ ft.

Thus, the correct answer would seem to
be somewhere in between, but closer to the
second guess.

Let us try a third guess: $v_3 = 7,000$ ft/sec.
This gives us

$$\sin i_3 = (7,000)\,(0.037)/1,000 = 0.259,$$
$$i_3 = 15°.$$

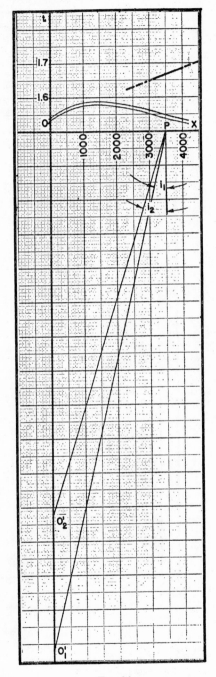

Fɪɢ. 26

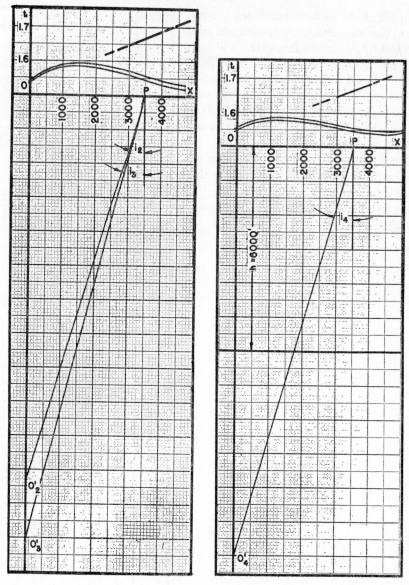

Fig. 27　　　　　　　　　　　Fig. 28

In Figure 27 we show the results of the second and third guesses. $O_3'P$ is measured as 3,500/0.259 (about 13,500) and should be $(7,000)(1.668)=11,680$ ft. This leads us to try

$$v_4 = 7,500 \text{ ft/sec,}$$

$$\sin i_4 = (7,500)(0.037)/1,000 = 0.2775,$$

$$i_4 = 16°10'.$$

Drawing up the answer, we measure $O_4'P$ as 3,500/0.2775; *i.e.*, 12,600 ft, and it should be $(7,500)(1.668)=12,500$—a pretty good check. Thus, we conclude that the data show that

$$v = 7,500 \text{ ft/sec.}$$

This solution, as is seen in Figure 28, shows that $h=6,000$ ft, *i.e.*, one-half the distance $O_4'P$.

Ex. 34: Compute in similar manner the v and h if we have found $t=1.110$ at $x_1=1,500$, $t_2=1.132$ at $x_2=2,500$.

A final word on the method: The weakness lies in the fact that a small error in Δt may well lead to a large error in v and h, as a little analysis will show. Consequently, the method should be tried and tested often. If the reflections are good and the Δt's definitely readable (and reliable) over a large area, the recurrence of v by this method as a "reasonably constant" value over the area is usually sufficient evidence of its reliability.

Lesson No. 9

REFLECTIONS FROM A DIPPING INTERFACE. I

We propose to consider now the problem of reflections obtained from a single plane dipping reflector under ideal conditions, similar to those implied in all previous work.

Let $S'S$ represent the trace of the flat horizontal surface of the earth in the direction of the *true dip* of a bed $R'R$, dipping at an angle ϕ in the direction $\overrightarrow{S'S}$ with respect to the horizontal. On $S'S$ let the point O represent a shot-point. The velocity of the medium lying between $S'S$ and $R'R$ will be represented by v.

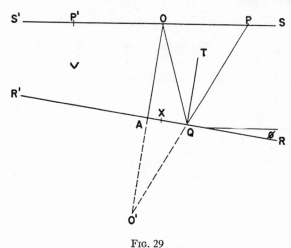

FIG. 29

To get the reflection path from the shot-point O to a receiving point P on the surface of the earth, we proceed in a manner similar to that used heretofore. From O drop a perpendicular to the bed $R'R$, the foot of which is the point A. Extend OA to the point O' so that $OA = AO'$. This point O' is the *image* point of O with respect to the reflector $R'R$. Joint P to O' by the line $O'P$, which intersects $R'R$ in Q. The *desired wave path of the reflection consists of OQ and QP*.

Ex. 35: Prove $OQ + QP = O'P$.

If at the reflecting point Q, QT is drawn perpendicular to $R'R$, then

$$\angle OQT \text{ is called the } angle\ of\ incidence$$

and

$$\angle PQT \text{ is called the } angle\ of\ reflection$$

of the wave path OQP.

Ex. 36: Prove, in Figure 29, that the angle of incidence is equal to the angle of reflection.

38

Ex. 37: In Figure 29, draw the reflected wave path from O to the point P', and thus, also, find the position of the point of reflection, Q', on $R'R$ for this path.

Ex. 38: Let X be any point on $R'R$ other than Q. Draw the lines OX and XP, and show that

$$OX + XP > OQ + QP.$$

As a consequence of the result of Exs. 36 and 38, we can state the following important result:

The reflected path OQP, drawn as described, is the *shortest* path consisting of two straight line segments joining a point (such as X) of $R'R$ to the shot-point O and receiver point P. This reflected path is such that the angle of incidence equals the angle of reflection.

Our next problem is to discuss, qualitatively at first, the type of *time-distance* curve to be expected from the travel-times of the waves from O being reflected from $R'R$ to the surface $S'S$. As a consequence of our preceding results, a surprising amount of important information can be obtained, all of which has its value in showing us how to think of these reflected wave paths. For this discussion we refer to Figure 30.

In this figure, the dipping bed $R'R$ is brought to its "outcrop" at R' with the surface $S'S$. The angle of dip is indicated by ϕ and we assume the dip is down to the right. The shot-point is at O, and its image point O' with respect to $R'R$ is, of course, such that OO' is perpendicular to $R'R$ and is bisected by $R'R$ at the point Q_0.

The points P_{-2}, P_{-1}, $\overline{P}$, O, P_1, P_2, P_3, $\cdots$, on the surface are intended to indicate various positions of pickups, up and down dip relative to the shot-point O. To obtain the reflected wave paths to any of these points, we proceed as usual, namely, the point (P)* is joined to the image point O' by a straight line which intersects $R'R$ at the corresponding reflection point (Q). This last point is then joined to O to form the complete path $O(Q)(P)$.

As we move to the right—down dip—from O through the points P_1, P_2, P_3, and beyond, the paths of the reflected waves, are

$$OQ_1P_1, \qquad OQ_2P_2, \qquad OQ_3P_3, \text{ etc.,}$$

and, in length, they are equal respectively to

$$O'P_1, \qquad O'P_2, \qquad O'P_3, \text{ etc.}$$

It should be apparent that these lengths continually increase as we move to the right. Let the distance of P_1, P_2, etc., from O be indicated, as in the figure, by x_1, x_2, etc. This, then, means that the travel-times increase and that conse-

---

* The symbols (P) and (Q) indicate respectively any point of P_1, P_2, etc., and the corresponding point of Q_1, Q_2, etc.

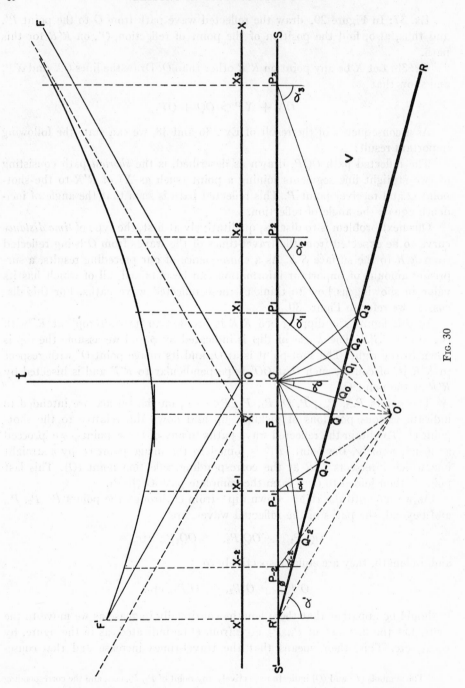

Fig. 30

quently the *time-distance* curve continuously rises. The travel-time t increases with increasing x.

The emergence angles at P_1, P_2, P_3, $\cdots$, are indicated by α_1, α_2, α_3, $\cdots$. These angles are continuously *increasing* as we move to the right and approaching 90° as an upper limit.

Let us indicate the slope of the *time-distance* curve at P_1, P_2, P_3, $\cdots$, by the values:

$$(dt/dx)_1, \qquad (dt/dx)_2, \qquad (dt/dx)_3, \cdots$$

respectively. Our fundamental relation is that

$$\sin \alpha_1 = v(dt/dx)_1,$$

where v is the velocity of propagation in the medium, with similar equations for each of the other positions (P).

Now as we move to the right and the α's increase to 90°, $\sin \alpha$ approaches 1. That means that

$$v(dt/dx)$$

approaches 1; and that, in turn, means that

$$(dt/dx)$$

approaches $1/v$. *As x increases to the right, (dt/dx) increases to a maximum of $1/v$.*

Thus, the *time-distance* curve in this case, too, approaches an *asymptotic slope* which is that of the straight line through the shot-point O representing the *time-distance* curve for the "first kicks." This latter line is indicated by OF in the figure.

The ray from O which strikes $R'R$ at Q_0 at right angles of $R'R$ is reflected back to O. The emergence angle here is α_0. But clearly, $\alpha_0 = \phi$, the angle of dip. Consequently, at O, the slope of the *time-distance* curve, $(d^t/dx)_0$, satifies the relation

$$\sin \phi = v(dt/dx)_0,$$

i.e.,

$$(dt/dx)_0 = \sin \phi/v.$$

Now, we raise the question: Of all the reflected wave paths from O to the surface, which is the shortest? Obviously, it is the one for which the travel-time is least. This occurs for that path which corresponds to the shortest distance from O' to $S'S$, and which obviously is the perpendicular $O'\overline{P}$ to $S'S$. At this point the emergence angle is 0°. But, from our relation

$$\sin \alpha = v(dt/dx),$$

$dt/dx = 0$, since $\alpha = 0$. This, of course, means that the slope of the *time-distance* curve is zero at $\overline{P}$, the minimum of the curve; which is what was to be expected.

In the figure, this point $\overline{P}$ is shown and its distance from O is indicated by the coordinate $\bar{x}$. Note that it is to the left (on the up-dip side) of O.

For receiving points P_{-1}, P_{-2}, etc., to the left (up-dip side) of $\overline{P}$, the travel-times of the reflected waves again increase with increasing distance, so that the *time-distance* curve rises again.

However, this *time-distance* curve comes to an abrupt end at the "outcrop" point R'. Clearly, the reflected wave-path from O to R' is precisely that of the "first-kick" path. Hence, the reflection *time-distance* curve intersects the "first-kick" *time-distance* curve, indicated by OF', at the point R', at which point both curves cease abruptly, insofar as physical significance is concerned.

Ex. 39: Show that the *time-distance* curve is symmetrical about the vertical line through $\overline{P}$ by showing that the reflected wave paths from O to any pair of points on $S'S$, one on each side of and at the same distance from $\overline{P}$, are equal.

Another matter of practical interest is that for *any spread of pickups*, the observed Δt across a record will be in the "normal direction" *except* the shot-point O and the point $\overline{P}$, in which region the Δt will be "back-handed." And, as has been mentioned before, in no case does

$$\Delta t / \Delta x \text{ exceed } 1/v \text{ in value; } i.e.,$$

$$\Delta t < \Delta x / v.$$

Other facts about the importance of the *time-distance* curve can be shown easily from the analytic standpoint, which will be treated later. We shall content ourselves by stating that the *time-distance* curve is a *hyperbola* whose asymptotes (shown dashed in the figure) intersect at $\overline{P}$ and are parallel to the surface "first-kicks" straight lines (OF and OF'). The point $\overline{P}$ is the point of least reflected-path-time and, consequently, the hyperbola is symmetric with respect to the vertical through $\overline{P}$ as stated in Ex. 39.

Ex. 40: What is the slope of the *time-distance* curve in Figure 30 at the point over R', at which the curve ends abruptly?

Lesson No. 10

REFLECTIONS FROM A DIPPING INTERFACE. II

Before proceeding to an analytic discussion of our problem, it might be well to discuss a numerical case.

In Figure 31, we have represented a reflecting bed, $R'R$, dipping at an angle of 5° to the right and such that its depth below the shot-point O is 5,000 ft; that is, in the figure, $OT = 5,000$ ft.

Between this dipping reflector and the surface $S'S$ is a homogeneous, isotropic medium in which the seismic speed of propagation is $v = 7,500$ ft/sec.

As described previously, we first construct the image point O' of O with respect to $R'R$, by drawing OQ_0 perpendicular to $R'R$ and extending it to O', so that $OQ_0 = Q_0O'$.

Since $\angle OQ_0T = 90°$ and $\angle TOS = 90°$, it follows that $\triangle OQ_0T$ is a right triangle in which

$$\angle TOQ_0 = 5°,$$

the amount of dip of $R'R$.

Ex. 41: Show that the distance $\overline{OQ_0} = 4,981$ ft, and that, therefore, $\overline{OO} = 9,962$ ft.

The wave path starting along OQ_0 is reflected back to O since the ray strikes $R'R$ at right angles. The length of the total path is

$$2\overline{OQ_0} = 9,962 \text{ ft},$$

and, at 7,500 ft/sec, it will take

$$9,962/7,500 = 1.328 \text{ sec}.$$

Thus, our *time-distance* curve passes through the point $x = 0$ (for O) and $t = 1.328$ sec.

At this point, the emergence angle is 5°. Thus, the *slope* of our *time-distance* curve, $(dt/dx)_0$, at the corresponding point is such that

$$\sin 5° = 7,500 \ (dt/dx)_0;$$

i.e.,

$$(dt/dx)_0 = 0.0872/7,500 = 0.012/1,000.$$

The reason for the last reduction above is to point out that *a spread of 1,000 ft straddling the shot-point O (500 ft on either side) will indicate a $\Delta t = 0.012$ and a time of 1.328 sec for the "center string."*

Now consider the reflected wave-path $O\overline{Q}P$ which arrives at right angles to $S'S$ and which will give a minimum time for our *time-distance* curve.

Ex. 42: Why is the path $O\overline{Q}P$ the earliest possible reflection arrival from RR'? What is the slope of the *time-distance* curve at the point? Show that the path $O\overline{Q}P = 9,924$ ft; that $O\overline{P} = 868$ ft; and that the travel-time for this path ($O\overline{Q}P$) is 1.323 sec.

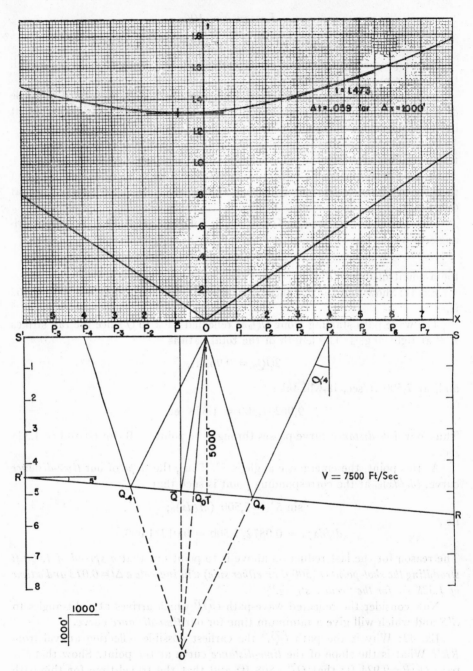

Fɪɢ. 31

(THE READER IS URGED TO FOLLOW THROUGH ALL THE CAL-CULATIONS AND REPEAT THE FIGURE ON A MUCH LARGER SCALE THAN IS POSSIBLE HERE, SO THAT THE SMALL DIFFER-ENCES CAN BE PLOTTED WITH GREATER ACCURACY.)

For the point $\overline{P}$, then, the travel-time is $t = 1.323$ sec, and at that point the tangent to the *time-distance* curve is horizontal. It is the lowest point of the curve. A spread, straddling this point $\overline{P}$, symmetrically, will show a $\Delta t = 0$ for this reflection.

Let us now go out 4,000 ft to the right of O to the point P_4 in Figure 31.

In length, the wave path OQ_4P_4 is equal to $O'P_4$. By the trigonometric law of cosines:

$$\overline{O'P_4}^2 = \overline{OP_4}^2 + \overline{OO'}^2 - (2\overline{OP_4})(\overline{OO'}) \cos \measuredangle P_4OO'.$$

Now,

$$\overline{OP_4} = 4{,}000,$$

$$\overline{OO'} = 9{,}962,$$

$$\measuredangle P_4OO' = 90° + 5° = 95°,$$

and

$$\cos \measuredangle P_4OO' = \cos 95° = -\sin 5°.$$

Thus, our formula becomes numerically:

$$\overline{O'P_4}^2 = (4.000)^2 \, 10^6 + (9.962)^2 \, 10^6 + 2(4{,}000)(9.962) \, 10^6 \sin 5°$$

$$= [(16.00 + 99.24 + (79.70) \, (0.0872)] \, 10^6$$

$$= (122.19) \, 10^6$$

from which

$$\overline{O'P_4} = 11{,}054 \text{ ft.}$$

At 7,500 ft/sec, the travel-time of the reflection to P_4 will be 1.473 sec, and it is shown on the *time-distance* curve of the figure.

To obtain the angle of emergence, α_4, at P_4, we note that

$$\alpha_4 = 90° - \measuredangle OP_4O',$$

and that, by the law of sines in $\triangle P_4OO'$:

$$\sin \measuredangle OP_4O' / \sin \measuredangle O'OP_4 = \overline{OO'}/O'P_4,$$

i.e.,

$$\sin \measuredangle OP_4O' = 9{,}962 \, (\sin 95°)/11{,}054,$$

$$= 9{,}962 \, (0.9962)/11{,}054,$$

$$= 0.8978,$$

and

$$\angle OP_4O' = 63°52'.$$

Thus, $\alpha_4 = 26°8'$, or, for practical purposes,

$$\alpha_4 = 26°.$$

The slope of our *time-distance* curve at the point P_4, i.e., $(dt/dx)_4$, will be obtained from the relation

$$\sin \alpha_4 = v(dt/dx)_4;$$

i.e.,

$$0.4405 = 7,500(dt/dx)_4.$$

We thus find

$$(dt/dx)_4 = 0.4405/7,500 = 0.059/1,000.$$

Thus, for a spread, 1,000 ft long, centering at P_4, there would be

$$\Delta t = 0.059 \text{ sec.}$$

We can now continue in the same fashion for a series of points along $S'S$. However, it must be noted that for points to the left (up-dip side) of O, the law of cosines will introduce a change in sign for the cosine of the contained angle, $\angle S'OO'$, which is equal to $85°$. For example, for the point P_{-4}, the equation would read

$$\overline{O'P_{-4}}^2 = \overline{OP_{-4}}^2 + \overline{OO'}^2 - (\overline{2OP_{-4}})(\overline{OO'}) \cos \angle P_{-4}OO',$$

$$= (4.00)^2\, 10^6 + (9.962)^2\, 10^6 - 2(4.00)(9.962)\, 10^6\, (\cos 85°),$$

$$= [(16.00 + 99.24) - (79.70)\, (0.0872)]\, 10^6,$$

$$= (108.29)\, 10^6.$$

Whence

$$O'P_{-4} = 10,410,$$

and the corresponding travel-time is 1.388 sec.

Ex. 43: Compute the necessary quantities and show that the following table is correct. The *time-distance* curve of Figure 31 was so obtained.

Ex. 44: At some of these points, compute the Δt to be expected for a spread (Δx) 1,000 ft long straddling those points.

Ex. 45: In the following table, the times to P_3 and P_4 are, respectively, 1.420 and 1.473 sec. What, then, is the emergence angle at their midway point, namely 3,500 ft to the right of O? Draw the emergent ray at this point.

Ex. 46: In the following table, the times to P_{-3} and P_{-4} are, respectively, 1.353 and 1.388 sec. What, then, is the emergence angle at their midway point,

Point	Length of Reflected Wave Path (ft)	Travel-Time (sec)
P_{-5}	10,750	1.433
P_{-4}	10,410	1.388
P_{-3}	10,150	1.353
P_{-2}	9,990	1.332
P_{-1}	9,920	1.323
O	9,960	1.328
P_1	10,100	1.347
P_2	10,330	1.377
P_3	10,650	1.420
P_4	11,050	1.473
P_5	11,530	1.537
P_6	12,070	1.609
P_7	12,660	1.688
P_8	13,310	1.775

namely 3,500 ft to the left of O? Draw the emergent ray at this point.

Ex. 47: What point of Figure 31 will be the intersection of the emergent rays of Exs. 45 and 46?

Ex. 48: Join the point of Ex. 47 with O and bisect this line by a perpendicular bisector. Show that this bisector is the trace $R'R$.

REFLECTIONS FROM A DIPPING INTERFACE. III

At this point, it is probably advisable to study the problem before us from an analytic point of view. Accordingly, referring to Figure 32, we shall indicate the dipping reflecting interface by $R'R$ whose dip is ϕ down to the right. The velocity of transmission of the medium between the surface $S'S$ and $R'R$ is indicated by v, and the depth to $R'R$ measured vertically from a shot-point O is h.

If we indicate the foot of the perpendicular from O to $R'R$ by Q_0, the distance $\overline{OQ_0}$ is $h \cos \phi$, which distance we shall indicate by H, *i.e.*,

$$H = h \cos \phi.$$

The image point O' of O with respect to $R'R$ is such that

$$\overline{OO'} = 2\overline{OQ_0} = 2H = 2h \cos \phi.$$

For the purpose of obtaining the equation of the *time-distance* curve of the waves originating at O and reflected by $R'R$, we first set up a coordinate system of axes, the x-axis being along the surface $S'S$ and we arbitrarily orient it positively to the down-dip side, as in the figure. The time-axis is erected vertically at the shot-point O.

Consider a pickup position P at a distance x from O; which distance x is positive on the down-dip side and negative on the up-dip side, in accordance with our agreement on the orientation of the positive x-axis. The length of the reflected wave path to P, namely OQP, is equal to that of the straight line $O'QP$, *i.e.*, $O'P$. By the law of cosines:

$$\overline{O'P^2} = \overline{OO'^2} + \overline{OP^2} - (2\overline{OO'})\,(\overline{OP}) \cos \measuredangle O'OP.$$

If x is positive, *i.e.*, if P is on the down-dip side, $\measuredangle O'OP = 90° + \phi$, in which ϕ is the dip of $R'R$. In this case

$$\cos \measuredangle O'OP = -\sin \phi.$$

If x is negative, *i.e.*, if P is on the up-dip side, $\measuredangle O'OP = 90° - \phi$, and

$$\cos \measuredangle O'OP = \sin \phi.$$

Now

$$\overline{OO'} = 2H,$$
$$\overline{OP} = x$$

and

$$\overline{O'P} = vt,$$

in which t is the travel-time of the reflected wave to P, and v is its velocity of travel. All these quantities put into the preceding equation, reduce it to

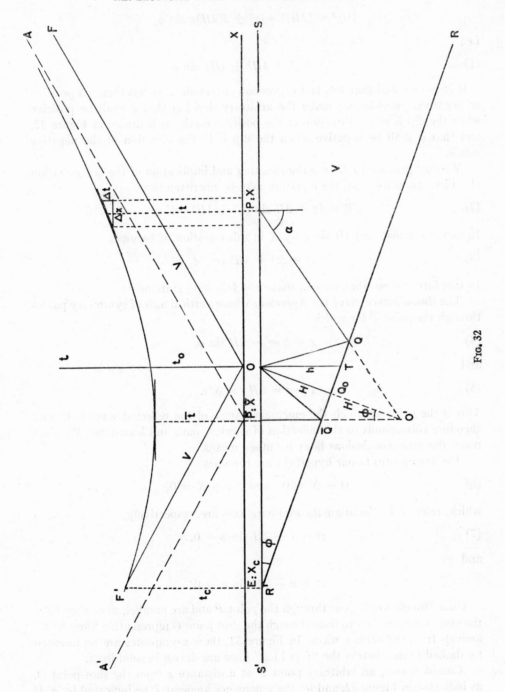

FIG. 32

$$(vt)^2 = (2H)^2 + x^2 \pm 2(2H)x \sin \phi,$$

i.e.,

(1) $$v^2 t^2 = x^2 + 4H^2 + 4Hx \sin \phi.$$

It is to be noted that this last expression covers all cases whether x is positive or negative, provided we make the arbitrary decision that ϕ shall be positive when the dip is in the direction of the positive x-axis, as is drawn in Figure 32, and that ϕ shall be negative when the dip is in the direction of the negative x-axis.

We now proceed to discuss the meaning and implication of the last equation (1). First, as to its form, the equation may be rewritten thus:

(2) $$v^2 t^2 = (x + 2H \sin \phi)^2 + 4H^2 \cos^2 \phi.$$

If, now, we replace $x + 2H \sin \phi$ by X in this equation, it becomes

(3) $$v^2 t^2 = X^2 + 4H^2 \cos^2 \phi.$$

In this form we see that we can make the following statement:

The *time-distance* curve is a *hyperbola* whose vertical axis of symmetry passes through the point $\overline{P}$ for which

(4) $$x = \bar{x} = -2H \sin \phi,$$

and

(5) $$t = \bar{t} = 2H \cos \phi / v.$$

This is the point at which the emergence angle of the reflected wave is $0°$ and therefore corresponds to the reflection of shortest path and least-time. We shall reach the same conclusions later by other means.

The asymptotes to our hyperbola are the lines

(6) $$vt - X = 0 \quad \text{and} \quad vt + X = 0,$$

which, referred to the original coordinate axes are, respectively,

(7) $$vt - x + 2H \sin \phi = 0,$$

and

$$vt + x - 2H \sin \phi = 0.$$

These two obviously pass through the point $\overline{P}$ and are parallel, since they have the same slope, to the two lines through the shot-point O representing "first-kick" arrivals from the surface wave. In Figure 32, these asymptotes are represented by dashed lines, whereas the "first-kick" lines are drawn in solid lines.

Consider, now, an arbitrary point P at a distance x from the shot-point O, as indicated in Figure 32, and let the emergence angle at P be indicated by α. If we represent the travel-time of the reflected wave from O to $P(x)$ by t, then the length of the path OQP, which, of course, is equal to $O'P$ is vt, *i.e.*,

$$O'P = vt.$$

Also,

$$OO' = 2H.$$

By the law of sines

(8) $$\sin \sphericalangle OPO'/\sin \sphericalangle POO' = OO'/O'P.$$

Now

$$\sphericalangle OPO' = 90° - \alpha,$$

and

$$\sphericalangle POO' = 90° + \phi,$$

in which ϕ is the angle of dip. (If P is on the up-dip side of O, $\sphericalangle POO' = 90° - \phi$, but the argument and result, it will be noted, are still valid.) With all this substitution, equation (8) becomes:

(9)
$$\sin \sphericalangle OPO'/\sin \sphericalangle POO' = \sin (90° - \alpha)/\sin (90° + \phi) = \cos \alpha/\cos \phi$$
$$= 2H/vt,$$

i. e.,

(10) $$\cos \alpha = 2H \cos \phi/vt.$$

This may be connected, by means of the identity

$$\sin \alpha = (1 - \cos^2 \alpha)^{1/2},$$

into

(11)
$$\sin \alpha = (1 - 4H^2 \cos^2 \phi/v^2t^2)^{1/2}$$
$$= (v^2t^2 - 4H^2 \cos^2 \phi)^{1/2}/vt.$$

If, now, we use relation (1) in this last expression, we find

$$\sin \alpha = [(x^2 + 4H^2 + 4Hx \sin \phi) - 4H^2 \cos^2 \phi]^{1/2}/vt,$$
$$= (x^2 + 4Hx \sin \phi + 4H^2 \sin^2 \phi)^{1/2}/vt,$$
(12) $$\sin \alpha = (x + 2H \sin \phi)/vt.$$

Let us now recall the fundamental relation of the emergence angle, namely,

(13) $$\sin \alpha = vdt/dx,$$

in which dt/dx is the slope of the *time-distance* curve. If we equate the right-hand sides of equations (12) and (13), we find that, for our *time-distance* curve:

(14) $$dt/dx = (x + 2H \sin \phi)/v^2 t.$$

It may be argued, and quite correctly, that this result is obtainable by direct differentiation of the equation of the *time-distance* curve (1), namely,

(15) $$2v^2 t \, dt/dx = 2x + 4H \sin \phi,$$

from which (14) follows directly. However, the purpose of our procedure above was to show, again, the connection between the slope of a *time-distance* curve (called, it will be remembered, the "apparent velocity") and the emergence angle of the corresponding wave.

Referring back to (14), the reflection which comes in "earlier" than any other is that for which $dt/dx=0$; this means at a distance x for which $x+2H \sin \phi=0$; *i.e.*, for

$$x = -2H \sin \phi.$$

It will now be recalled that this point has already been singled out in equation (4) by a different line of argument.

Ex. 49: The outcrop of the interface $R'R$ occurs at the point E whose x-coordinate is indicated by x_c. Show that

$$x_c = -H/\sin \phi,$$

that the emergence angle for the reflected wave approaches $90° - 2\phi$ at that point, and that, therefore, the slope of the *time-distance* curve there is

$$(dt/dx)_{x_c} = -\cos 2\phi/v.$$

Show, also, that the travel-time for the reflection to this point is the same as that for the direct surface "kick", *i.e.*,

$$t_c = H/v \sin \phi;$$

that, therefore, at this point E, the surface refraction *time-distance* curve (the straight line $t=x/v$ intersects our hyperbola). What is the seismic significance of this situation as reflected in the figure by the abrupt ending of both *time-distance* curves?

Ex. 50: Follow through all the details of this lesson for the numerical case mentioned in Lesson No. 10—or make your own numerical case.

Ex. 51: Show that the slope of the *time-distance* curve at the shot-point O ($x=0$) is $\sin \phi/v$, in which ϕ is the angle of dip of RR'.

Ex. 52: At what interval for a seismograph spread, in Figure 32, would the "Δt" be "back-handed"? (Ans. The interval between O and $\overline{P}$.)

A *very important* consequence of the result of Ex. 51 is that the dip of a reflecting horizon can be readily determined by a reflection spread, centered at the shot-point, if the velocity is known. For, if the length of the spread is Δx (one-half of Δx on each side of the shot-point), and if we measure a difference in time of Δt across this spread, then the formula for the emergence angle at the shot-point yields

$$\sin \phi = v\Delta t/\Delta x,$$

in which ϕ is the angle of dip. This follows from the fact that at the shot-point the angle of emergence is equal to the angle of dip.

This Lesson No. 11 is almost entirely a mathematical treatment. Some of the readers, because of their limited mathematical training, may find some difficulty in understanding its contents. It seems to me that in all cases an honest and conscientious attempt should be made to learn both the methods and the results, but particularly the latter. In any case, however, the reader should not be discouraged if his success with this lesson is not too good. One should be able to go on with the further lessons in any case. Lessons of this type are put in to round out the theory to completeness and will be of value to a full mathematical treatment.

It is perhaps advisable to emphasize once again that each reader or group of readers should adjust the pace of progress to its convenience and absorptive capacities and not try to follow these lessons as they appear.

M. M. SLOTNICK

Lesson No. 12

DETERMINATION OF VELOCITY AND INTERFACE
FROM REFLECTION DATA—GENERAL CASE

It might already have occurred to some of the readers that the methods described in Lesson No. 8 (pp. 31 *et seq.*) can readily be extended to cover the more general case of reflection data from a dipping interface. It is the purpose of this lesson so to extend those methods; and, as before, we shall do so by a numerical example. We might mention here, too, as we have mentioned before, that the method has its analytic analogue. The numerical method here described has been found to be the most practical for solving the problem with the type of data usually available.

To be specific, then, suppose that we have a spread on one side of a shot-point O running from 2,000 ft to 3,000 ft and that the corrected travel-times to the first and last pickups are, respectively, 1.332 and 1.353 sec. Suppose, further, that on the other side of O and in line with this spread we have another spread from 2,000 ft to 3,000 ft and that the travel-times to the first and last pick-up are, respectively, 1.377 and 1.420 sec. The situation is indicated in Figure 33.

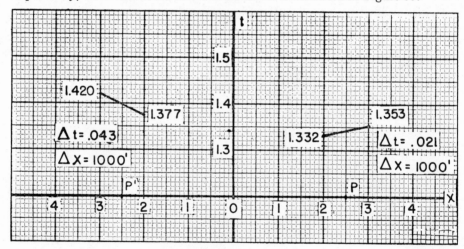

Fig. 33

Assuming the time-distance curves to be linear over each of these 1,000 ft-spreads, we can say that on one side of O (taken as on the right side in Figure 33), the travel-time to 2,500 ft from O (to the point P) is

$$(1/2) \ (1.332 + 1.353) = 1.342 \text{ sec.}$$

Similarly, on the other side of O we shall have the travel-time to 2,500 ft (to the point P') equal to

54

$$(1/2) (1.377 + 1.420) = 1.398 \text{ sec.}$$

Suppose, now, we *guess* that the velocity of our wave propagation is v_1 = 6,000 ft/sec. Then, at P, the angle of emergence, α_1, is obtained from the fact that

$$\sin \alpha_1 = (6,000) (0.021)/1,000 = 0.126,$$

and

$$\alpha_1 = 7°15'.$$

Similarly, at P', the angle of emergence, α_1', is obtained from the relation

$$\sin \alpha_1' = (6,000) (0.043)/1,000,$$
$$= 0.258;$$

so that

$$\alpha_1' = 15°.$$

The situation is drawn to scale in Figure 34. Emergent rays through P and P' are drawn whose angles with the vertical are, respectively, α_1 and α_1'. These are brought to intersection at the point O_1'.

If the guess of $v_1 = 6,000$ ft/sec is correct, then

(a) O_1' would be the image point of O with respect to the reflecting bed and

(b) the distances $O_1'P$ and $O_1'P'$ would be, respectively,

$$O_1'P = (6,000) (1.342) = 8,052 \text{ ft}$$

and

$$O_1'P' = (6,000) (1.398),$$
$$= 8,388 \text{ ft,}$$

since the travel-times to P and P' are, respectively, 1.342 and 1.398 sec.

A simple scaling of these distances from Figure 34, which is drawn to scale, shows these distances to be, respectively, about

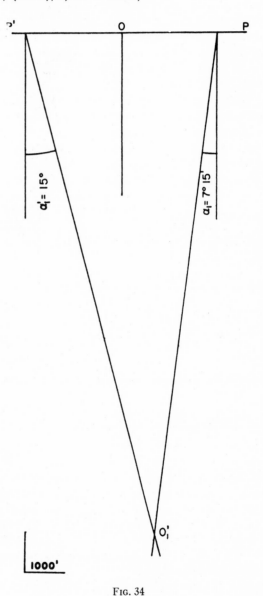

FIG. 34

$$O_1'P = 12,800 \text{ ft,}$$

and

$$O_1'P' = 13,300 \text{ ft.}$$

We conclude, therefore, that our guess of 6,000 ft/sec was far from the mark. Moreover, a little consideration will indicate that the guess was too small.

Consequently, we proceed to a guess of $v_2 = 8,000$ ft/sec and continue as before. With such a velocity, and referring to Figure 35, at P:

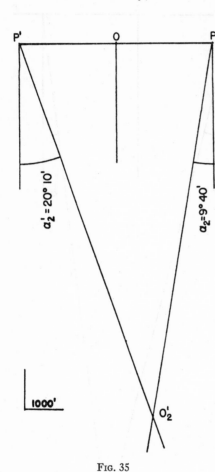

$$\sin \alpha_2 = (8,000)(0.021)/1,000 = 0.168,$$

$$\alpha_2 = 9°40';$$

at P':

$$\sin \alpha_2' = (8,000)(0.043)/1,000 = 0.344,$$

$$\alpha_2' = 20°10'.$$

Drawn to scale, the image point of O is now O_2' and, if our guess of the velocity of 8,000 ft/sec is the correct one, we should now have:

$$O_2'P = (8,000)(1.342) = 10,736 \text{ ft,}$$

and

$$O_2'P' = (8,000)(1.398) = 11,184 \text{ ft.}$$

Scaling off these distances in Figure 35 shows that

$$O_2'P = 9,600 \text{ ft,}$$

and

$$O_2'P' = 10,000 \text{ ft.}$$

FIG. 35

Again, our guess is not too good, but we are nearer our goal, and a check of this set of figures with the preceding set shows that

(1) we have gone too far in increasing the velocity from 6,000 ft/sec to 8,000 ft/sec but that

(2) the correct answer is nearer the latter figure. Accordingly, let us try $v_3 = 7,500$ ft/sec.

As before, but referring to Figure 36, at P:

$$\sin \alpha_3 = (7{,}500)\,(0.021)/1{,}000 = 0.1575,$$
$$\alpha_3 = 9°5';$$

at P':

$$\sin \alpha_3' = (7{,}500)\,(0.043)/1{,}000 = 0.3225,$$
$$\alpha_3' = 18°50'.$$

Drawn to scale as in Figure 36, O_3' is the image point of O, and, if our velocity of 7,500 ft/sec is the correct one, we should have:

$$O_3'P = (7{,}500)\,(1.342) = 10{,}065 \text{ ft},$$

and

$$O_3'P' = (7{,}500)\,(1.398) = 10{,}485 \text{ ft}.$$

Scaling off these distances in Figure 36 shows that we have

$$O_3'P = 10{,}100 \text{ ft},$$

and

$$O_3'P' = 10{,}550 \text{ ft}.$$

This agreement is as close as we can hope to attain, considering the accuracy of the data and of the drawing. Accordingly, we conclude that a velocity of 7,500 ft/sec is a good estimate of the true value.

It follows, also, that the perpendicular bisector of OO_3' in Figure 36, namely, the line RR', is the trace of the reflecting horizon which, it will be noted, is at a depth of 5,000 ft vertically below O and that it is dipping to the left in the manner and amount shown.

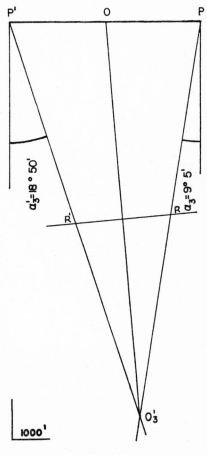

Fig. 36

It may be noted that it is *not* necessary to have the two sets of data used in our problem symmetrically spaced with respect to the shot-point. In fact, the reader is asked to solve the same problem as before but with different data as in the following example.

Ex. 53: Determine the position of a reflecting horizon if we are given the following reflection data, all *from the same side* of and in line with the shot-point:

Distance from Shot-point (Ft)	Travel-time of Reflection (Sec)
2,000	1.377
3,000	1.420
5,000	1.537
6,000	1.609

Lesson No. 13

ELEMENTS OF "DIP-SHOOTING"

It has probably occurred to some of the readers that the basis of interpretation by means of the so-called "dip-shooting" method can be found in the last two lessons. It is therefore opportune at this stage to include some pages in which we shall attempt to outline the general ideas and, by a few exercises, to direct the reader's attention to the possibilities of the method.

Suppose, then, that centering about a point P, at a distance x from a shot-point O, we have a spread of pickups, Δx in overall length, in line with O and over which a reflected wave-front shows a difference in travel-time of Δt (of Figure 37). If, as usual, we indicate the emergence angle of this wave-front at P by α, then we have, for practical purposes, the relation

$$\sin \alpha = v\Delta t/\Delta x.$$

As usual, too, we indicate the velocity of the reflected wave by v.

Suppose, now, that on the opposite side of the shot-point O and in line with the spread of pickups described in the preceding paragraph, we have another spread whose length is also Δx and which is centered at the point P', whose distance from O is also x (of Figure 37). Over this spread we assume the difference in travel-time is $(\Delta t)'$ and that, at P', the emergence angle of the reflected wave is α', so that

$$\sin \alpha' = v(\Delta t)'/\Delta x.$$

Now, as has been shown repeatedly in the last few lessons, once α and α' are determined, it is a simple matter to find the image point, O', of O with respect to the reflecting surface, and the trace of the reflecting surface is, in fact, the perpendicular bisector, $R'R$, of the line OO'.

Of the two values, Δt and $(\Delta t)'$, let

$$\Delta t \geq (\Delta t)',$$

i.e., since the two quantities are either equal to each other or not, let Δt be the greater if they are unequal. Then

$$\alpha \geq \alpha',$$

and a little thought will show that the dip is toward the side of the greater value, Δt.

All this is indicated in Figure 37. It should be obvious in Figure 37 that

$$\angle PO'P' = \alpha + \alpha'.$$

Ex. 54: Prove $\angle PO'P' = \alpha + \alpha'$.

59

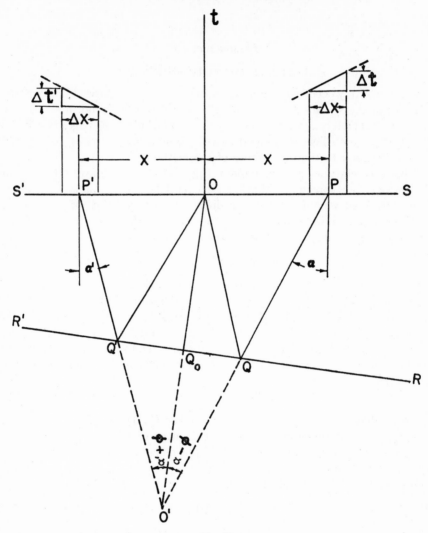

It should also be obvious that
$$\angle OO'P = \alpha - \phi,$$
$$\angle OO'P' = \alpha' + \phi.$$

Ex. 55: Prove the last two relations.

By the law of sines, in $\triangle OO'P$,
$$OP/OO' = \sin(\alpha - \phi)/\sin(90° - \alpha) = \sin(\alpha - \phi)/\cos\alpha,$$
and, in $\triangle OO'P'$:
$$OP'/OO' = \sin(\alpha' + \phi)/\sin(90° - \alpha') = \sin(\alpha' + \phi)/\cos\alpha'.$$

Now, in these two sets of equations, the left-hand sides are equal, since

$$OP' = OP = x.$$

Hence, the right-hand sides are equal and we have,

$$\sin (\alpha - \phi)/\cos \alpha = \sin (\alpha' + \phi)/\cos \alpha'.$$

We now borrow from our knowledge of trigonometrical relations to expand the numerators:

$$\sin (\alpha - \phi) = \sin \alpha \cos \phi - \cos \alpha \sin \phi,$$
$$\sin (\alpha' + \phi) = \sin \alpha' \cos \phi + \cos \alpha' \sin \phi.$$

If, then, these relations are put into the last equations, and if, further, we recall that

$$\sin \alpha/\cos \alpha = \tan \alpha,$$

the result may be written:

$$\tan \alpha \cos \phi - \sin \phi = \tan \alpha' \cos \phi + \sin \phi.$$

This, in turn, by dividing through by $\cos \phi$ and rearranging terms, can be written

$$\tan \phi = (1/2) (\tan \alpha - \tan \alpha').$$

This is the basic result upon which the various methods of dip-shooting rest. As has been described in the preceding lessons and in the earlier part of this one, the values of α and α' can be determined provided we obtain Δt and $\Delta t'$ for a suitable Δx and have the value of v. From these values of α and α', the values of $\tan \alpha$ and $\tan \alpha'$ can be readily obtained, and thereafter it is a simple matter to find $\tan \phi$ from the relation above.

In practice, the steps described can be, and have been, reduced to tables and charts which render the actual arithmetic and conversion a matter of simple operations. If, for example, field practice is such that Δx, the length of the spread, is fixed and if, further, the velocity v, also, is assumed constant, then $\tan \alpha$ is directly a function of Δt alone. We should then tabulate $\tan \alpha$ as a function of Δt, from the fact that

$$\sin \alpha = v\Delta t/\Delta x.$$

From this table, then, $\tan \alpha$ and $\tan \alpha'$ are read immediately, once Δt and $\Delta t'$ are given. The value of $\tan \phi$ and of ϕ then follow at once.

This, in brief, is a description of the method and its use. We do not propose to go into more detail here on this matter, since it is felt that there is no need to do so at this time.

It is customary to indicate at each shot-point on a map the direction and amount of dip so determined—assuming it to be true dip and direction. Often the shooting is done in a four-way pattern from which better estimates of true dip and direction are obtained. On this score we shall have more to say in some future lesson.

Ex. 56: Given $\Delta t = 0.045$ for a spread of $\Delta x = 1,000$ ft, centering at a distance of 4,500 ft from the shot-point and a $(\Delta t)' = 0.064$ for a spread of similar length centering at the same distance on the other side of the shot-point. What is the dip of the reflecting bed if the velocity of wave travel is 7,500 ft/sec? Note that the travel-times are not necessary for the solution of the problem. They are nonetheless determined by the given data. What are the travel-times? Hint: Draw the picture of the wave-paths and get the image point O' of the shot-point O.

Lesson No. 14

PLOTTING REFLECTION POINTS ON DIPPING REFLECTING HORIZONS

The contents of this lesson will, for the most part, be immediate consequences of the last few lessons, insofar as computing techniques are involved. However, the lesson will furnish an opportunity for stating some broad and important considerations which, it is to be hoped, will be studied by the reader to the extent that a full understanding of the implications for interpretation is obtained.

We begin by repeating the hypotheses with which we are still working:

(a) that our "profile" of shooting is in the direction of true dip;
(b) that there is a constant velocity, v, of wave propagation in the medium involved;
(c) that the dipping reflecting surface is plane.

We propose to discuss, under these conditions, the concept which has become generally known as "migrating the reflecting point." We shall *studiously avoid* the use of this term since we feel it to be definitely and needlessly misleading. If the reflecting bed is flat or inclined at a very gentle dip, it is customary to plot the "reflection points" on a vertical line *midway* between the shot-point and pickup location, or directly under the shot-point, whether the section is carried on a *time* or *depth* basis. If, however, the dip is sizeable and, therefore, the "more exact positioning" of the reflection point is necessary, we can no longer content ourselves with such a simple procedure. The attempt to place the reflection point correctly in the section has been termed the "migration of the reflection point." From such a phrase one might infer that the reflection point has been moved to its present position from its *correct* position. This is exactly opposite to the facts. Accordingly, we shall speak of *placing* the reflection point where *it ought to be*, rather than "migrating" it.

The second concept that we must mention is that the correct placing of the reflection point for a dipping bed *must* take into consideration some velocity information. There is no way of accounting for the amount of dip and position of the dipping reflecting bed on a section carried on a time basis only. One must use velocity information, directly or in a method which carries, implicit in it, such information. It is well to consider this fact thoroughly, for very often the question of how to account for large dips on sections carried on a *time* basis is raised. The proper answer is, of course, that there is no way except to convert to sections carried in depth, and this, in turn, means that velocities are being used.

To introduce the topic, consider Figures 38 and 39. In the first of these figures we consider a dip (of 10°), and in the second a steep dip (of 45°). To understand the succeeding paragraphs, it is recommended that while reading them the reader do the next exercise, which follows the description of the figures.

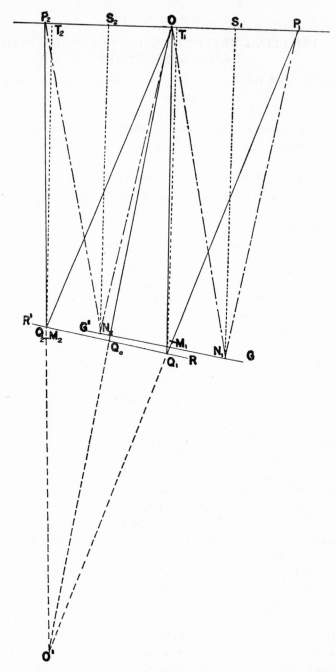

Fig. 38

Here is how the figures were made:

(1) $R'R$ is the trace of a dipping bed.

(2) Draw OQ_0 from the shot-point O perpendicular to $R'R$.

The path OQ_0 is that of the ray from O which is reflected back to O from $R'R$. The travel-time would be

$$2(OQ_0/v)$$

in which v is the velocity of propagation.

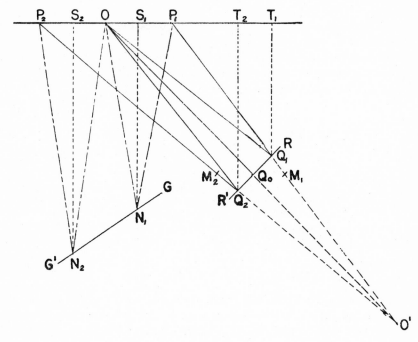

Fig. 39

(3) Extend OQ_0 to O' so that

$$OQ_0 = Q_0O'.$$

The point O' is the image point of O with respect to $R'R$.

(4) Join O' to P_1 and P_2 where P_1 and P_2 are pickup locations, equidistant and in line with O. Call the intersections of $O'P_1$ and $O'P_2$ with $R'R$, Q_1 and Q_2 respectively.

As we have seen repeatedly in the last several lessons, the points Q_1 and Q_2 are the reflecting points we seek. The wave paths from O to P_1 and P_2 are OQ_1P_1 and OQ_2P_2 respectively.

(5) Thus, *if our section* were being carried properly, we should locate the reflecting points Q_1 and Q_2 under their projections at the surface (at T_1 and T_2),

and, by joining Q_1 and Q_2, we would have the desired trace, $R'R$, of the reflecting surface.

Now, let us see where the trace would be drawn if no account were taken of the "Δt" of the record, which means, of the dip. Where would the section show the trace, in other words, if only the travel-times to P_1 and P_2 were used and the corresponding depths were plotted directly under the midpoints, S_1 and S_2, of the distances OP_1 and OP_2?

The distances $O'P_1$ and $O'P_2$ are equal to the distances travelled by the reflections OQ_1P_1 and OQ_2P_2. Suppose:

(1) We locate the points M_1 and M_2 as the bisecting points of the line segments $O'P_1$ and $O'P_2$ respectively.

(2) On the perpendiculars S_1N_1 and S_2N_2 to the surface of the earth through the midpoints, S_1 and S_2, of the distances OP_1 and OP_2, locate the points N_1 and N_2, respectively, so that

$$ON_1 = P_1N_1 = P_1M_1,$$

and

$$ON_2 = P_2N_2 = P_2M_2.$$

Then

(3) since by this construction

$$ON_1P_1 = 2\overline{ON_1} = 2\overline{O'M_1} = \overline{O'P_1},$$

and

$$ON_2P_2 = 2\overline{ON_2} = 2\overline{O'M_2} = \overline{O'P_2},$$

the true reflecting paths OQ_1P_1 and OQ_2P_2 are respectively equal in length to the paths ON_1P_1 and ON_2P_2, if the same velocity is used in both cases. We should then locate the points N_1 and N_2 and draw $G'G$ through these two points, as the desired trace.

The two cases in Figures 38 and 39 are intended to show how to find the **errors** which can accrue if due regard is not taken for locating the reflection point as determined from the "Δt's." It may be noted, also, that the error introduced by "midpoint" plotting increases with the angle of dip.

Ex. 57: Assume a dipping bed $R'R$ of 22° which is at a depth of 7,200 ft directly below a shot-point O. Draw a figure for this situation similar to Figures 38 and 39. If the wave velocity is 8,000 ft/sec, find the travel-times to points P_1 and P_2 each 2,000 ft from, but on opposite sides of, the shot-point O, in line with the direction of dip, P_1 being on the down-dip side. What is the $\Delta t/\Delta x$ for the *time-distance* curve at P_1 and P_2?

This exercise will form the basis of the rest of the discussion of this subject in Lesson No. 15.

Lesson No. 15

PLOTTING REFLECTION POINTS ON DIPPING
REFLECTING HORIZONS (*Continued*)

At the end of the preceding lesson it was mentioned that we shall continue the subject under discussion by using Ex. 57 as a numerical case.

The following facts can be ascertained for the solution of that problem. The travel-time of the reflection to P_1 is 1.778 sec, and to P_2 it is 1.592 sec. At P_1 we have $\Delta t/\Delta x = 0.062/1{,}000$, and at P_2 we have $\Delta t/\Delta x = 0.029/1{,}000$. The corresponding angles of emergence are:

at P_1

$$\sin \alpha_1 = 0.496, \qquad \alpha_1 = 29°45',$$

and at P_2

$$\sin \alpha_2 = 0.232, \qquad \alpha_2 = 13°25'.$$

The reader is now urged to do carefully the problems which follow and to make the necessary drawings to scale.

Given the three points P_2, O, P_1 in line on the surface in the direction of true dip of a reflecting plane, with

$$P_2O = OP_1 = 2{,}000 \text{ ft.}$$

Ex. 58a: If the velocity of propagation is 8,000 ft/sec and the travel-time from the shot-point O to P_1 is 1.778 sec, plot the reflecting point N_1 under the assumption that it is vertically under a point midway between O and P_1.

Ex. 58b: The travel-time from O to P_2 is 1.592 sec. Plot the reflecting point N_2 under a similar assumption.

The line joining N_1 and N_2 is, then, the trace that would be indicated if *no attention* were paid to the information contained in the Δt's of the corresponding seismograms.

Suppose, now, that P_1 and P_2 are central points of spreads of pickups extending 500 ft on each side of these points and in line with O. Thus, for the corresponding seismograms, $\Delta x = 1{,}000$ ft.

Ex. 59a: Given that the travel-time to P_1 is 1.778 sec and given also that $\Delta t = 0.062$ sec for $\Delta x = 1{,}000$ ft around P_1. If, as before, $v = 8{,}000$ ft/sec, show that the emergence angle α_1 at P_1 is 29°45'. Draw the path of the emerging ray and extend it to the image point O' of O, by making $P_1O' = (8{,}000)(1.778)$ sec. Draw OO' and bisect it at Q_0. At Q_0 draw $R'R$ at right angles to OO'. The intersection $R'R$ with $O'P_1$ is Q_1, the *true reflection point*, and $R'R$ is the extended *true trace* of the reflecting plane.

Ex. 59b: Repeat the steps in the preceding problem for the point P_2, for which the travel-time is 1.592 sec, and $\Delta t = 0.029$ sec for $\Delta x = 1{,}000$ ft.

Ex. 60: A spread of pickups, 1,000 ft long, is in line with the true dip of a reflecting bed extending across a shot-point O and 500 ft on either side of that point. The travel-time to the center pickup (at O) is 1.669 sec and the Δt across the full spread (1,000 ft) is 0.047 sec. If the velocity of propagation is 8,000 ft/sec,

    a. What is the emergence angle of the reflecting wave at O? This is equal to the dip of the reflecting bed. Why?

    b. Draw this emergent ray and extend it to the image point O', which is such that $\overline{OO'} = (8,000)\,(1.669)$ ft. Why?

    c. The midpoint of $\overline{OO'}$ is the corresponding true reflecting point. Why?

    d. The perpendicular bisector of $\overline{OO'}$ is the true trace of the reflecting bed. Why?

To the Readers of the Lessons:

With the accompanying Lessons Nos. 14 and 15, the first part of the projected series comes to an end. We have tried to cover the elements of the simple seismic reflection problem in the first part, and we shall now turn to the elements of the simple seismic refraction problem, after which we hope to fuse both problems into work of more advanced nature.

We have found that the value of the lessons can be greatly enhanced by holding group discussions at periodic intervals, each led by a qualified person. Such valuable criticisms and comments as have been evoked have, in fact, arisen from such group meetings. It has been a very distinct source of happiness to me personally to be able to take part in such meetings and to lend such advice and recommendations for covering the subject matter as seemed proper. I shall try to continue these visits with the same purpose in mind; but I emphasize again that group meetings be arranged at which one or more of the participants act as teachers to discuss these lessons. The pace with which the lessons are covered should be decided among the group, and in no way should one feel that this pace need be related to the frequency with which the lessons are "published." That frequency, frankly, hinges entirely on the mood, schedule and temperament of the writer. It should be evident that I enjoy writing the lessons all the more as reports of an enthusiastic response come in.

There are two tasks which should be accomplished before the second series of lessons is started. The first is the very happy one, albeit somewhat delayed, of acknowledging the splendid cooperation of the young lady who has done all the typing of these lessons. Such mistakes as are found are in no way hers, since the lessons are read and reread before "publication." For these mistakes I alone assume the responsibility. But for the excellence of their appearance and the efficiency of distribution, I owe and acknowledge a debt of thanks to Miss Louise Bodron. The figures accompanying the lessons are drafted by Mr. Hugh W. Hardy, whose work attests his ability and for which I am indeed grateful. Here, too, I must take all the responsibility for any errors which have appeared.

The second task is one of enumeration. Our circulation is reaching close to 300 copies, and we wish to find out how many of these are actually in use. There is no desire to keep these lessons from anyone in our organization who feels that he can profit from them. Nonetheless, we feel that we do not want to have any of the lessons wasted. Consequently, in order to give us a "look-see," please fill in the enclosed form at once and send it to me. If no reply is forthcoming, you may find yourself and your colleagues *off the list*. This, of course, we do not want to happen.

M. M. Slotnick

Lesson No. 16

SNELL'S LAW

The preceding lessons have shown the very fundamental and important role played by the relationship existing between the slope of the *time-distance* curve (dt/dx) of a seismic "event" and the emergence angle of the corresponding wave.

There is yet another concept of equal importance in the study of "geometrical acoustics," to coin a phrase, which we shall now introduce.

Consider a moving *plane* wave front which assumes the successive positions of the members of a family of parallel planes. Let its velocity of propagation in the medium be v_1. Now suppose that this medium is bounded by a *plane* surface, called the interface, on the other side of which is a medium in which the velocity of propagation is v_2, different from v_1.

As the *plane* wave front in the first medium moves towards and across the plane interface into the second medium, some of its energy is *reflected* back into the first medium in a manner which has been previously discussed. The energy which passes across the interface into the second medium is said to be "refracted."

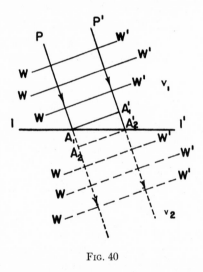

FIG. 40

As the *plane* wave front in the first medium moves across the interface into the second medium it *cannot* continue to occupy the successive positions of the same family of parallel planes extended into this medium but must, instead, change direction into another family of parallel planes (except in the very special case in which the plane wave front is parallel to the interface). To show this, consider the situation sketched in Figure 40. Here we have a simplified section a plane wave front in the upper medium represented by the traces of successive positions of this front, WW'. The motion of this plane wave toward the plane interface, whose trace is II', is further indicated by two wave paths, P and P', at right angles to the fronts represented by WW'.

Suppose that the wave passed into the second medium and continued so that its front persisted in occupying successive planes parallel to the original family, WW', in the first medium, as shown by dotted lines.

The wave front A_1A_1', in which A_1 is on the interface II', would move into the wave front A_2A_2', parallel to A_1A_1', in an amount of time equal to that necessary for transit from A_1 to A_2 or A_1' to A_2', which requires that these times of transit, $A_1'A_2'/v_1$ and A_1A_2/v_2, *should be equal*. Since v_1 and v_2 are assumed *not* equal and since $A_1'A_2' = A_1A_2$, these times are *not* equal except in the case of

70

WW' being all parallel to II'. Thus, the plane wave front must change in direction on crossing the interface. The change in direction is called the refraction of the wave, and the amount of the change, *i.e.*, the law of refraction, is governed by the relation called Snell's Law.

We proceed to discuss this fundamental relation. Consider, then, a plane wave front, W_1W_1', travelling at a velocity v_1 toward a plane interface II', and let P_1 and P_1' be two wave paths indicating the direction of propagation, all of which is shown in section in Figure 41. Let A_1 be a point on the path P_1 at which the wave front strikes the interface. At the instant at which the wave front strikes A_1, it also passes through such points as A_1', for which the corresponding path is P_1'. The *angle at which the wave front, A_1A_1', strikes the interface II'*, indicated by θ_1 in Figure 41, is called the *angle of incidence*. This angle is equal to the angle between wave path P_1 and the normal (perpendicular) to II'.

In the second medium the plane wavefronts are represented by the parallel traces A_2A_2' and W_2W_2', and the corresponding wave paths by P_2 and P_2'. The angle which A_2A_2' makes with II' is equal to the angle which P_2 makes with the normal to II', and is indicated by θ_2 in Figure 41.

Since both A_1A_1' and A_2A_2' are plane wave fronts of the same wave, the time of travel from A_1 to A_2, which is

$$A_1A_2/v_2,$$

must equal the time of travel from A_1' to A_2', which is

$$A_1'A_2'/v_1;$$

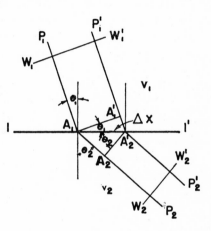

FIG. 41

that is to say, if we call this time τ, then

$$\tau = A_1A_2/v_2 = A_1'A_2'/v_1.$$

We now recall that the relationship between wave fronts and wave paths is such that

$$\angle A_1A_1'A_2' = \angle A_1A_2A_2' = 90°.$$

Thus, from basic definitions,

$$\sin \theta_1 = A_1'A_2'/A_1A_2',$$

and

$$\sin \theta_2 = A_1A_2/A_1A_2'.$$

If we designate the distance A_1A_2' by σ, then

$$A_1'A_2' = \sigma \sin \theta_1,$$

and
$$A_1A_2 = \sigma \sin \theta_2.$$

These last two results we now insert in the preceding equations for τ and get
$$\tau = \sigma \sin \theta_2/v_2 = \sigma \sin \theta_1/v_1.$$

This last result may be simplified into either form of the desired result:
$$\sin \theta_1/v_1 = \sin \theta_2/v_2,$$
or
$$\sin \theta_1/\sin \theta_2 = v_1/v_2.$$

This is known as *Snell's Law*.

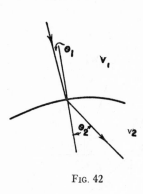

FIG. 42

We have indicated the proof of Snell's relation by the use of plane waves. It can be shown that, for purposes such as we have in mind, and by limiting processes, Snell's Law in the form shown above can be used for wave paths, or rays, not necessarily associated with plane waves, and across interfaces, not necessarily plane. In other words, we shall use Snell's Law in situations such as are indicated in Figure 42.

Ex. 61: If a ray in a medium of wave velocity 7,200 ft/sec strikes an interface at an angle of 24°, at what angle with the normal to the interface will it enter the second medium in which the velocity is 9,600 ft/sec? Draw a sketch of this case, to scale.

Ex. 62: Through a shot-point O in a medium in which the velocity is 8,150 ft/sec a number of rays are drawn to indicate schematically the energy going off in "all" directions, as shown in Figure 43. Suppose that a plane interface, II', exists below which is a medium in which the velocity is 10,250 ft/sec. Some of the energy is reflected, and the situation for the reflected energy has been studied in Lesson No. 4 (see Figure 15b). Draw the rays into which the given rays, striking II', are *refracted* into the lower medium. Assume

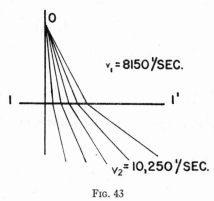

FIG. 43

the rays from O strike II' at 0°, 5°, 10°, 15°, 20°, $\cdots$, 45°.

Ex. 63: Do the preceding problem if the velocities in the media are interchanged; *i.e.*, the upper one has a velocity of 10,250 ft/sec, and the lower one 8,150 ft/sec.

Consider, again, the relation called Snell's Law:
$$\sin \theta_1/\sin \theta_2 = v_1/v_2.$$

It should be evident from the figures already shown that we can always restrict both angles θ_1 and θ_2 to lie between 0° and 90°. The angles, in fact, may also attain these end values. Thus, if $v_2 > v_1$, $\theta_2 > \theta_1$, and vice versa.

One important point should be realized, which stems from the fact that the *sine of an angle is at most equal to unity*. Suppose that

$$v_2 > v_1,$$

and let us write Snell's Law in the form:

$$\sin \theta_2 = (v_2/v_1) \sin \theta_1.$$

For all values of $\sin \theta_1$ from O to v_1/v_2 (which <1, by our supposition) there is a corresponding value of $\sin \theta_2$ and, therefore, of θ_2. However, at the end value for which $\sin \theta_1 = v_1/v_2$, $\sin \theta_2 = 1$, and $\theta_2 = 90°$. This particular value of

$$\theta_1 = (\sin^{-1} v_1/v_2)*$$

for which $\theta_2 = 90°$ is called the *critical angle* for the two media, and we shall usually indicate it by ϕ.

Let us repeat the argument, for it is an important one.

If two media, in which the velocities are v_1 and v_2, and such that

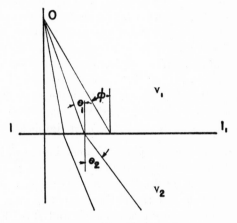

FIG. 44

$v_2 > v_1$, are separated by an interface, then a ray from the first medium striking the interface at an angle θ_1 with the normal to the interface will be refracted into the second medium at an angle θ_2 with that normal. The relation between the angles is governed by

$$\sin \theta_1/\sin \theta_2 = v_1/v_2.$$

Since v_2 is assumed greater than v_1, θ_1 is limited in magnitude to lie between O and $\sin^{-1} (v_1/v_2)$. The latter value of $\theta_1 = [\sin^{-1} (v_1/v_2)]$ is referred to as the critical angle and will usually be indicated by ϕ; *i.e.*,

$$\sin \phi = v_1/v_2.$$

The corresponding value of θ_2 is 90°.

Ex. 64: What is the critical angle between two media in the first of which the velocity is 8,150 ft/sec and in the second 10,250 ft/sec?

Ex. 65: The critical angle between two media is 48° and the velocity in the faster one is 12,400 ft/sec. What is the velocity in the other medium?

There is yet another and very significant property of wave propagation which leads to Snell's Law, which we shall leave for the next lesson.

* It should be recalled that the symbol $\sin^{-1} \alpha$ means the *angle* whose sine is α.

Lesson No. 17

SNELL'S LAW—PRINCIPLE OF LEAST TIME

A fundamental result in the mathematical discussion of wave propagation is the concept known as *Fermat's Principle*. Stated for our purposes, it runs somewhat like this: The study of the propagation of waves may be reduced to the study of wave paths which are defined as the paths along which the travel-times are minimal. We proceed to expand on this subject.

Consider a moving wave front. Corresponding to it is a family of wave paths (see Lesson No. 1). Choose any two points lying on any one of these wave paths. Of all possible paths joining those two points, the *wave path* is that for which the travel-time is least. In other words, the travel-time along any other path (within suitable limits) joining those two points would be greater than along the *wave path*.

It is for this reason that Fermat's Principle is sometimes referred to as the *Principle of Least Time*. We take this principle as basic to our development, and we shall now seek some of its implications.

In the first place, in a medium in which the *velocity* is *constant*, the *wave paths* are *straight lines*. For, obviously, if the velocity, v, in a medium is constant, the travel-time t, along a path of length L joining any two points A and B (of Figure 45) in the medium is

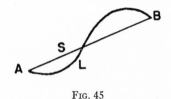

$$t = L/v.$$

FIG. 45

The smallest value of t will be for the path S which is the straight line joining A and B.

Now, let II' in Figure 46 be the trace of a plane interface separating two media in which the velocities are v_1 and v_2. Let the points A_1 in the first medium and A_2 in the second medium be connected by the wave path L_1L_2. The two parts L_1 and L_2 are straight-line segments, in accordance with the earlier statement, since v_1 and v_2 are assumed constant. Moreover, the straight-line segments L_1 and L_2 are such that the total travel-time along them, namely

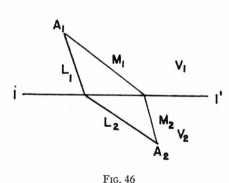

FIG. 46

$$t = L_1/v_1 + L_2/v_2,$$

is less than the travel-time for any

74

other path, such as, for example, M_1M_2. That is to say, for this latter path the travel-time $M_1/v_1 + M_2/v_2$, is greater than that for L_1L_2.

We seek the distinguishing characteristic of the wave path L_1L_2 over any other path M_1M_2. In Figure 47, let R be any point on II' and join the given points A_1 and A_2 to R. At R draw the normal to II' and let

$$\measuredangle A_1RN_1 = \theta_1,$$
$$\measuredangle A_2RN_2 = \theta_2.$$

As R takes on various positions along II', the angles θ_1 and θ_2 take on different values. Then, too, for each position of R, the travel-time

$$t = \overline{A_1R}/v_1 + \overline{RA_2}/v_2$$

takes on a different value. *For what position of R is this time a minimum, that is, the least value?* For this position of R, what is the relation between θ_1 and θ_2? These questions we desire to answer.

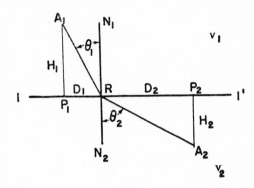

FIG. 47

Let the perpendicular distance from A_1 to II', that is, $\overline{A_1P_1}$, be indicated by H_1 and the perpendicular distance from A_2 to II', that is, $\overline{A_2P_2}$, by H_2. As R moves along II', H_1 and H_2 do *not* vary; they are constant. Let the distances $\overline{P_1R}$ and $\overline{RP_2}$ be represented by D_1 and D_2, respectively. For any position of R, we have

$$\overline{A_1R} = H_1/\cos\theta_1 \quad \text{and} \quad D_1 = \overline{P_1R} = H_1 \tan\theta_1.$$

Also, we have

$$\overline{RA_2} = H_2/\cos\theta_2 \quad \text{and} \quad D_2 = \overline{RP_2} = H_2 \tan\theta_2.$$

The travel-time for the path, $\overline{A_1R}$ and $\overline{RA_2}$, is therefore

(1) $$t = H_1/v_1 \cos\theta_1 + H_2/v_2 \cos\theta_2.$$

This travel-time varies with different positions of R, as do also θ_1 and θ_2. On the other hand,

(2) $$\overline{P_1P_2} = D_1 + D_2 = H_1 \tan\theta_1 + H_2 \tan\theta_2,$$

does *not* vary with different positions of R.

Let us recall that we desire to find the position of R for which (1) has the least possible value. We shall use the method of differentials:

From equation (1), by differentiating,

(3) $$dt = (H_1 \sin\theta_1/v_1 \cos^2\theta_1)d\theta_1 + (H_2 \sin\theta_2/v_2 \cos^2\theta_2)d\theta_2.$$

From equation (2), bearing in mind that the left-hand side does *not* change with different positions of R—that is, it is *constant*—we have

(4) $$O = (H_1/\cos^2 \theta_1)d\theta_1 + (H_2/\cos^2 \theta_2)d\theta_2.$$

Now, for the least value—minimum—of t in (1), the differential of t, dt in (3), must be O. We therefore rewrite (3) with this condition, and also (4) in these forms:

(5) $$(H_1 \sin \theta_1/v_1 \cos^2 \theta_1)d\theta_1 = - (H_2 \sin \theta_2/v_2 \cos^2 \theta_2)d\theta_2,$$

and

(6) $$(H_1/\cos^2 \theta_1)d\theta_1 = - (H_2/\cos^2 \theta_2)d\theta_2.$$

If, finally, we divide (5) by (6), we have:

$$\sin \theta_1/v_1 = \sin \theta_2/v_2,$$

which will be recalled as being *Snell's Law*.

Consider the result. The *path of minimum time from A_1 to A_2 occurs at that point R on II', for which Snell's Law obtains.*

We thus see that the approach to Snell's Law of the preceding lesson leads to the same result as is obtained from using the *minimum time* principle of Fermat.

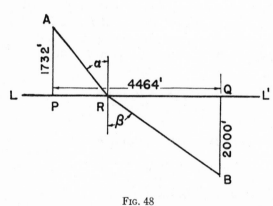

FIG. 48

Ex. 66: The point A is 1,732 ft offshore from a straight coast line, LL_1, and the point B is 2,000 ft inland from that coast line (Figure 48). The point P on LL' nearest A is 4,464 ft from the point Q on LL' nearest to B. If one must row at 10,000 ft/hr from A to some point R on the coast line and then walk from that point to B at 20,000 ft/hr, at what point R should one aim (in still water, of course) to get from A to B in the least possible time? How much time is actually involved in this least time? At the point R for the least time what are the values of angles α and β? Is the answer the same if the direction of travel is from B to A?

Ex. 67: A pipe line is to be laid from a well location A in a marsh to a gathering point B on high land, the two areas separated by a straight line LL' (see Figure 49). If all the costs of pipe and laying are \$2/ft on the high land and \$4/ft in the marsh, what is the least cost at which the line can be laid? How much pipe will be needed? Note that it is *not* the least length of pipe possible.

There is an *important limiting* case of this minimum time problem which we shall illustrate in the following manner.

In Figure 50, the point A is assumed to be 5 miles from the nearest point R on a straight road LL'. Let B be a point on the road 20 miles from R. If an automobile travels 15 mph from A towards any point of the road and can travel 30 mph on the road, to what point P should the car aim starting from A so that his path APB will be the fastest? To solve this problem, let us first find the time for any path, APB. Let $\angle RAP = \phi$. Then, the time needed is

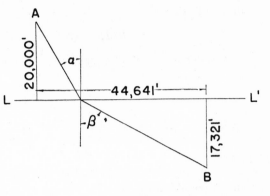

FIG. 49

$$t = \overline{AP}/15 + \overline{PB}/30,$$

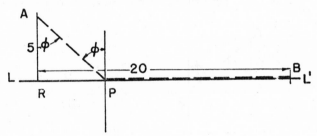

FIG. 50

in which

$$\overline{AP} = \overline{R}/\cos\phi = 5/\cos\phi$$

and

$$\overline{PB} = \overline{RB} - \overline{RP} = 20 - 5\tan\phi.$$

Thus,

$$t = 5/15\cos\phi + (20 - 5\tan\phi)/30;$$

i.e., simplifying,

$$t = 1/3\cos\phi + (4 - \tan\phi)/6.$$

Since $\tan\phi = \sin\phi/\cos\phi$, we have again by simplification,

$$t = (2 - \sin\phi)/6\cos\phi + 2/3.$$

To find ϕ for which t is a minimum, it is necessary (and in this case, also sufficient) that

$$dt/d\phi = 0.$$

By differentiating,

$$dt/d\phi = (2 \sin \phi - 1)/6 \cos^2 \phi.$$

When this derivative is set equal to 0 as a condition for the minimum t, we find that

$$\sin \phi = 1/2;$$

whence,

$$\phi = 30°.$$

Thus our problem is answered to the extent that we know that the path of minimum possible time is such that $\angle RAP = 30°$.

Ex. 68: In this discussion, is the answer the same if the direction of travel is from B to A?

Ex. 69: In the problem above compute the travel-time from A to P to B if $\angle RAP = 0°$, $5°$, $10°$, $15°$, $20°$, $\cdots$, $40°$, $45°$, and plot the corresponding travel-times as functions of the angle. Note that the minimum time occurs for $30°$.

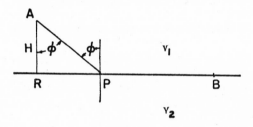

FIG. 51

Ex. 70: Show that for the general case illustrated in Figure 51, with the velocities of v_1 and v_2 as shown, the minimum travel-time from A to B will occur for that point P for which

$$\sin \phi = v_1/v_2.$$

Thus, we see that the *limiting* case of *Snell's Law* which occurs at the *critical angle* of incidence is also a limiting case of the minimum travel-time problem.

APPENDIX I

SOLUTION TO EXERCISE 66 OF LESSON NO. 17

J. A. BROOKS, JR.

It has probably already occurred to some of the readers that the actual numerical evaluation of the answer to Exercise 66 of Lesson No. 17 presents some difficulties. Many such problems are best solved by methods which consist of "trial and error" techniques. These methods are far more universal in their adaptability than elementary mathematical tools. For this reason, we are indicating such a method for solving Exercise 66 to obtain the desired numerical solution.

In this exercise, the solution requires that the angles α and β satisfy Snell's Law; that is, one condition for our answer is that

$$\sin \alpha / \sin \beta = 10,000/20,000,$$

which we can write in the form:

$$(1) \qquad\qquad 2 \sin \alpha = \sin \beta.$$

Another condition is obtained by rewriting equation (2) of page 75 for our purposes; namely,

$$(2) \qquad\qquad S = 1,732 \tan \alpha + 2,000 \tan \beta = 4,464.$$

From equation (1) it can immediately be determined that in this problem the angle α must be less than 30°. For if α is 30°, $\sin \alpha = 0.5$, $\sin \beta = 1$, $\beta = 90°$, and the point B in the problem would not be reached. For values of α greater than 30°, $\sin \beta$ is meaningless.

If we select values for α within the range in which we suspect the correct value of α to occur, then β is determined for each α by equation (1). By substituting these related values of α and β in equation (2), we can check the validity of our selection. The simplest way to make these calculations is to arrange the work in tabular form as shown below:

I	II	III	IV	V	VI	VII	VIII
α	$\sin \alpha$	$\sin \beta$	$\tan \alpha$	$1,732 \tan \alpha$	$\tan \beta$	$2,000 \tan \beta$	$S = 1,732 \tan \alpha$ $+2,000 \tan \beta$
10	0.1736	0.3472	0.1763	0.3054×10^3	0.3702	0.7404×10^3	1.046×10^3
15	0.2588	0.5176	0.2680	0.4642×10^3	0.6049	1.2098×10^3	1.674×10^3
20	0.3420	0.6840	0.3640	0.6304×10^3	0.9377	1.8754×10^3	2.506×10^3
25	0.4226	0.8452	0.4663	0.8076×10^3	1.581	3.162×10^3	3.970×10^3

In column I, the values selected for α are listed. Column II is a list of the values of $\sin \alpha$ for these values of α. The values in column III ($\sin \beta$) are twice the corresponding values of column II because of equation (1). Columns IV and VI list the

79

values of tan α and tan β as read from tables, and columns V and VII consist of these tangents multiplied by the indicated distances; namely, 1,732 and 2,000, respectively, as indicated in equation (2). Column VIII contains the sums of the values in columns V and VII. Because of equation (2), we seek that pair of values of α and β which makes this sum in column VIII equal to 4,464. Since the terms in column VIII in the tabulation increase with increasing values of α, and since the sum for $\alpha = 25°$ is 3,970 (which is still less than 4,464), we know the correct value for α lies between 25° and 30°.

We now extend our tabulation by choosing values for α of 26°, 27° and 28° and continue the computations as follows:

I	II	III	IV	V	VI	VII	VIII
α	sin α	sin β	tan α	1,732 tan α	tan β	2,000 tan β	$S = 1,732$ tan α $+2,000$ tan β
26	0.4384	0.8768	0.4877	0.8447×10^3	1.823	3.646×10^3	4.491×10^3
27	0.4540	0.9080	0.5095	0.8825×10^3	2.1675	4.335×10^3	5.218×10^3
28	0.4695	0.9390	0.5317	0.9209×10^3	2.7302	5.460×10^3	6.381×10^3

The value 4,491 for column VIII where $\alpha = 26°$ is greater than the required value 4,464, which indicates that the desired value for α lies between 25° and 26°. Since for $\alpha = 25°$, $S = 3,970$, and for $\alpha = 26°$, $S = 4,491$, a linear interpolation of the desired value, 4,464, will yield $\alpha = 25°55'$. If higher accuracy is desired, the interval for linear interpolation should be reduced. Thus, we continue our tabulation as follows:

I	II	III	IV	V	VI	VII	VIII
α	sin α	sin β	tan α	1,732 tan α	tan β	2,000 tan β	$S = 1,732$ tan α $+2,000$ tan β
25°55'	0.4371	0.8742	0.4859	0.8416×10^3	1.8003	3.601×10^3	4.443×10^3
25°56'	0.4373	0.8746	0.4863	0.8423×10^3	1.804	3.608×10^3	4.450×10^3
25°57'	0.4376	0.8752	0.4867	0.8430×10^3	1.809	3.618×10^3	4.451×10^3
25°58'	0.4379	0.8758	0.4870	0.8435×10^3	1.814	3.628×10^3	4.472×10^3
25°59'	0.4381	0.8762	0.4874	0.8442×10^3	1.818	3.636×10^3	4.480×10^3

The above tabulation gives a value of $S = 4,472$ when $\alpha = 25°58'$, which is nearest to the desired value of $S = 4,464$. (If still higher accuracy is desired, one could interpolate linearly between $\alpha = 25°57'$ and 25°58' and thus obtain $\alpha = 25°57.6'$.)

To the nearest minute, therefore, $\alpha = 25°58'$. The corresponding value of β is determined from the fact that sin $\beta = 2$ sin $\alpha = 0.8758$, as shown in column III. Thus, $\beta = 61°08'$. For these values of α and β, cos $\alpha = 0.8991$ and cos $\beta = 0.04828$. The equation for the travel-time is

$$t = 1,732/10,000 \cos \alpha + 2,000/20,000 \cos \beta;$$

and, substituting the values for $\cos \alpha$ and $\cos \beta$,

$$t = 1.732/8.991 + 1/4.828,$$
$$= 0.193 + 0.207,$$
$$= 0.400 \text{ hours or 24 minutes.}$$

The solution to Exercise 67 can be obtained similarly.

Lesson No. 18

SINGLE LAYER REFLECTION AND REFRACTION PATHS

Consider a shot-point O on the surface, SS', of the ground under which we have a medium in which the velocity of propagation is v_1. We shall assume this medium, or bed, to have a thickness of h_1 and to be separated from the next deeper medium, or bed, by a plane interface, II'. In this lower bed the velocity of propagation is v_2, which we assume to be greater than v_1, $(v_2 > v_1)$. (See Figure 52.)

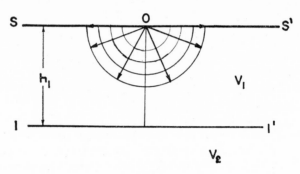

Fig. 52

The shot at O generates a wave front which expands spherically. Consider the corresponding rays, or wave paths, associated with this wave front. One wave path moves along the surface SS' at a velocity v_1. If detectors were placed along SS', this wave, sometimes called "first-kick" wave, would arrive in a travel-time t proportional to the distance x from the shot-point; $i.e.$, for the travel-time of this wave, we have

$$t = x/v_1.$$

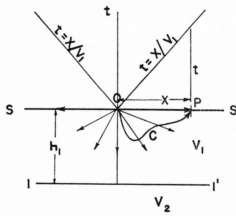

Fig. 53

Note that the minimum time principle obtains. For if P is a typical pickup position at a distance x (Figure 53), the shortest time of travel from O to P is along the straight line from O to P, a distance equal to x, for which the travel-time is $t = x/v_1$. In this bed, any other path—as for example the path C in Figure 53—from O to P would obviously consume more time than the direct, straight-line path.

82

For this wave, then, the *time-distance* curve is the straight line through O, whose slope is $1/v_1$. It may be trivial, but it is nonetheless worthy of note, to see that the "emergence angle" (see Lesson No. 1) for this wave is 90°, and that the *slope* of the corresponding *time-distance* curve is

$$dt/dx = \Delta t/\Delta x = 1/v_1.$$

Accordingly, our relation of Lesson No. 1,

$$\sin \alpha = v_1(\Delta t/\Delta x),$$

becomes an identity in which $\alpha = 90°$, $\sin \alpha = 1$, and $(\Delta t/\Delta x) = 1/v_1$.

Ex. 71: Draw the *time-distance* curve for the "first-kicks" in Figure 53 if $v_1 = 8,150$ ft/sec.

As we have discussed in previous work, some of the energy from the shot at O travels in a wave front to the interface II' and is reflected back to SS'. A typical reflected path might be ORP (Figure 54). As we have seen, this path, too, satisfies the requirement of least travel-time from O to P with the additional requirement of being reflected by II'.

In Figure 54, there is included the *time-distance* curve of this *reflected wave*, in addition to the "first kick"—that is, the refraction, *time-distance* curve of Figure 53. As we have seen, this is a hyperbola whose asymptotes are percisely the previously-drawn refraction *time-distance* curves. Let us recall some more pertinent facts about this hyperbola.

For example, corresponding to a typical pickup position, P, at a distance $OP = x$ from the shot-point O, the travel-time of the reflected wave ORP is

$$t = (x^2 + 4h_1^2)^{1/2}/v_1,$$

and this time is plotted at the point T of the *time-distance* curve in Figure 54. Also, as discussed previously, the direct refracted wave travels to P in time

$$t = x/v_1,$$

and this is plotted as the point U in Figure 54.

The slope of the hyperbola at T is (see page 24)

$$dt/dx = x/v_1(x^2 + 4h_1^2)^{1/2}.$$

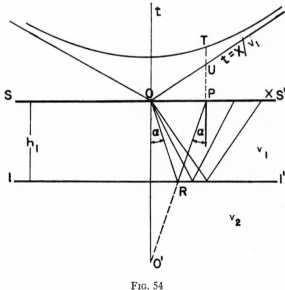

Fig. 54

If the emergence angle of the reflected wave at P be indicated by α, then (see Lesson No. 1)

$$\sin \alpha = v_1(dt/dx),$$

and the combination of these results gives

$$\sin \alpha = x/(x^2 + 4h_1^2)^{1/2},$$

a result which can be noted geometrically and directly in Figure 54.

This relation then holds for the typical pickup position P at a distance x from O, the depth to II' being h_1.

As P moves outward away from O, α increases from $0°$ and becomes larger and larger, approaching but never quite getting equal to $90°$. The slope of the hyperbola (dt/dx), too, starts at O at the shot-point and increases as P moves outward from O to, but never quite attains, the value $1/v_1$, which is the slope of the asymptote, which, in turn, is the refraction *time-distance* ("first-kick") curve.

At this point, it is perhaps advisable to insert

Ex. 72: Draw the *time-distance* curve of the refracted wave ("first-kicks") and the reflection for the following case. Since this same *numerical case* will be used for many exercises, the reader is *urged to draw the necessary figures carefully and to scale.*

$$v_1 = 8{,}150 \text{ ft/sec.}$$

$$h_1 = 4{,}570 \text{ ft.}$$

Draw the *time-distance* curves to a distance of 20,000 ft from the shot-point O. Now consider this problem:

Ex. 73: Suppose that in the preceding exercise, $v_2 = 10{,}250$ ft/sec. At what distance from O will the emergence angle, α, be equal to

$$\sin^{-1} (8{,}150/10{,}250)?$$

What is the slope of the *time-distance* hyperbola at that distance? What is the travel-time of the reflection to this point?

The answer to the first part of Exercise 73 may be obtained easily by referring back to the formula for $\sin \alpha$ on page 24. The problem then reduces to solving for x in the equation

$$\sin \alpha = 8{,}150/10{,}250 = x/[x^2 + (2) (4{,}570)^2]^{1/2}.$$

(A very easy method to use here would be to find, first, $\tan \alpha$ from the tables, knowing $\sin \alpha$. Then, since

$$\tan \alpha = x/2h_1 = x/(2) (4{,}570),$$

x is easily found.)

Now, in this example, it is important to note that this value of α we have chosen is precisely that of the critical angle for the two velocities being used. In other words, in Exercise 73, we have asked about the reflected path which strikes the interface II' at the *critical angle* for the two velocities used.

Let us return to the general case shown in Figure 54. As we move away from the shot-point O and the *slope* of the hyperbola increases from O to $1/v_1$, it passes through the value of $1/v_2$. For, since

$$0 < v_1 < v_2,$$

it follows that

$$1/v_2 < 1/v_1.$$

This slope, dt/dx, attains the value $1/v_2$ at the point for which the emergence angle α is such that

$$\sin \alpha = v_1 \, (dt/dx),$$
$$= v_1/v_2.$$

We thus have the important result: *The slope of the time-distance reflection hyperbola at the point where the emergence angle is equal to the critical angle for velocities v_1 and v_2 $(v_1 < v_2)$ is $1/v_2$.*

The reader is urged to study this relation in Figure 55 carefully and to draw the situation for the numerical case of Exercises 72 and 73.

ϕ, is the critical angle $\left[\sin^{-1} (v_1/v_2)\right]$. The emergence angle equals critical angle at C. The slope at C is $1/v_2$. At O, the slope is 0. The slope increases as we move from O to and beyond A. At C, it has attained the value $1/v_2$. It continues to increase to B and on, getting nearer and nearer to $1/v_1$, which is the slope of the refraction *time-distance* curve OR. Always, we have

$$\sin \alpha = v_1 \, dt/dx,$$

or

$$dt/dx = \sin \alpha/v_1.$$

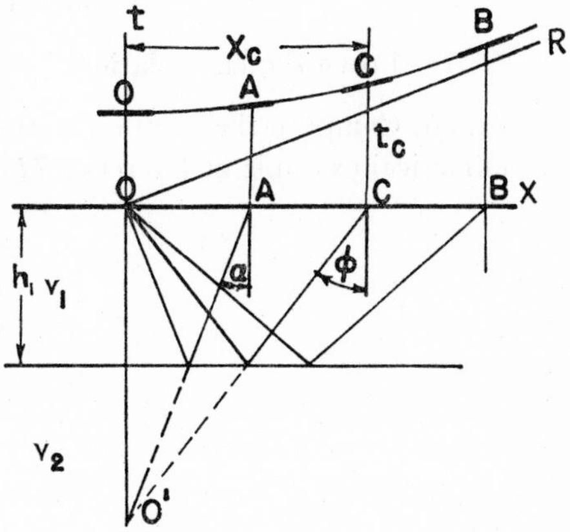

FIG. 55

At O,

$$dt/dx = 0, \quad \text{and} \quad \alpha = 0°.$$

At C,

$$dt/dx = 1/v_2,$$
$$\alpha = \phi, \text{ and } \sin \alpha = \sin \phi = v_1/v_2.$$

At C, in Figure 55, we have

$$\sin \alpha = \sin \phi = v_1/v_2 = x_c/(x_c{}^2 + 4h_1{}^2)^{1/2},$$

where

$$x_c = OC.$$

Thus, the point C is located at

$$x_c = 2h_1(v_1/v_2)/[1 - (v_1/v_2)^2]^{1/2},$$
$$= 2h_1v_1/(v_2{}^2 - v_1{}^2)^{1/2},$$
$$= 2h_1 \tan \phi.$$

Ex. 74: Prove the last relation.

One more item must be obtained for future work. What is the travel-time, t_c, to this point C? Since the travel-time to any point at a distance x is

$$t = (x^2 + 4h_1{}^2)^{1/2}/v_1,$$

all we need do is to use the last value on x_c and compute the travel-time

$$t_c = (1/v_1)\,[4h_1{}^2v_1{}^2/(v_2{}^2 - v_1{}^2) + 4h_1{}^2]^{1/2},$$
$$= (1/v_1)\,[4h_1{}^2v_2{}^2/(v_2{}^2 - v_1{}^2)]^{1/2},$$
$$= 2h_1(v_2/v_1)/(v_2{}^2 - v_1{}^2)^{1/2},$$
$$= 2h_1/v_1 \cos \phi.$$

Ex. 75: Prove the last relation.

Ex. 76: Compute the location of travel-time to, and slope at, the point C for the numerical example of Exercises 72 and 73.

Lesson No. 19

SINGLE LAYER REFLECTION AND REFRACTION PATHS
(*Continued*)

In addition to the two "minimum time" paths from O to P of Figure 54 (the "direct," straight line path OP, and the reflected path ORP) that we have discussed in the last lesson, there is yet another of basic importance, insofar as the problem of two beds is concerned, provided that the velocity of propagation, v_2, in the lower bed is greater than the velocity, v_1, in the upper bed. This third path which we shall now introduce is a *refraction* path.

We begin by reconsidering the wave *fronts* involved in these two minimum time paths. As a consequence of the shot explosion at O (Figure 56), the energy radiates from that point so that the successive positions of the wave front are

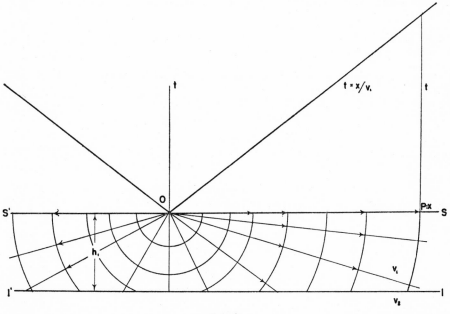

Fig. 56

spheres and the corresponding paths are the straight lines radiating from O. We consider simply a vertical plane section of this situation and, for the present, also assume the interface $I'I$ to be a plane parallel to the surface $S'S$, so that all vertical sections through O are alike.

Figure 56 shows some positions of the wave front and some wave paths of the direct wave. Here we note, again, that we shall have the "direct" wave arrive at a typical pickup position, P, when the expanding wave front arrives there, which corresponds to the arrival of the wave path, OP, travelling at a velocity v_1.

87

Corresponding to this expanding wave front, there is the time-distance curve which is the straight line whose equation is $t = x/v_1$, in which x is the distance OP and t is the travel-time thereto from O.

Figure 57 shows some positions of the wave fronts and corresponding wave paths which describe the wave reflected from $I'I$. As we have seen, the wave

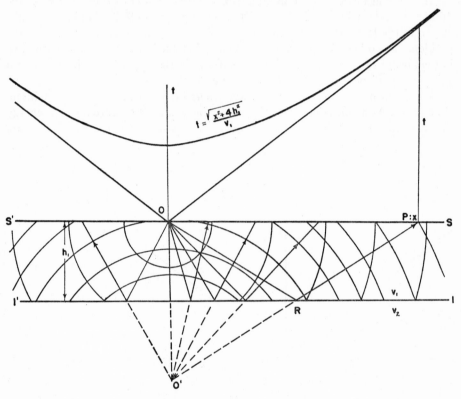

$$t = \frac{\sqrt{x^2 + 4h_1^2}}{v_1}$$

FIG. 57

front positions after reflection from $I'I$ are circles whose common center is at the image point O'. The corresponding wave path to any typical point P, at a distance x from O, is the broken line ORP, in which R is the intersection of $I'I$ with $O'P$. The arrival of the reflected wave front at P indicates the travel-time of the reflection ORP which we have found to be

$$t = (x^2 + 4h_1^2)^{1/2}/v_1,$$

in which h_1 is the thickness of the first medium.

Now, consider the energy which is transmitted into the next lower bed. When the radiating paths through O "extend" into the lower bed, as in Figure 58, they will be refracted in accordance with the relation expressed in Snell's Law. The typical wave path, OY, which strikes $I'I$ at an angle θ_1 to its normal, is refracted into the lower medium into the path YT, which is at an angle θ_2 with the normal to $I'I$, and the relation between the angles is $\sin \theta_1 / \sin \theta_2 = v_1 / v_2$. We thus have wave paths in the lower medium which are straight lines (see fourth paragraph, p. 74), but which, it can be shown, do *not* radiate from a central point even when extended "backward." That is to say, if all the wave paths, of which YT is a typical one, were extended, they would not converge to one point. This means that the corresponding wave *front* positions in the second medium, which must, in plane vertical section, be curves intersecting the paths at right angles, are *not* circles but are, in fact, other and more "complicated" curves. We do not propose to discuss these wave front curves analytically in these lessons (although we recommend the study of them to those interested in such mathematical treatment), but we must indicate some important properties which will be, we believe, intuitively evident.

For the present, we repeat, we shall be interested only in the case for which the velocity v_2 in the lower medium is greater than that in the upper medium, v_1; *i.e.*, $v_2 > v_1$. Let C, in Figure 58, be the point on $I'I$ for which the line OC makes the *critical angle* ϕ, $\sin^{-1} (v_1/v_2)$, with the normal to $I'I$. This means that any path such as OY, making an angle $\theta_1 < \phi$ with the normal to $I'I$, will be refracted into the medium below as indicated by YT; and because $v_2 > v_1$ and

$$\sin \theta_2 / \sin \theta_1 = v_2 / v_1,$$

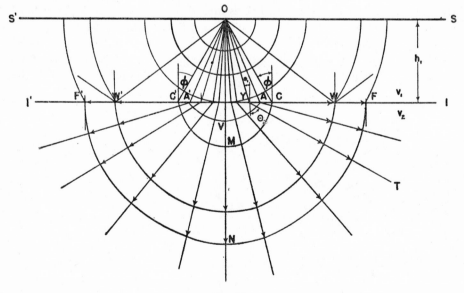

Fɪɢ. 58

the angle θ_2 will be greater than θ_1. For a path such as OW for which the similar angle of incidence $\theta_1 > \phi$, no refraction into the lower bed is possible, as is indicated by Snell's Law. For if $\phi_1 > \phi$, sin $\theta_1 > $ sin ϕ; *i.e.*, sin $\theta_1 > v_1/v_2$. Thus, since Snell's Law states that

$$\sin \theta_2 = (v_2/v_1) \sin \theta_1,$$

it would mean that sin $\theta_2 > 1$, an obvious impossibility.

Now, a careful drawing and a little thought will show that a wave front, like $A'VA$ in which its points of intersection, A' and A, with $I'I$ lie "within" the double critical length $C'C$, will *not* intersect $I'I$ at right angles, but that a wave front $F'NF$ for which the "end" point F' and F lie "beyond" the double critical length $C'C$ will intersect $I'I$ at right angles. In Figure 58 we have tried to show this situation by drawing the tangents to the wave fronts at F and F'.

The points F and F', beginning at the critical points C and C', move out along $I'I$ with the expanding wave front in the second medium at a velocity v_2. This follows, of course, from the fact that all the wave paths in the lower medium are traversed by the corresponding expanding wave front at the velocity v_2.

We now must introduce a special case of what is known as "Huygens' Principle." As the point F (and F', too) moves outward along $I'I$ with the expanding wave front, $F'NF$, at a velocity v_2, we may consider that there is started at each of its positions a new disturbance which has the effect of setting up spherical wave fronts in the *upper medium*. The "net" effect of all these new disturbances is to integrate themselves into a single wave front which is the envelope of the individual ones of these disturbances. Let us investigate this wave front "envelope" in our two-dimensional case. The points F_1, F_2, F_3, of Figure 59, represent positions of the moving point F.

During an elapsed time, t, during which the point F moves a distance v_2t, the radius of the circular wave front in the upper medium centered at F at the be-

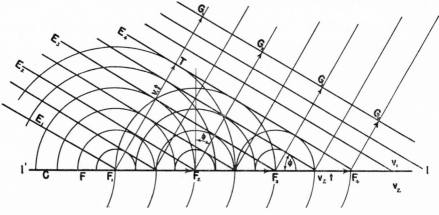

Fig. 59

ginning of the time t has grown to the value v_1t. This is shown in Figure 59 in which F_1 is chosen as a position of F from which t is measured. Let t, in fact, be the time that F moves from F_1 to F_4, so that

$$F_1F_4 = v_2t.$$

During that time, the disturbance starting at F_1 has grown into a circular wave front whose radius

$$F_1T = v_1t,$$

since the velocity in the upper medium is v_1.

Huygens' Principle in effect, states that we have a wave front which is the envelope of these circular wave fronts started by the moving point F. A little thought on the matter will convince the reader that the envelopes of these circles in our vertical section are, successively, a family of parallel straight lines like E_1F_1, E_2F_2, E_3F_3, E_4F_4, $\cdots$, and the members of this family are, therefore, effectively, the positions of a wave front moving "upward" through the first medium.

Ex. 77: The portions of the wave front represented by the straight lines E_1F_1, E_2F_2, $\cdots$, are inclined at an angle ϕ with $I'I$; *i.e.*,

$$\angle E_1F_1C = \angle E_2F_2C = \cdots = \phi,$$

where

$$\sin \phi = v_1/v_2;$$

i.e., ϕ is the critical angle for the velocities v_1 and v_2.

The wave *paths* corresponding to this moving wave front represented by the lines E_1F_1, E_2F_2, etc., will be the curves which cut these lines at right angles. Obviously, these curves form another set of straight lines—F_1G_1, F_2G_2, etc. We recall that we should expect these paths to be straight lines (see p. 74, fourth paragraph).

Ex. 78: The wave path segments, F_1G_1, F_2G_2, etc., of Figure 59, are inclined at the critical angle ϕ with the normal to the interface $I'I$.

All this argument, then, indicates that in addition to the two minimum-time arrivals from the shot-point O to a point P already described (the "direct" wave and the reflected wave), there is yet another, provided $v_2 > v_1$ and P (Figure 60) is sufficiently far removed from O. The path of this wave we refer to as the *refracted* wave from O to P through the interface $I'I$. This path, although seemingly a mathematical fiction, is nonetheless explained, as we have seen, by Huygens' Principle.

It is now our purpose to clarify all this into an argument similar to those we have used in the lessons thus far.

From the shot-point O we draw the ray OF at the critical angle ϕ for the velocities v_1 and v_2:

$$\sin \phi = v_1/v_2.$$

The point F is the one at which the disturbances which form the "rising" wave fronts begin. Thus, from the point F onward, in the manner indicated at points $F, F_1, F_2, F_3, \cdots$, we conceive of the wave paths $FQ, F_1P_1, F_2P_2, F_3P_3, \cdots$, all rising from $I'I$ at the critical angle ϕ with its normal.

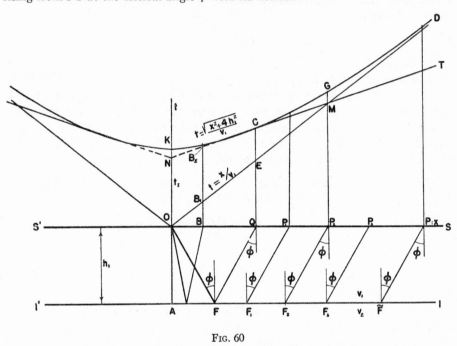

Fig. 60

Ex. 79: Show that of all paths from O to a point such as P in Figure 60, consisting of straight lines and traversing into and through some of the lower medium the path $OF\widetilde{F}P$ is that of minimum time.

Our next problem is to determine the type of *time-distance* curve produced by this refracted wave which corresponds to the wave paths OFF_1P_1, OFF_2P_2, $OFF_3P_3, \cdots$, (Figure 60) and the relation of this *time-distance* curve to the other two already discussed.

We must repeat that for the present we are discussing only the case in which $I'I$ is parallel to $S'S$. In this case, the emergence angle of the wave paths under discussion are all equal to ϕ, the critical angle, as should be evident in Figure 60. In the relation of Lesson No. 1:

$$\sin \alpha = v_1(\Delta t/\Delta x),$$

α is the emergence angle of a wave path, and $\Delta t/\Delta x$ is the slope of the corresponding *time-distance* curve. In our case,

$$\alpha = \phi$$

and, ϕ being the critical angle,

$$\sin \phi = v_1/v_2.$$

These facts, put together, yield the result that for our *time-distance* curve

$$\Delta t/\Delta x = 1/v_2.$$

Thus, as is evident from the fact that the emergence angle is the same, ϕ, at all the points P_1, P_2, P_3, $\cdots$, and as follows from the concomitant fact that the slope of the time-distance curve is $1/v_2$, a constant, the *time-distance curve is a straight line* whose slope is $1/v_2$. We sometimes say the *apparent velocity* indicated by this straight-line section of the *time-distance* curve is v_2.

To say that we have a straight line of slope $1/v_2$ is not sufficient to characterize it. We still need at least *one point* of the straight line in order to fix it, and this we now propose to find.

Let F in Figure 60 be the point on $I'I$ for which the incident ray from O, namely OF, makes an angle equal to ϕ, the critical angle with the normal to $I'I$; and let Q be the point on $S'S$ at which the ray OF is reflected back. Then, at Q, *the travel-time for OFQ is a point on the reflection hyperbola*, since OFQ is a reflected path. At that point, the slope of the hyperbola dt/dx is again obtained from the fact that since the emergence angle is ϕ,

$$\sin \phi = v_1 dt/dx,$$

and

$$\sin \phi = v_1/v_2.$$

That is, for the hyperbola, at Q, the slope is

$$dt/dx = 1/v_2.$$

But also, the travel-time for OFQ is a point on the refraction *time-distance* curve, too, since it is the *first* of the refracted paths exemplified by $OFFQ$, $OFF_1 P_1$, OFF_2P_2, OFF_3P_3, etc., which have for their *time-distance* curve the straight-line of slope $1/v_2$. It follows, therefore, that this refraction *time-distance* straight line is the tangent to the reflection hyperbola at the point C corresponding to Q.

All three *time-distance* curves discussed to this point are shown schematically in Figure 60. They are plots of the travel-times of arrivals of significance. Each of these arrivals (and all other similar arrivals) is, *by definition*, called a *seismic event*. (We recall that we are restricting ourselves to longitudinal—compressional —waves only, assuming no dispersion and not considering the *amount* of energy involved; that is, the amplitude.) Referring to Figure 60:

(a) the *direct refracted* wave. Its travel-time curve is the straight line, OD, passing through the origin O, whose slope is $1/v_1$ and whose equation is $t = x/v_1$.

(b) the *reflected wave* from $I'I$. Its travel-time curve is a hyperbola, KCD. This hyperbola cuts the t-axis at K such that $OK = 2h_1/v_1$. At K it has zero slope, and the slope increases outward approaching $1/v_1$ as a limit, the hyperbola having the straight line described under (a) as an asymptote.

(c) the *refracted wave from the interface* $I'I$. Its travel-time curve is the straight line CT whose slope is $1/v_2$. It is the tangent to the hyperbola of (b) at the point C which is over the point Q at which the angle of emergence is the critical angle, ϕ.

In all this it is important to bear in mind that $v_2 > v_1$. If this is not the case, there will be *no refraction* arrivals from $I'I$. For the present, too, we recall another assumption: that $I'I$ is parallel to $S'S$. We shall discuss later the refraction problem when $I'I$ dips with respect to $S'S$.

For points lying between O and Q of Figure 60, exemplified by B, there will be two seismic events: the direct wave arrival, whose arrival time is plotted as B_1; and the reflected wave whose arrival time is plotted as B_2.

At the point Q, we have the first *possible* arrival of the second refracted wave whose time-distance curve is CT, the tangent to KCD at C. We recall that the angle of emergence at Q is the critical angle, ϕ.

Let M be the intersection of OD and CT, and let P_2 be the corresponding position on $S'S$. Then for points lying between Q and P_2, such, for example, as P_1, there are *three seismic events*. In this interval, the points in the segment EM represent the *first refracted arrivals* ("first kicks"). The points in the segment CM are sometimes called *secondary refraction arrivals*. Then comes CG, whose points represent the *reflection wave arrivals*.

At P_2, both refracted events arrive simultaneously.

From the point P_2 onward, the *refraction* events reverse in order of arrivals, and MT now represents the "first kicks," MD the *secondaries*, and GD, of course, the reflection arrivals.

We desire to emphasize to the reader the meaning of *secondary refraction arrivals*, or, briefly, *secondaries*. They can occur *only* after some distance from the shot-point. In Figure 60, that point is Q. For some distance (QP_2) the *secondaries* are from the horizon $I'I$, and the *primary refraction* wave is still from the surface $S'S$. Beyond P_2 the situation is reversed. And, finally, at no point does the reflection wave arrival precede either refraction wave arrival.

As an immediate consequence of the minimum-time principle, it should be quite clear that if v_2. the velocity in the lower medium, is less than v_1, there will be no refracted path from the interface $I'I$.

There are finally, two more items of some interest in this discussion which we should mention before going on to the actual and practical applications of our results.

In the first place, based on the coordinate system indicated in Figure 60, what is the equation of the refraction *time-distance* straight line CT? We can answer this question in two ways.

The first, and "analytic," method is simply to write the equation of the tangent line to the hyperbola KCD at the point C. As seen in Figure 60, the point C has the coordinates:

$$C: (2h_1 \tan \phi, \; 2h_1/v_1 \cos \phi),$$

in which, of course, $\sin \phi = v_1/v_2$.

Ex. 80: Show that the coordinates of C are as stated, recalling that the equation of the hyperbola is

$$v_1^2 t^2 = x^2 + 4h_1^2.$$

Ex. 81: Show by the usual analytic methods that the equation of line CT is

$$t = x/v_2 + 2h_1(v_2^2 - v_1^2)^{1/2}/v_1 v_2.$$

The second method is to go back to fundamentals, as indicated in Figure 60. Let P be an arbitrary point on the x-axis to which we assign the coordinate x. The travel-time of the wave we seek is, of course,

$$t = OF/v_1 + F\tilde{F}/v_2 + \tilde{F}P/v_1,$$

which, since $OF = \tilde{F}P$, becomes

$$t = 2(OF/v_1) + F\tilde{F}/v_2.$$

Now,

$$OF = h_1/\cos \phi$$

and

$$F\tilde{F} = OP - 2AF$$
$$= x - 2h_1 \cdot \tan \phi.$$

Thus,

$$t = 2h_1/v_1 \cos \phi + (x - 2h_1 \tan \phi)/v_2.$$

Recalling that

$$\sin \phi = v_1/v_2,$$

we obtain by algebraic and trigonometric manipulation the result desired;

$$t = x/v_2 + 2h_1(v_2^2 - v_1^2)^{1/2}/v_1 v_2.$$

Ex. 82: Obtain this result by the proper manipulations.

One final word: We have mentioned that, physically, this *refraction* time-distance line is meaningless between the shot-point N and its point of contact, C, with the reflection hyperbola. Nonetheless, its extension to the t-axis, as shown by the dotted segment NC in Figure 60, has a mathematical significance which will be of importance later in deriving certain useful conclusions. The "intercept time," ON, is obtained from the equation of the line by setting $x=0$ and thus obtaining

$$t_1 = 2h_1(v_2{}^2 - v_1{}^2)^{1/2}/v_1v_2.$$

Ex. 83: Can you ascribe a pseudo-physical meaning to the fictitious arrival times on the straight line from N to C?

Lesson No. 20

THE TWO-LAYER HORIZONTAL REFRACTION PROBLEM

In practice, refraction techniques can often be used to great advantage, and the exploration seismologist would do well to have an understanding of the values and limitations of the refraction method. As we shall see, the method does not yield as much detail as do the reflection seismograph techniques, nor does it, generally speaking, effectively explore to as great depths. Nonetheless, for the delineation of basin boundaries and determinations of velocities in media (which often serve to characterize those media), it can be of tremendous value. If the basement is not too deep, the thickness of the sediments can often be readily found by suitably placed refraction profiles. With variations of the basic method, other specialized problems can be solved. From time to time we shall indicate the possibilities inherent in the refraction method as we proceed to develop its various facets.

Our first chore is to study the most elementary problem: that of a bed in which the velocity, v_1, is bounded above by the horizontal plane of the earth and below by a parallel plane which serves as an interface between this bed and the next lower one in which the velocity is v_2, which is greater than v_1.

Suppose, then, that along the line $S'S$ (Figure 61) we have pickups, suitably spaced, beginning with the shot-point O. In practice, this usually requires successive movements of the pickup spread in such manner that eventually the

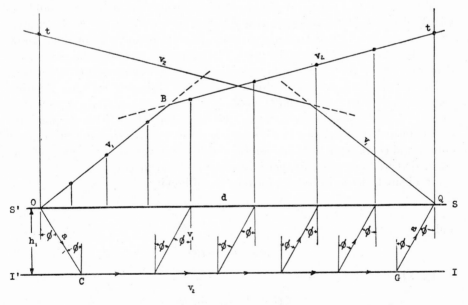

FIG. 61. Reversed time-distance refraction profile for one horizontal interface. "Interpretation" paths from shot point O, only.

97

entire profile is covered. After each movement, the spread having been laid down, a charge is exploded at the fixed shot-point, O. For reasons that will soon become apparent, each profile is "reversed." That is to say, at the end of the profile another shot-point, Q, is located; and, as each spread is laid down, the travel-times to the pickup positions from *each* of the *two* shot-points, O and Q, are obtained. The optimum length of the profile OQ is determined by the problem in hand and varies from as little as a mile to as much as six or more miles. The factors of the problems which determine the length OQ and the "pickup interval" will become apparent in the course of our discussion.

We are interested, as we have said, in the ideal, simple case in which $S'S$ is a horizontal trace representing the "corrected" trace of the earth, corrected in a manner which will be discussed later. And, it is assumed that the travel-times, too, have been properly corrected.

Now, since the velocity of propagation immediately below $S'S$ is v_1, we would have the data ("first kicks") for some distance from O, when plotted, indicate a straight line radiating from O with slope $1/v_1$, as shown in Figure 61.

It is common practice to say that this line has an apparent velocity of v_1 and to show this fact by writing the value of v_1 above this line.

At some distance from O, the data would indicate a "bend" in the time-distance curve and the "first kicks" would line up along another and "faster" line. The slope of this second line, in our case, would be $1/v_2$, and we say that it shows an apparent velocity of v_2 (see p. 92).

The position at which this bend occurs—namely, the point B—would obviously depend on the velocities v_1 and v_2 and on the thickness h_1. If we were presented *only* with these data originating from shot-point O, we would not know, as we shall see later, whether the desired interface, $I'I$, is horizontal or not. For that reason it is important to obtain similar data from a shot-point Q at the other end of the profile. It should be obvious that for a horizontal interface the time-distance curve originating from Q would be the same as that from O, except, of course, that the one is in the reverse direction of the other. If we are presented with data such as are shown in Figure 61 in which the *time-distance* curves from both O and Q are replicas of one another, although reversed, we would feel confident that we have a single-layer horizontal problem to solve.

In Figure 61 let us introduce, for the sake of brevity, the notations

$$d = \overline{OQ}$$

and

$$a = OC = GQ.$$

Ex. 84: Show that

$$CG = d - 2a \sin \phi$$

$$= d - 2av_1/v_2.$$

The travel-time of the wave from O to Q is, of course, equal to the travel-time in the reverse direction, from Q to O. Let us indicate this total travel-time by t. Then, clearly, (Figure 61)

$$t = OC/v_1 + CG/v_2 + GQ/v_1,$$
$$= 2a/v_1 + (d - 2av_1/v_2)/v_2.$$

Ex. 85: From the previous relation solve for a to obtain the *important formula*

$$a = (v_2t - d)/2(v_2/v_1 - v_1/v_2).$$

We proceed now to indicate the actual solution of a numerical problem. The following table contains a set of data suitably corrected for elevation and shot-depth with reference to the surface of the earth, whose trace, OQ, is used as the datum line.

	Distance from O (ft)	Distance from Q (ft)	Corrected Travel-Time fom O (sec)	Corrected Travel-Time from Q (sec)
1st spread	0	10,000	0	1.621
	500	9,500	0.087	1.553
	1,000	9,000	0.174	1.488
	1,500	8,500	0.261	1.421
	2,000	8,000	0.347	1.355
	2,500	7,500	0.435	1.287
2nd spread	2,500	7,500	0.432	1.287
	3,000	7,000	0.522	1.221
	3,500	6,500	0.609	1.131
	4,000	6,000	0.697	1.043
	4,500	5,500	0.782	0.956
	5,000	5,000	0.869	0.870
3rd spread	5,000	5,000	0.870	0.870
	5,500	4,500	0.957	0.783
	6,000	4,000	1.043	0.695
	6,500	3,500	1.130	0.610
	7,000	3,000	1.220	0.522
	7,500	2,500	1.286	0.434
4th spread	7,500	2,500	1.288	0.434
	8,000	2,000	1.353	0.348
	8,500	1,500	1.421	0.260
	9,000	1,000	1.486	0.172
	9,500	500	1.554	0.087
	10,000	0	1.621	0

The common practice of "overlapping" the last pickups on each spread has been used in this table, which accounts for two entries at distances of 2,500 ft, 5,000 ft and 7,500 ft from each shot-point. The spreads are each 2,500 ft long and contain six pickups, the pickup interval being 500 ft. At pickup locations, common to two adjacent spreads, the corrected travel-times are averaged—if such averaging is reasonably indicated, of course.

A study of the table reveals that each profile is practically the reverse of the other. Each, in fact, is plotted individually in Figure 62. *The over-all time from O to Q must be the same as from Q to O*, otherwise we would have a contradiction and an impossible situation.

Here we wish to bring out a point which we shall repeat and stress over and over again as we proceed: While it is commendable and, in fact, necessary to be as accurate in one's work as is justifiable by reason of the type of data, it is never purposeful or useful to extend the accuracy of one's work over and beyond the limits of the accuracy of the data. This principle plays a fundamental role in the refraction interpretation techniques, as it does in any other type of numerical work.

The travel-times listed are indicated to the nearest thousandth of a second as read on the customary seismograph record. Experience indicates that, at best, the travel-times can always be altered by as much as 0.002 sec in either direction of the value read in them. Very often this "error" can be twice as great or even more. In drawing the *time-distance* curves through the points of such data, then, one should not hesitate to avail oneself of the flexibility which this state of affairs allows.

The data of the table are plotted as points in the upper half of Figure 62. To argue that one could increase the (vertical) time scale and plot the points more "accurately" is, in the light of the preceding statements, rather specious. The best scale to be used is one justified by the data.

Through the "nearer" points so plotted, the *best* lines (using the eye, in this case) of the same slope are drawn through O and Q. These lines are marked 5,750, which is the reciprocal of the common slope and corresponds to the v_1 of Figure 61. Through the further points, beyond the "break" or "bend" in the *time-distance* curves of Figure 62, straight lines are drawn which are marked 7,500, corresponding to the v_2 of Figure 61.

This, then, is a typical *time-distance* curve of a two-layer, *horizontal* interface problem, which we proceed to solve.

I. The slopes of the "outer" segments of the *time-distance* curves of Figure 62 are both 1/7,500. This, of course, could be obtained from the data in some such fashion as this:

$$\text{Distance } OQ = 10{,}000 \qquad \text{Travel-time from } O \text{ to } Q\text{: } 1.621$$
$$\underline{\text{Distance } OS = 7{,}000} \qquad \underline{\text{Travel-time from } O \text{ to } S\text{: } 1.221}$$
$$\Delta x = 3{,}000 \qquad\qquad\qquad\qquad \Delta t = 0.400$$
$$\Delta t / \Delta x = 0.400/3{,}000 = 1/7{,}500$$

II. The wave from O to Q emerges at an angle α, in which

$$\sin \alpha = v_1 \, \Delta t / \Delta x.$$

In fact, of course, the wave path from O to any point lying in the interval SQ could have been used. As we note,

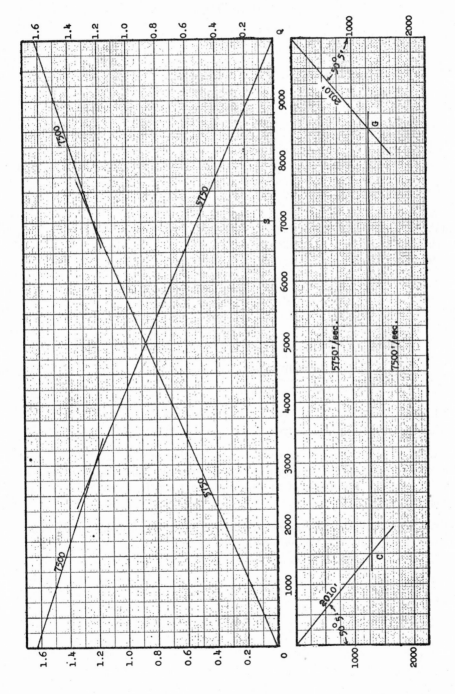

FIG. 62

$$v_1 = 5{,}750 \text{ ft/sec,}$$

$$\Delta t / \Delta x = 1/7{,}500.$$

Thus,

$$\sin \alpha = 5{,}750/7{,}500 = 0.767$$

and

$$\alpha \cong 50°5'.$$

III. Because the *time-distance* curves of the reversed profiles are replicas of one another, the interface is horizontal. And, for that reason, the angle of emergence is equal to the critical angle, ϕ; that is,

$$\sin \phi = v_1/v_2 = 5{,}750/7{,}500 = \sin \alpha.$$

IV. Accordingly, as in Figure 62, we draw GQ through Q, and its counterpart, CO, through O, each at an angle of 50°5′ with the vertical. In practice, this is best done by careful use of a protractor.

V. We then use the result in Ex. 85.

$$a = (v_2 t - d)/2(v_2/v_1 - v_1/v_2);$$

i.e.,

$$a = [(7{,}500)\,(1.621) - 10{,}000]/2(7{,}500/5{,}750 - 5{,}750/7{,}500),$$
$$\cong (12{,}160 - 10{,}000)/2(1.304 - 0.767)$$
$$= 2{,}160/2\,(0.537) \cong 2{,}010 \text{ ft.}$$

VI. Thus, we scale off $OC = QG = 2{,}010$ ft, and the line through C and G, so determined, is the interface desired. Note that it is 1,270 ft below the surface.

Ex. 86: The *time-distance* curves over a refraction profile 12,000 ft long and its reverse indicate a horizontal interface and show velocities of 6,000 ft/sec and 12,000 ft/sec. Let the depth of the interface be 1,800 ft. Construct the *time-distance* curves.

Ex. 87: Solve the *time-distance* curves of the preceding problem for the depth of the interface, following the method of this lesson.

Lesson No. 21

SINGLE DIPPING INTERFACE REFRACTION PROFILE

The method of solving the elementary refraction problem which we have presented is easily made adaptable to the next problem we must solve: that of a profile over a single dipping interface. In this lesson we shall discuss some of the basic ideas and proceed to a numerical case in the next lesson.

We assume that the upper bed, in which the seismic velocity is v_1, is separated from a lower bed, in which the seismic velocity is v_2 by a *dipping plane* serving as

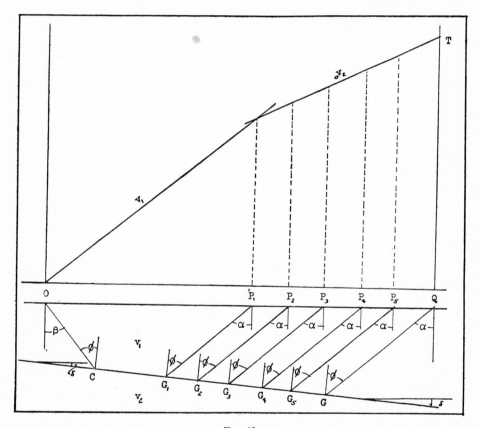

Fig. 63

an interface, and that $v_2 > v_1$. A refraction profile is laid out along the surface of the earth in the *direction of true dip* (and such that the interface does not outcrop within the profile). In vertical section, then, the situation is as sketched in Figure 63. Here OQ represents the trace of the plane surface of the earth, with O and Q serving as shot-points at each end of the "reversed profile." The trace CG is that

103

of the dipping interface which, to be specific, is oriented so that it dips down-ward from O to Q; and the *angle of dip*, δ, is the true angle of dip.

Using, first, the shot-point at O and shooting down-dip, what kind of time-distance curve may we expect?

Clearly, for some distance beginning with O we shall have the travel-times indicate a velocity of v_1; *i.e.*, the first section of the *time-distance* curve will be a straight line through O with slope equal to $1/v_1$. In Figure 63, this is the situation in the interval between O and P_1.

The point P_1 is at such distance from O that the travel-time from O to P_1 along the straight line OP_1 with a velocity v_1 is exactly equal to the travel-time represented by the wave path OCG_1P_1 in which the segments OC and G_1P_1 are traversed with a velocity v_1, and the segment CG_1 with a velocity v_2. In accordance with the Minimum Time Principle and the related Huygens' Principle, the *time-distance* curve for points beyond P_1 towards Q is obtained by evaluating the travel-times for the refracted wave paths, as shown in Figure 63. For example, at P_4, the travel-time corresponds to that of the wave path OCG_4P_4, in which OC and G_4P_4 both are straight lines inclined at the critical angle ϕ with the normal to the dipping interface, CG. We recall that this angle ϕ is defined by the relation:

$$\sin \phi = v_1/v_2.$$

Since the parts of the refraction paths typified by G_1P_1, G_2P_2, G_3P_3, G_4P_4, $\cdots$, GQ are parallel lines, their angles of emergence at the surface are all equal. Let their common value be α. The slope of the corresponding part of the *time-distance* curve, dt/dx is then obtained from the fact that

$$\sin \alpha = v_1 dt/dx,$$

i.e.,

$$dt/dx = \sin \alpha/v_1,$$

a constant. *This part of the time-distance curve is also, therefore, a straight line,* and we may write, as we usually do,

$$\Delta t/\Delta x = \sin \alpha/v_1.$$

Ex. 88: The emergence angle α, *shooting down-dip*, the critical angle ϕ, and the dip angle δ, are related to one another by the fact that

$$\alpha = \phi + \delta.$$

If we use this expression for α in the slope relation above, we have

$$\Delta t/\Delta x = \sin (\phi + \delta)/v_1.$$

The angle δ being positive,

$$\phi + \delta > \phi,$$
$$\sin (\phi + \delta) > \sin \phi,$$

and

$$\sin (\phi + \delta)/v_1 > \sin \phi/v_1.$$

But

$$\sin \phi/v_1 = 1/v_2,$$

ϕ being the critical angle. Thus, the slope of this section of the *time-distance* curve, *shooting down-dip*, is *greater* than it would be for the same velocities but a horizontal interface; or, put otherwise and in its more usual form, the reciprocal of the slope of this section of the time-distance curve, called the *apparent velocity* of the arriving wave, is *less than the true velocity*, v_2, in the lower bed.

In Figure 63, this section of the *time-distance* curve is denoted by $_0v_2$, indicating the *apparent velocity* measured when shooting at O. And, as we have just pointed out,

$$_0v_2 < v_2,$$

since we are shooting *down-dip*.

Note, too, that the apparent velocity is the rate at which the emerging wave "sweeps" across the ground in line with the profile—it is the velocity with which P_1 moves to P_2 to P_3, $\cdots$, etc.

To summarize, then: shooting down-dip, the lower (high-speed) bed will manifest itself on the *time-distance* curve by a segment of a straight line whose slope is

$$\Delta t/\Delta x = dt/dx = \sin \alpha/v_1,$$

in which

$$\alpha = \phi + \delta,$$

where ϕ is the critical angle ($\phi = \sin^{-1} v_1/v_2$), and δ is the angle of dip of the interface. The apparent velocity of this section is *less than the true velocity*, v_2.

Now let us consider the same subsurface section and assume the profile shot in the reverse direction; that is, what may we expect for our time-distance curve shooting up-dip from Q?

For some distance from Q—specifically, for the interval QN_1 in Figure 64— we shall have a straight line emanating from Q with slope $1/v_1$, indicating a velocity of v_1 for the upper bed.

Ex. 89: In the common subsurface situation illustrated in Figures 63 and 64, of the two distances, OP_1 and QN_1, which is the greater and why?

The point N_1 is at such distance from Q that the travel-time of the wave from Q to N_1 along the straight line QN_1, with a velocity v_1 is exactly equal to the travel-time for the wave path QGC_1N_1. From N_1 and beyond, the minimum-time paths are typified in Figure 64 by QGC_1N_1, QGC_2N_2, QGC_3N_3, QGC_4N_4, $QGCO$, where

QG and the segments C_1N_1, C_2N_2, etc., are inclined at the critical angle ϕ with the normal to the interface CG.

Since the segments C_1N_1, C_2N_2, etc., are parallel lines, their angles of emergence at the surface are all equal to a common value, β. The slope of the corresponding *time-distance* curve, dt/dx determined by

$$\sin \beta = v_1 dt/dx,$$

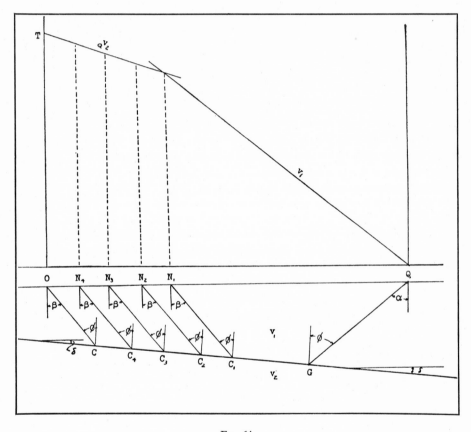

FIG. 64

is, therefore, a constant:

$$dt/dx = \sin \beta/v_1,$$

which we write as

$$\Delta t/\Delta x = \sin \beta/v_1.$$

Thus, this section of the time-distance curve, too, is a straight line.

Ex. 90: The emergence angle β, *shooting up-dip*, the critical angle ϕ, and the dip angle δ are related to one another by the formula:

$$\beta = \phi - \delta.$$

If we use this expression for β in the slope relation above,

$$\Delta t/\Delta x = \sin (\phi - \delta)/v_1.$$

Since

$$\phi - \delta < \phi,$$
$$\sin(\phi - \delta) < \sin \phi$$

and

$$\sin(\phi - \delta)/v_1 < \sin \phi/v_1.$$

But $\sin \phi/v_1 = 1/v_2$, ϕ being the critical angle. Thus, the slope of this section of the *time-distance* curve shooting up-dip is *less* than it would be for the same velocities but a horizontal interface; or, put otherwise and in its customary usage, the reciprocal of the slope of this section of the *time-distance* curve, called the *apparent velocity* of the arriving wave, is *greater than the true velocity*, v_2, in the lower bed.

In Figure 64, this section of the *time-distance* curve is denoted by $_Qv_2$, indicating the *apparent velocity* when shooting at Q. And, as we have pointed out,

$$_Qv_2 > v_2,$$

since we are shooting *up-dip*.

Here, too, the apparent velocity is the rate at which the emerging wave sweeps horizontally across the surface in line with the profile; that is, it is the velocity with which N_1 moves to N_2, to N_3, etc.

To summarize, then: shooting up-dip, the lower (high-speed) bed will manifest itself on the *time-distance* curve by a segment of a straight line whose slope is

$$\Delta t/\Delta x = dt/dx = \sin \beta/v_1,$$

in which

$$\beta = \phi - \delta,$$

where ϕ is the critical angle ($\phi = \sin^{-1} v_1/v_2$) and δ is the angle of dip of the interface. The apparent velocity of this section is *greater than the true velocity*, v_2.

Now let us superimpose both *time-distance* curves of Figures 63 and 64—the one down-dip shot from O, and the other up-dip shot from Q--over the same section and profile, as is done in Figure 65.

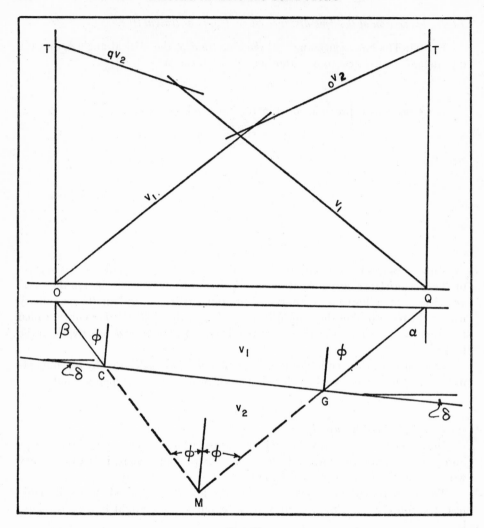

FIG. 65

The refracted path from O to Q is $OCGQ$; and from Q to O it is $QGCO$, which, in either direction, is covered in time

$$t = OC/v_1 + CG/v_2 + GQ/v_1.$$

The segments OC and QG are inclined at the critical angle ϕ ($\sin^{-1} v_1/v_2$) with the normal to the interface CG.

The angle of emergence at Q is

$$\alpha = \phi + \delta,$$

and

$$\sin \alpha = \sin (\phi + \delta) = v_1/_Ov_2,$$
$$= v_1(\Delta t/\Delta x)_O,$$

since the value of

$$_Ov_2 = (\Delta x/\Delta t)_O,$$

the latter measured on the outer segment of the *time-distance* curve emanating from O.

Similarly, the angle of emergence at O is

$$\beta = \phi - \delta,$$

and

$$\sin \beta = \sin (\phi - \delta) = v_1/_Qv_2,$$
$$= v_1(\Delta t/\Delta x)_Q,$$

since the value of

$$_Qv_2 = (\Delta x/\Delta t)_Q,$$

the latter measured on the outer segment of the *time-distance* curve emanating from Q.

Clearly, from the relations above, the angles α, β, ϕ satisfy the inequality:

$$\alpha > \phi > \beta.$$

Ex. 91: Extend OC and QG, in Figure 65, to the intersection at M. Prove geometrically that

$$\angle OMQ = \alpha + \beta = 2\phi.$$

This is a result of greatest importance.
Another result of great importance is

Ex. 92: In Figure 65, the triangle CMG is isosceles with $CM = MG$.

Finally, we add

Ex. 93: Show geometrically that the dip angle

$$\delta = (\alpha - \beta)/2.$$

Lesson No. 22

NUMERICAL SOLUTION FOR A REFRACTION PROFILE OVER A SINGLE DIPPING INTERFACE

As a consequence of the discussion and exercises of the preceding lesson, we are now in a position to solve a numerical problem, based on corrected field data, of a two-layer refraction profile in which the interface is dipping along the line of the profile.

The solution should be studied not only for its intrinsic value as a step toward learning the interpretation techniques for this and for more complicated refraction problems, but also because this type of solution is often used to study low-velocity layers for the purpose of making corrections for other types of seismic data (particularly reflection travel-times). It should be apparent that the disposition of the interface between the low-velocity layer and the beds beneath can often be detailed by short reversed refraction profiles of the type we are discussing here.

Consider, then, the data in Figure 66. We assume that the proper corrections to the travel-times have already been applied. The profile from O to Q is 9,000 ft long, and the over-all travel-time between O and Q is 1.600 sec.

We continue by itemizing the arguments and procedures.

I. The 6,500 on the t-d* curve indicates that in the neighborhood of Q the "best line" through the data is such that for that line

$$\Delta x/\Delta t = 6,500;$$

or, reciprocally, the slope of that line is

$$\Delta t/\Delta x = 1/6,500.$$

Consequently, at Q, the emergence angle α of the wave is obtained from the fact that

$$\sin \alpha = v_1(\Delta t/\Delta x),$$

in which

$$v_1 = 5,250.$$

Thus,

$$\sin \alpha = 5,250/6,500 = 0.808.$$

From a table of sines we find that, to the accuracy we need,

$$\alpha = 53°50'.$$

Thus, at Q, we draw the line QG making an angle of 53°50' with the vertical through Q.

* We shall often use "t-d" for *time-distance*, for the sake of brevity.

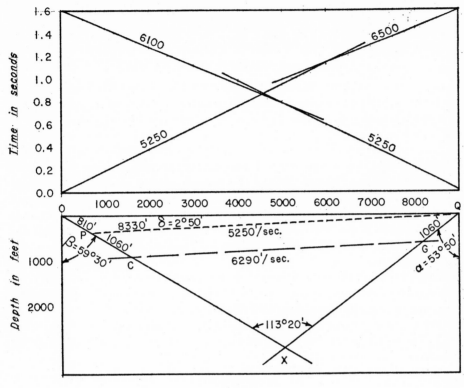

FIG. 66

II. At O, the emergence angle of the wave from shot-point Q is β in which

$$\sin \beta = v_1(\Delta t/\Delta x).$$

At this end,

$$\Delta t/\Delta x = 1/6,100,$$

since 6,100 is the apparent velocity of the wave emerging at O. Thus,

$$\sin \beta = 5,250/6,100 = 0.861,$$

and

$$\beta = 59°30'.$$

At O, therefore, we draw the line OC making an angle of 59°30' with the vertical through O.

III. We extend the two lines QG and OC to intersection at M. Then, (*cf.* Ex. 91)

$$\measuredangle OMQ = \alpha + \beta,$$
$$= 53°50' + 59°30',$$
$$= 113°20'.$$

As a consequence of the result of Exercise 91, this angle, $\measuredangle OMQ$, is equal to 2ϕ, in which ϕ is the critical angle; *i.e.*,

$$2\phi = 113°20'$$

and

$$\phi = 56°40'.$$

IV. Because

$$\sin \phi = v_1/v_2,$$

we have

$$v_2 = v_1/\sin \phi.$$

For this numerical case,

$$\sin \phi = \sin 56°40' = 0.835.$$

Thus, since $v_1 = 5{,}250$ ft/sec,

$$v_2 = 5{,}250/0.835 = 6{,}290 \text{ ft/sec.}$$

We have in this way found the *true velocity* in the *lower medium*. Note that it is *not*, as is often implied, the average of the two apparent velocities of 6,100 ft/sec and 6,500 ft/sec. (This average is, in fact, a good approximation if the two apparent velocities are not too far apart in value. The greater the difference between the indicated apparent velocities, which means the greater the dip of the interface, the greater will be the error in averaging the apparent velocities for the true velocity.) The method for obtaining v_2 which we have shown is sound in all cases, no matter how great the dip, from the theoretical standpoint.

Returning to our problem: Because the *time-distance* curves are not the reverses of each other, $\alpha \neq \beta$. In fact, we found

$$\beta > \alpha.$$

Thus,

$$OM > QM.$$

V. We mark the point P on OM so that

$$MP = MQ,$$

and draw the dotted line QP.

The $\triangle PMQ$ is isosceles and, as a consequence of the result of Exercise 92, the interface we are seeking is *parallel* to PQ. Moreover, because of the result of Exercise 93, the dip of this interface is

$$\delta = (\beta - \alpha)/2 = (59°30' - 53°50')/2,$$

$$= 2°50'.$$

Now, by *measurement* (or trigonometrical calculation, which would be tedious and unnecessary) we find that

$$OP = 810 \text{ ft.}$$

This part, OP, of the wave path is traversed with a velocity of 5,250 ft/sec and therefore takes

$$810/5,250 = 0.154 \text{ sec.}$$

Since the total travel-time is 1.600 sec, the rest of the path $PCGQ$ takes

$$1.600 - 0.154 = 1.446 \text{ sec;}$$

that is to say,

$$1.446 = PC/5,250 + CG/6,290 + GQ/5,250.$$

VI. From this point on the problem is exactly the equivalent of that discussed on page 98, in which

$$a = PC = GQ$$

and

$$PQ = d.$$

Also,

$$t = 1.446, \qquad v_1 = 5,250, \qquad v_2 = 6,290.$$

We obtain

$$PQ = d = 8,330$$

by measurement in Figure 66. Then, using the formula for a on page 99, we have

$$a = [(6,290)\ (1.446) - 8,330]/2(6,290/5,250 - 5,250/6,290),$$

$$= 1,060 \text{ ft.}$$

VII. We scale off PC and QG to determine the points C and G by making each of these distances equal to 1,060 ft.

The trace CG is then the desired interface.

Check: As a rapid check that our solution is probably the correct one, we make the following observations:

i) The interface dips downward in the direction of the slower apparent velocity; *i.e.*, from Q to O.

ii) The true velocity, $v_2 = 6,290$ ft/sec, lies in value between the two apparent velocities: 6,100 ft/sec and 6,500 ft/sec.

iii) The critical angle, ϕ, is the arithmetic average of the values of the two emergence angles, 53°50′ and 59°30′.

iv) The angle of dip, δ, is one-half the difference between the values of the two emergence angles.

v) Finally, a time-check is made thus:

$$OC = 810 \text{ ft} + 1,060 \text{ ft} = 1,870 \text{ ft},$$

$$GQ = 1,060 \text{ ft},$$

$$CG = 6,550 \text{ ft}.$$

For practical purposes, the last value is best obtained by scaling the distance in Figure 66.

Thus, the travel-time for the wave path $OCGQ$ is

$$1,870/5,250 + 6,550/6,290 + 1,060/5,250,$$

$$= 2,930/5,250 + 6,550/6,290,$$

$$= 0.558 + 1.041 = 1.599 \text{ sec},$$

which checks unusually well with the observed time of 1.600 sec. A time-check within ± 0.005, or even greater, is usually sufficient.

THE READER IS URGED TO DO THE NUMERICAL WORK OF THE PRECEDING PROBLEM IN DETAIL FOR HIMSELF, FIRST DRAWING THE *TIME-DISTANCE* CURVES AND THEN FOLLOWING THE STEPS OF THE SOLUTION UNTIL THE MECHANICS OF THE PROCEDURE ARE WELL UNDERSTOOD.

In addition, we suggest

Ex. 94: A refraction profile is shot over a distance OQ under which is an interface whose depth directly under O is 2,000 ft and dips toward Q at the rate of 500 ft for every horizontal 10,000 ft. Above the interface the velocity is 5,700 ft/sec, and below the interface it is 6,500 ft/sec. Draw a sketch to show the situation and continue with the example:

a) What might be a reasonable length for OQ?

b) Draw the theoretical refraction *time-distance* curves from O and Q.

c) Reverse the problem and solve for the interface from these *time-distance* curves.

Lesson No. 23

THE ANALYTIC BASIS OF THE ELEMENTARY REFRACTION PROBLEM

At this stage in the development of the refraction problem, it seems advisable to discuss it from the analytic standpoint. In Lesson No. 19, some of this ground has been covered. Nonetheless, by setting up the analysis for the general two-layer refraction problem (along direction of true dip) we shall be able not only to get the earlier results again but also to obtain others of value.

Suppose, then, we consider the situation illustrated in Figure 67, which is essentially the same as was used in Figure 65.

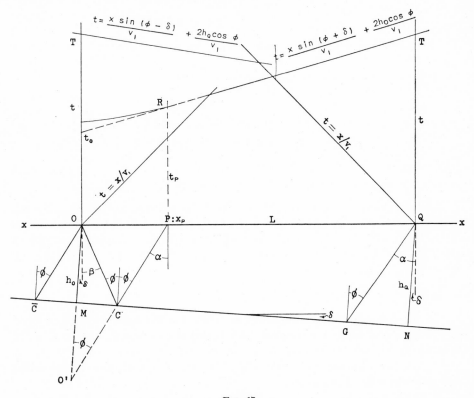

Fig. 67

First, consider a time- (t-) axis at shot-point O and an x-axis along OQ oriented positively from O to Q in the direction of true dip. Based on this coordinate system, what are the equations of the two sections of the *time-distance* curve emanating from O?

For reasons which will become apparent, it is desirable to use the *perpendicu-*

115

lar distance from O to the dipping interface CG. In Figure 67, this is the distance OM, which we indicate by h_O.

It should be obvious that the first section of the *time-distance* curve originating at O has the equation

(1) $$t = x/v_1.$$

We have seen that the second section is also a straight line. Using the notation of Lesson No. 21, the slope of this line is

$$dt/dx = \sin \alpha/v_1,$$
$$= \sin (\phi + \delta)/v_1.$$

We recall that

$$\sin \phi = v_1/v_2,$$

ϕ being the critical angle, and that δ is the angle of true dip.

Knowing the slope of this line, its equation must be of the form

(2) $$t = x \sin (\phi + \delta)/v_1 + K,$$

in which the constant K is to be determined by finding the coordinates of some one point on that line.

It will suit our purposes to choose this point as that corresponding to the travel-time of the *reflection* from the interface CG which is reflected at the critical angle ϕ. The reflection point is at C, and the wave arrives at the surface at the point P. On the *time-distance* curve of Figure 67 the desired point is indicated by R.

Ex. 95: Using the notation in Figure 67 and indicating the distance OP by x_P and the travel-time of the reflection OCP by t_P, show that the coordinates of R are

$$x_P = 2h_O \sin \phi/\cos \alpha$$
$$t_P = 2h_O \cos \delta/v_1 \cos \alpha.$$

These values must satisfy the equation (2) of the line forming the "outer" part of the *time-distance* curve as indicated above, since the point R is on the desired line. In other words, the value of K is found from the fact that

$$2h_O \cos \delta/v_1 \cos \alpha = [(2h_O \sin \phi/\cos \alpha)(\sin (\phi + \delta)/v_1)] + K.$$

Recalling that

$$\phi + \delta = \alpha,$$

we have

$$K = 2h_O \cos \delta/v_1 \cos \alpha - 2h_O \sin \phi \sin \alpha/v_1 \cos \alpha,$$
$$= (2h_0/v_1 \cos \alpha) (\cos \delta - \sin \phi \sin \alpha),$$
$$= [2h_0/v_1 \cos (\phi + \delta)] [\cos \delta - \sin \phi \sin (\phi + \delta)],$$
$$= [2h_0/v_1 \cos (\phi + \delta)] (\cos \delta - \sin^2 \phi \cos \delta - \sin \phi \cos \phi \sin \delta),$$

$$= [2h_0/v_1 \cos (\phi + \delta)] (\cos^2 \phi \cos \delta - \sin \phi \cos \phi \sin \delta),$$
$$= [2h_0 \cos \phi/v_1 \cos (\phi + \delta)] [\cos (\phi + \delta)],$$
$$= 2h_O \cos \phi/v_1.$$

Thus, the desired equation is:

(3) $$t = x \sin (\phi + \delta)/v_1 + 2h_O \cos \phi/v_1.$$

Ex. 96: If, at Q, we erect a time- (t-) axis and orient an x-axis positively from Q toward O—that is, *up-dip*—the refraction *time-distance* curve will consist of segments of the straight lines

$$t = x/v_1,$$

and

(4) $$t = x \sin (\phi - \delta)/v_1 + 2h_Q \cos \phi/v_1.$$

Here h_Q is the perpendicular distance QN, from Q to the interface CG.

Ex. 97: Show that for a horizontal interface, $\delta = 0$, equations (3) and (4) reduce to the result of Exercise 82.

If we designate the length of the profile OQ by L, and the over-all travel-time from O to Q by T, then, using equation (3):

(5) $$T = L \sin (\phi + \delta)/v_1 + 2h_O \cos \phi/v_1$$

Ex. 98: Using Figure 67, show that

$$h_Q = h_O + L \sin \delta;$$

and then show that the total travel-time T, from Q to O, from the relation (4) of Exercise 96, is equal to that obtained above from O to Q, namely (5).

Ex. 99: The point R of Figure 67, used in the derivation of the value of K, is also a point on the t-d curve of the reflection from the interface CG. Show that at R the slope of the *reflection t-d* curve (hyperbola) is the same as the refraction t-d straight line and that therefore the latter is tangent to the reflection hyperbola.

Ex. 100: Find the relationships pertaining to the point S (not shown in Figure 67) analogous to the point R for the data originating from shot-point Q.

A result of important practical value is to be obtained from a consideration of the intercept of the straight line (3) with the t-axis. This value, indicated by t, is of course obtained by setting $x = 0$; *i.e.*,

(6) $$t_0 = 2h_O \cos \phi/v_1.$$

Consider first the "fictional" refraction path from O to C to G to Q. Then consider the path from O to C to any point between Q and P; and let that point move continuously from Q to P. Now continue moving in the same direction from P

arriving at O. The corresponding path is from O to C to $\overline{C}$ back to O, with the distance $C\overline{C}$ covered negatively, so to speak. All this is physically fictional, but it is effective in seeing the meaning of the result and using it in a manner to be indicated. With this concept, we see that t_0 is the time of travel from O to C with a velocity v_1, then from C to $\overline{C}$ with a velocity v_2 counted *negatively*, then from $\overline{C}$ to C, *i. e.*,

$$t_0 = OC/v_1 - C\overline{C}/v_2 + \overline{C}O/v_1,$$
$$= (h_0/v_1 \cos \phi) - (2h_0 \tan \phi/v_2) + (h_0/v_1 \cos \phi,)$$
$$= (2h_0/v_1 \cos \phi) - (2h_0 \sin^2 \phi)/(v_1 \cos \phi),$$

since $\tan \phi = \sin \phi/\cos \phi$, and $v_2 = v_1/\sin \phi$. Reducing the last expression, we have

$$t_0 = (2h_0/v_1 \cos \phi)(1 - \sin^2 \phi)$$
$$= 2h_0 \cos \phi/v_1;$$

which is in agreement with the result (6) above.

Note what this result means. If, with O as a shot-point we shoot a profile in any azimuth, the straight-line section of the refraction *time-distance* curve from the interface will have this last value for its intercept. This intercept is independent of the azimuth. It depends only on h_0 and the velocities involved, provided only that the refracting interface is a monoclinal plane over this shooting area. *The same argument will later be found to be valid for the multi-layered problem.* Thus, as long as profiles from a given shot-point are shot over layers separated by planes, with no change in dip over the effective shooting area, the intercepts of the corresponding straight-line segments of the refraction *time-distance* curves with the time-axis through the shot-point will be the same.

This is of tremendous help in drawing the *time-distance* straight-line segments from the corrected data when two or more profiles have a common shot-point. In fact, using this property is just as important and just as effective as making certain that over-all travel-times, which should be equal, actually are equal.

Ex. 101: Show that the intercept at Q has the value

$$t_Q = 2h_Q \cos \phi/v_1.$$

The student interested in pursuing the analysis further is now in a position to do so, and will be rewarded with some results of more than passing interest.

Ex. 102: Write the equations of the two *time-distance* curves based on *one* coordinate system only. Then find the point of intersection of the two curves, which should be at $x = L/2$, if $\delta = 0$.

Ex. 103: Where do the two segments of the refraction *time-distance* curve from a shot-point intersect, expressed in distance from the shot-point and in travel-time?

Lesson No. 24

CORRECTIONS FOR SEISMIC DATA

I. INTRODUCTION

Up to this point, all our discussions were based on the premise that the seismic data to be interpreted had been suitably corrected to a flat and horizontal surface which, in each case, serves as a *datum plane* and below which the medium is one of constant seismic velocity. It is our present purpose to discuss the needs for corrections to the raw data and the various types of corrections which may be used.

Corrections to data are applied in order to reduce the problems to situations which in each case approximate as closely as possible the ideal from the theoretical standpoint and the solutions to which will yield results which, in turn, it is hoped will approximate "reality" from the practical standpoint. Experience alone shows that this goal is reasonably well realized in petroleum exploration seismology, for there is no laboratory for testing the over-all results except that of the years of successful experience.

In the interpretation of seismic data, the existence of media in which the elastic constants are constant is implied; we assume the interfaces to be clearly and sharply defined; we make assumptions as to continuity of beds and their properties; in short, we reduce the number of all the many, varied and changing parameters to a minimum and idealize their properties.

The resultant interpretation is affected by these idealizations and assumptions. It is affected, too, in the manner with which the travel-times of seismic events are read. In the case of the refraction techniques some attempt is made to obtain actual travel-times, whereas in reflection techniques these are not even ascertainable.

Compounded on all these details are those of correcting the travel-time data in order that they be amenable to solutions of the types we have been discussing. We must correct the data to a datum plane—preferably a horizontal one—below which we assume media in which our solutions are intended to apply. We therefore have corrections by virtue of the medium lying between the earth's surface and this datum plane which consist of topography and elevation effects and so-called "low velocity" effects. The depth of the shot enters as part of the problem. Then come corrections which must be applied over dipping interfaces whose strike may be at any angle to the line of shooting profile. Of this latter matter, more will be said as the lessons continue. For the present, the discussion will be that of low-velocity and elevation corrections.

To discuss all possible problems which may arise and the techniques which may be used in the solutions to those problems is an impossible assignment. All we shall try to do is to indicate the general nature of the problem and to instruct the reader in the methods and reasons for the general procedures we recommend.

119

We are interested in teaching the reader, in short, how to think about the problems, feeling that such procedure will be most fruitful in rendering the reader able to solve his own problems.

Basically, there are two different ways of attacking the problem of the corrections under consideration.

The point of view on which the first way is based is that of considering each particular "set-up" in a seismic survey as a problem unto itself and solving its attendant ramifications on that basis. That problem having been solved, the resultant piece of subsurface information is duly plotted in section or on contour map, again unto itself, and it is fitted into the over-all picture only as one of many individual parts.

One immediate advantage of such a method is that no universal—or, at least, widespread—datum plane, such, for example, as sea level, is necessary in the solution of the problem. The advantage accrues from the fact that a widespread datum plane, while important from the final and gelogical point of view, is not intrinsically tied into the physical problem of the individual set up.

The second method of making corrections rests on the adoption of a widespread datum plane, very often that of sea level, but always that of a plane parallel to sea level. Although such a datum plane is not tied intrinsically to the problem raised by each individual set-up, the methods based on this general type of attack usually have some advantage in yielding results equally well and which are amenable to mapping almost instantly.

The reader must learn for himself which types of corrections are necessary and applicable. Each area—and often each set up—is a small but important source of problems; and there cannot be any one idea in making corrections which yields the "best" results at all times.

It will be apparent, as we develop the ideas, that there is nothing of difficulty in any of the methods propounded; that, rather, it is almost always a matter of applying common sense arithmetic to some very simple physical assumptions.

The basic reason for the need of corrections to the travel-times is the existence of the so-called "low-velocity layer" at the surface. This layer is also, at times, called the "weathered layer." Perhaps, from the seismic standpoint, this latter term is less desirable than the former, since it may be confused with its geologic connotation. While very often the low-velocity layer and the weathered layer in its geologic sense are one and the same, it is also sometimes true that they are not. We shall therefore speak of the low-velocity layer—or l.v.l.—rather than of the weathered layer.

The l.v.l. varies from place to place in its geometric and seismic properties, and it is the existence of these variations which brings up the many problems and creates the situation already mentioned—that there is no one answer to all situations.

It is a very common peculiarity of the l.v.l. that its elastic properties are extremely variable. It is this fact that very often deprives this layer of consistency in what is generally meant by seismic velocity. Attempts to measure the speed of propagation in this medium usually yield extremely erratic and highly variable results. The lack of compaction, large variations in porosity and fluid content, the seismic irregularities of glacial drift, actual weathering itself—any of these conditions might occur in the l.v.l., and these tend to make it something less than a homogeneous elastic medium.

As a consequence of general usefulness, it is safe to say that, whenever feasible, corrections for the propagation of seismic waves through the l.v.l. are preferably to be made as *time* corrections. Rather than assign a velocity to the l.v.l.,—even though measured locally—it is better to adjust the data by using the *time* of transit of the wave through the l.v.l. than converting this time to depth or directly using depth; for it is almost always true that at the next location such velocity as has been used at one location will not be valid at the next.

The principle will be followed in the examples which follow.

II. DISCUSSION OF CORRECTIONS

In exciting the ground into seismic activity by the explosion of a charge, the center of the explosion is referred to as the shot-point. This shot-point is at some depth from the surface. The travel-time from the charge to a point immediately over it on the surface of the earth, that is, to the mouth of the shot-hole, is called the "up-hole time." It is common practice to obtain this up-hole time for each shot.

The depth of the shot-point may be a few feet or several hundred feet, the effectiveness of the shot being determined to a large extent by the depth and the formation in which the charge explodes. Consequently, the charge may be exploded in the l.v.l., below it, or even at its bottom. In most cases, unless strong arguments can be raised against the practice, it is most desirable to have the shot-point below the l.v.l.

Suppose, then, we have a situation somewhat as illustrated in Figure 68. The trace PP' indicates the trace of the localized datum plane in the immediate neighborhood of the shooting set up.

At location A the shot depth is represented by a, and the up-hole time by t_a.

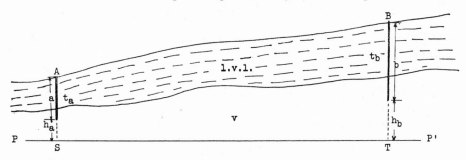

FIG. 68

The distance between the bottom of the shot-hole and the datum plane used is indicated by h_a. It is, of course, assumed that we know the elevations of the surface at A and that of PP' from which h_a is obtained as the differences between these two elevations and the shot-hole depth. If, then, the velocity immediately below the l.v.l. is v, the travel-time of a wave from the datum plane to the surface, that is, for the distance SA, is

$$t_A = t_a + h_a/v.$$

This consideration is the basis of some of the most commonly used corrections.

The l.v.l. may be studied in its relation to the pickup locations and to the travel-times of the seismic events to these locations by using the first-arrivals to these locations and so obtaining a *refraction t-d* curve for them. This refraction profile method, sometimes referred to as "poop shooting," should, ideally, be reversed; but very often, from practical considerations, it is not. The travel-times are plotted, the "best" straight lines are drawn for the *t-d* curves, and the result interpreted in the usual manner. As we have stated, since the l.v.l. is generally not a good seismic medium, these *t-d* curves are, at best, approximations which, it must be hoped, are reasonably good ones. The worth of this method varies from area to area but, in general, is best in "hard" surface country as opposed to swampy and marshy lands.

It is generally of value, too, in long refraction profiles where the correction for each pickup for the l.v.l. is sizeable as well as changeable from location to location. Small refraction profiles over the pickup locations will serve to delineate the l.v.l. at these locations and in that way yield data for correcting the travel-times to each pickup.

The method of "continuous profiling" in reflection seismology entails the use of shot-holes at each end of a "set-up." Thus, in Figure 68, A and B would be successive shot-holes with the distance between A and B used as the spread of pickup locations. When A is the shot-point, the pickup spread extends from A to B; and when B is the shot-point, the same pickup locations in the reverse directions are used over the same spread, from B to A.

Using the previous relation obtaining at A to its counterpart at B, namely

$$t_B = t_b + h_b/v,$$

we note that the travel-time of an event from S to T on the datum plane PP' would be

$$t_{ST} = t_{AB} - [(h_a + h_b)/v + t_b],$$

in which t_{AB} is the observed travel-time from the bottom of the shot-hole A to the pickup at B.

Arguing similarly,

$$t_{TS} = t_{AB} - [(h_a + h_b)/v + t_a]$$

is the corrected travel-time from T to S, in which t_{BA} is the observed travel-time of the event from the bottom of shot-hole B to the pickup location at A. Obviously under correct correlation of the data, we should have

$$t_{TS} = t_{ST}.$$

The same arguments apply to any datum plane, although greater care must be used in the choice of v when the datum plane is at great depths below the surface. In that event, too, greater significance attaches to the implication we have used, in making our corrections, that the wave paths in the l.v.l. are at right angles to the datum plane. If the datum plane is very deep, this assumption may lead to sizeable errors in the corrections.

As we have said, it is not the purpose of the Lessons to supply the details of the routine chores and arithmetical procedures which are so necessary and important, but which must be learned by use and experience. Rather is it our purpose to show the basic concepts and ideas upon which the reader is expected to build a successful "practice." In this sense, then, this chapter on Corrections, it is hoped, has fulfilled its purpose, and we shall leave the matter, at least for the present.

To Readers of the Lessons:

It is now a year since the "Lessons in Seismic Interpretation" were begun. This fact, coupled with a desirable place for a pause such as we now have, provides an opportunity to make a few pertinent remarks.

The response to the lessons has been delightfully gratifying, but, for the most part, of an oral variety. At times, I have a wistful desire to see some of the comments in writing, even though they may be adverse. When written, such comments have a way of making a more definite and a permanent impression.

At the risk of repetition, I would point out again that the basic purpose of these lessons is to form the background for an understanding of the ideas in seismic interpretation rather than to help master the routine, but necessary and important, chores. And in establishing this background, the point of view is that of teaching a group who, for the most part, are not "professional mathematicians."

In the accompanying Lesson,* we treat in brief fashion the matter of correction to observed travel-times. As we have said, this seems to be a desirable place for a pause before the next series, which we shall designate as Part II, begins. This series will treat, in its three-dimensional aspects, the problem of reflection and refraction paths and travel-times in which a plane interface is inclined with respect to the horizontal plane of the surface and which forms the lower boundary of a medium in which the velocity is constant. From now on the discussions will assume a point of view which will have more mathematical analysis, for that is the only way the whole subject matter can be handled. We shall try to explain the arguments in as elementary a manner as we can with the aid of figures drawn as best we can.

There will still remain the "multi-layered" problem and that of continuous variation of velocity with depth. These problems and the associated ones which arise in their applications will follow. The problem of treating data of well-velocity surveys, too, must be considered. Although we shall continue to use substantially the same procedures as we have thus far used, and to insert numerical problems and examples whenever it seems desirable, we must point out again that the analytic treatment will occupy a larger part of the discussions which are to follow.

So much, then, for the plans. They are not rigid, and any suggestions of topics to be considered first in lieu of those outlined will be welcomed and, if agreeable, will be accepted.

Again, it is always pleasant to thank those who help with the preparation of these lessons. To Mrs. Brantley (*née* Bodron) for her excellent stenography, to M. Pruitt for his drafting, to Mr. H. W. Merritt and, more recently, Dr. L. W. Blau for their discovery of large and small *errata*, both before and after they have been committed—to all these and others, a huge basketful of hearty thanks.

M. M. Slotnick

* Lesson 24.

LESSONS
IN
SEISMIC COMPUTING

PART II

Lesson No. 25

THE THREE-DIMENSIONAL SEISMIC PATH PROBLEM—
SINGLE LAYER

I. INTRODUCTION

The seismic energy released at the shot-point by the explosion of the charge is transmitted over a three-dimensional region. The full interpretation of the data obtained must be considered therefore from that standpoint. Up to now we have reduced the problems in hand to two-dimensional ones by assuming that the profiles shot were at right angles to the strike of a dipping interface; in other words, that our vertical "section" of the subsurface included the direction of true dip of the bed involved.

If the interface involved in the problem is horizontal or, at worst, of very gentle dip as is quite often the case, the methods we have discussed apply. In fact, these methods are very often used even when the dip involved is sizeable, the questions of applicability of the methods being evaded. This, however, is not always as serious a matter as one might suspect since the "flat" areas, like tops of anticlines and bottoms of synclines, which enter the picture, ought to be mapped reasonably well in any case. It is at the adjacent dips that the two-dimensional interpretation would misplace the bed.

With the present greater need for higher accuracy in subsurface delineation, we shall have to pay more attention to the three-dimensional aspects of interpretation. It is the purpose of the next few lessons to lay the groundwork for an understanding of these problems and to indicate the methods of solving them.

The methods, of necessity, will have to be mathematical in treatment. We shall try to discuss these mathematical developments as best we can; and by figures and constant repetition, we believe the ideas will be understood by all who are genuinely interested. To those whose mathematical development is perhaps somewhat greater, matters will come easily; these people might do well to answer the many interesting geometrical and analytical by-products. On the other hand, we shall try to explain the *results*, in detail, so that if the mathematical manipulations necessary prove too burdensome to some readers, at least the results and their significance will be apparent.

A final word before we proceed. The figures we shall use try to illustrate spatial situations on the flat plane of the paper. To understand them properly and completely, we shall explain them in what we hope will be complete terms. Nonetheless, it would be well for each reader to make his own figures for a fuller understanding of them.

II. THE PLANE OF A REFLECTED WAVE PATH

Suppose that A and B of Figure 69 are two points in a medium in which the wave propagation velocity is constant and which has for a boundary a reflecting plane interface, p. Recalling the minimum-time principle, what is the path of a wave from the point A reflected by p to the point B?

In the first place, the total reflected wave path will consist of two straight-line segments, intersecting in a reflecting point on p, typified by the path $AR'B$. This follows from the fact that the wave paths within a medium in which the velocity is constant are straight-line segments.

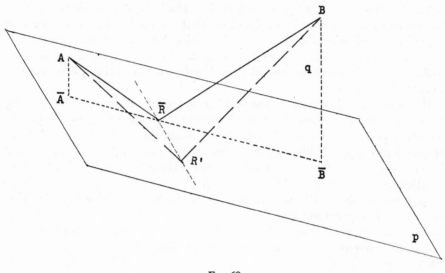

FIG. 69

Our first important result is:

The plane of the two straight-line segments of the reflected wave path is the plane through A and B which is at right angles to the reflecting plane p.

We proceed to prove this statement by showing that for every path $AR'B$ whose plane is *not* perpendicular to p, there is a shorter path (and therefore one of less travel-time, since the velocity is constant), $A\overline{R}B$, in the plane q which passes through A and B and is perpendicular to p. After showing this to be the case, all we need do is to find the shortest wave path in q which, of course, reduces the problem to that already discussed (pp. 38 and 39). We proceed to the argument.

From A and B drop perpendiculars $A\overline{A}$ and $B\overline{B}$, respectively, to the plane p, the points $\overline{A}$ and $\overline{B}$ being the feet of these perpendiculars. Then the points A, $\overline{A}$, $\overline{B}$, and B are four points in a plane q which is the plane through A and B perpendicular to p. Moreover, the line $\overline{AB}$ is in p, and angles $A\overline{AB}$ and $B\overline{BA}$ are right angles.

Ex. 104: Make your own drawing of Figure 69 and prove the assertion of the last paragraph.

Now let R' be any point of p, *not* on the line $\overline{AB}$, and from R' draw the perpendicular $R'\overline{R}$ to $\overline{AB}$, $\overline{R}$ being the intersection of this perpendicular with $\overline{AB}$ and therefore lying in the plane q as well as in p. The line $R'\overline{R}$ is perpendicular to the plane q and the lines $A\overline{R}$ and $\overline{R}B$. Why?

Ex. 105: Show that

$$A\overline{R} < AR'$$

and

$$\overline{R}B < R'B,$$

and, therefore, that

$$A\overline{R} + \overline{R}B < AR' + R'B.$$

From this exercise the fact follows that the minimum-time path from A to p to B, which must consist of two straight-line segments, must lie in the plane q which passes through A and B and is at right angles to the reflecting plane p.

In this plane q we now seek the reflection path—from A to some point on $\overline{AB}$ to B—the point on $\overline{AB}$ to be determined by the minimum time principle. As we have shown (p. 39), this point is obtained by extending $A\overline{A}$ to the point A' (Figure 70), the image of A with respect to p; *i.e.*, $A'\overline{A} = A\overline{A}$. This image point A' is joined to B and will intersect the line $\overline{AB}$ in a point R. (Why?) The path ARB is the reflection path.

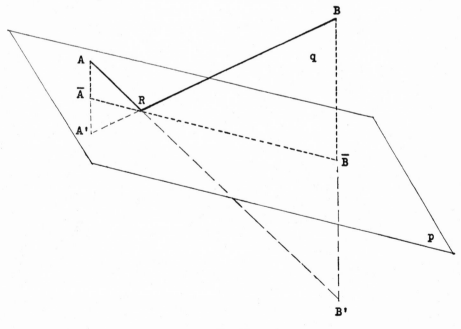

Fig. 70

Ex. 106: Prove directly that the path ARB of Figure 70 is that of minimum-time from A to a point on p to B. If B' is the image point of B with respect to p, show that the reflection path from B to A is the same as from A to B in the reverse direction. In other words, show that $B'A$ and $A'B$ intersect in a point R on $\overline{AB}$, the reflecting point for the wave.

Ex. 107: Using the definitions of page 11 as a basis, define the angles of incidence and of reflection in Figure 70 and show them to be equal.

Ex. 108: Discuss the special case of the path from A to B reflected when the line AB is perpendicular to p.

III. THE PLANE OF A REFRACTED WAVE PATH

Suppose, now, that the plane interface p separates two media in one of which the seismic velocity is v_1 and in the other v_2, with $v_1 \neq v_2$. Let A_1 be a point in the first medium and A_2 a point in the second (Figure 71). The wave path from A_1 to A_2 will consist of two straight-line segments (since the velocity in each medium is constant), A_1R' and $R'A_2$, in which R' is a point of p such that the travel-time over this path, namely

$$A_1R'/v_1 + R'A_2/v_2,$$

is a minimum.

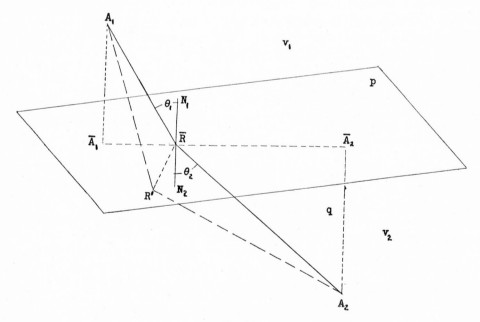

FIG. 71

The straight line through A_1 and A_2 is assumed *not* perpendicular to p. Let the feet of the perpendiculars from A_1 and A_2 to p be $\overline{A}_1$ and $\overline{A}_2$, respectively. The four points A_1, A_2, $\overline{A}_1$, $\overline{A}_2$ then lie in the plane q which is perpendicular to p.

The first important result is that *for a minimum travel-time the point R' will lie in the plane q.* We shall prove this by showing that we can always find a point $\overline{R}$ on $\overline{A}_1\overline{A}_2$ for which the travel-time

$$A_1\overline{R}/v_1 + \overline{R}A_2/v_2$$

is less than

$$A_1R'/v_1 + R'A_2/v_2,$$

which is the travel-time for the typical point R' in p but not on $\overline{A}_1\overline{A}_2$.

Since R' is *not* on $\overline{A}_1\overline{A}_2$, we drop a perpendicular from R' to this line—all in the plane p—and indicate the intersection as $\overline{R}$.

Ex. 109: The line $R'\overline{R}$ is at right angles to both $A_1\overline{R}$ and $\overline{R}A_2$, and also to q.

Ex. 110: Show that

$$A_1\overline{R} < A_1R'$$

and

$$\overline{R}A_2 < R'A_2.$$

If, now, we divide both sides of the first of these two inequalities by v_1 and the second by v_2 and add corresponding sides, we have proved our point.

At the point $\overline{R}$ draw the normal N_1N_2 to the plane p. This, of course, is parallel to $A_1\overline{A}_1$ and $A_2\overline{A}_2$ and lies in the plane q. Then, as we did on page 75, let us write

$$\sphericalangle A_1\overline{R}N_1 = \theta_1 \quad\text{and}\quad \sphericalangle A_2\overline{R}N_2 = \theta_2.$$

If we think of $\overline{R}$ as moving along $\overline{A}_1\overline{A}_2$, it will finally reach a position R (Figure 72), for which Snell's Law holds:

$$\sin\theta_1/v_1 = \sin\theta_2/v_2$$

(see p. 75). For this point R the travel-time will be a minimum and the line segments A_1R and RA_2 will therefore constitute the wave path.

To summarize: *The refracted wave path from a point A_1 in a medium in which the seismic velocity is v_1 to a point A_2 in another medium in which the velocity is v_2, which media are separated by a plane interface p, consists of two straight-line segments whose plane q is the plane through A_1 and A_2 perpendicular to the plane p. The point of refraction R on the intersection of p and q is that for which Snell's Law obtains:*

$$\sin\theta_1/v_1 = \sin\theta_2/v_2.$$

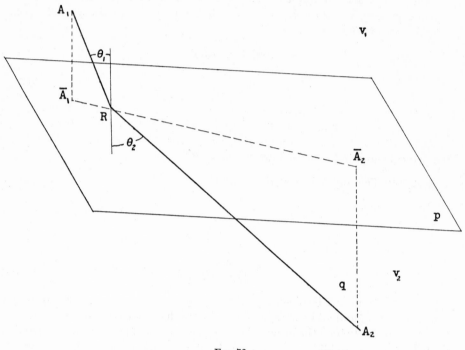

Fig. 72

We have shown the situation in Figure 72.

Ex. 111: What can be said on this matter if the line A_1A_2 is perpendicular to p?

Ex. 112: Show that the refracted path from A_2 to A_1 consists of the same two line segments traversed in the reverse direction.

There remains finally one more situation to be discussed.

Suppose that in the previous example that $v_2 > v_1$ and that the point A_2 lies in p, but sufficiently far removed from $\overline{A}_1$. We leave for the student to show the important result:

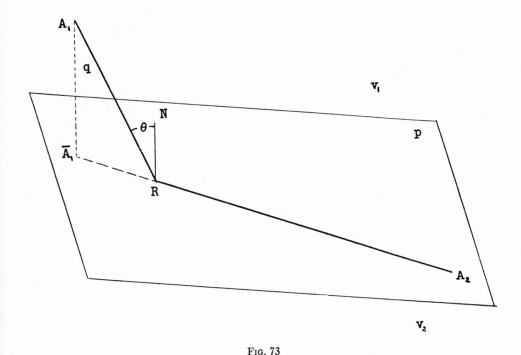

FIG. 73

Ex. 113: *The refracted wave path from a point A_1 in a medium in which the seismic velocity is v_1 to a point A_2 on the plane interface p separating that medium from another in which the seismic velocity is v_2, with $v_2 > v_1$, consists of two line segments in the plane q which is the plane through A_1 and A_2 at right angles to p. If we indicate the intersection of p and q by $\overline{A_1A_2}$, the segments are (1) the line joining A_1 to the point R of $\overline{A_1A_2}$ for which $\angle\overline{A_1}A_1R = \angle A_1RN = \theta = sin^{-1}(v_1/v_2)$, the critical angle for v_1 and v_2, and (2) the straight line RA_2.*

This is illustrated in Figure 73.

Lesson No. 26

REFLECTION FROM A SINGLE DIPPING INTERFACE—
ANALYTIC PRELIMINARIES

As has been mentioned, we must use mathematical methods to study our problem in its three-dimensional aspects. Accordingly, we shall have to use the usual three-dimensional Cartesian coordinate systems to get our results. However, it must be remembered that a coordinate system is only a device—analogous to a tool—to attain certain ends, and that these ends or results must therefore be independent of the coordinate system employed.

Experience has shown that many of our readers have difficulty in "seeing" three-dimensional pictures on the flat surface of a sheet of paper. This is unfortunate, and an attempt will be made to overcome this hurdle by developing

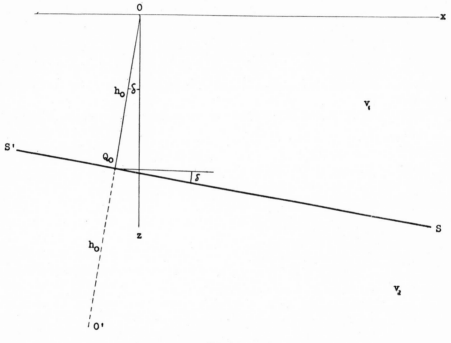

FIG. 74

the subject matter with a succession of figures. However, the best method of all is to have the *reader make his own figures*, expanding on them as the subject progresses. It has been suggested that the reader make cardboard models for many of the problems and in that way make matters easier to understand.

* * *

By way of a beginning, we indicate in Figure 74 a vertical section of the situation we are to discuss. Here the reader is asked to visualize the line Ox as the x-axis on the surface of the earth, oriented positively in the direction of the true dip of a plane interface whose trace in this vertical section is $S'S$. Thus the

134

direction of strike of this dipping plane is at right angles to the plane of the paper.

The angle δ at Q_0 is the true dip of the plane interface. A line through Q_0 at right angles to the sheet of paper is in the direction of the strike of the dipping plane interface.

If, from O, which we shall consider as a shot-point, we draw a perpendicular OQ_0 to $S'S$, then the angle between this line and the vertical Oz through O—which we shall use as the z-axis, oriented positively downward—is also δ, the angle of dip. The distance OQ_0 will be designated by h_0.

If we continue OQ_0 to the point O' such that

$$OQ_0 = Q_0O' = h_0,$$

and thus

$$OO' = 2h_0,$$

then O' is the *image point* of O with respect to $S'S$.

It is important to note that the image point of O with respect to the dipping plane whose trace is $S'S$ is O' *even in three-dimensional space*. For, from O one can draw one and only one perpendicular to the dipping plane—which perpendicular is OQ_0.

All these facts should now be clear as we proceed to a study of Figure 75. In making this illustration, we start with that of Figure 74. From O we draw a

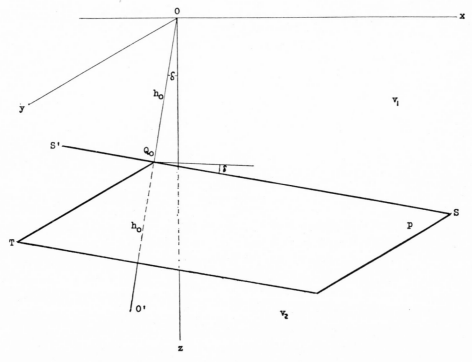

Fig. 75

y-axis which is to be considered as being at right angles to the plane of the sheet of paper and oriented positively from O toward the reader. This direction is that of the *strike* of the dipping interface. (Why?)

From Q_0 we have drawn a line Q_0T parallel to Oy which *lies in the dipping plane interface*, hereafter to be referred to as p. The plane p, let us repeat, is normal (at right angles) to the (x, z)-plane (the plane of the sheet of paper) and intersects it in $S'S$, which makes an angle δ with the horizontal x-direction.

Ex. 114: Show that the coordinates of Q_0 are $(-h_0 \sin \delta, O, h_0 \cos \delta)$; and those those of O' are $(-2h_0 \sin \delta, O, 2h_0 \cos \delta)$.

Our next step is to proceed to Figure 76. This figure is based on the preceding one, with some additions.

We have first chosen an arbitrary point P on the surface of the earth; that is, P is a point in the (x, y)- plane. The coordinates of the point P are:

the *directed* projection $\overrightarrow{OP_x}$ of $\overrightarrow{OP}$ on the x-axis for its x-coordinate,
the *directed* projection $\overrightarrow{OP_y}$ of $\overrightarrow{OP}$ on the y-axis for its y-coordinate,
and its z-coordinate is O, since P is in the (x, y)-plane.

Now we indicate the distance $\overrightarrow{OP}$ by ρ and the angle from the positive x-axis to $\overrightarrow{OP}$ (measured in the direction from the $+x$-axis to the $+y$-axis) by ψ. We

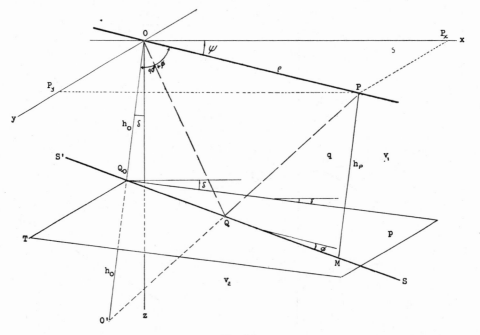

Fig. 76

may then write the coordinates of P as

$$P: (\rho \cos \psi, \rho \sin \psi, O).$$

Let us now think of the line OP as a line of pickups radiating from the shot-point O on the surface s of the earth (the (x, y)-plane), and that we are receiving at these pickups seismic energy which, generated at the shot-point O, is reflected to these pickups by the dipping plane interface p. The seismic velocity in the medium between the surface s and p is v_1, a constant.

To obtain the path of the reflected wave arriving at P, we proceed as before:

The image point O' of O with respect to p is joined to P by the straight line $O'P$, which pierces p in Q.

The point Q lies on $S'S$ (see footnote), the intersection of p with the plane of OO' and OP which we indicate by q. In fact, this plane q is at right angles to p and contains all the wave paths from O which are reflected at p to points on OP.

Thus, as P moves along the line OP, the reflecting point Q moves along the intersection $S'S$ of the two planes, p and q.

The length of the wave path OQP is equal to the length of the line segment $O'P$.

Ex. 115: Show this last statement to be true, again, referring to Figure 76, following the line of reasoning of page 12 but remembering that the problem now is three-dimensional.

If the travel-time of this reflected wave to P is t, then

$$OQP = O'P = v_1 t.$$

To express $O'P$ in terms of $OP = \rho$ and $OO' = 2h_0$ of triangle $O'OP$, we need the value of $\measuredangle POO'$ in terms of ψ and δ.

Referring back to the coordinates of

$$P: (\rho \cos \psi, \rho \sin \psi, O)$$

and to those of

$$O': (-2h_0 \sin \delta, O, 2h_0 \cos \delta),$$

the square of the distance between those points is:

$$\overline{O'P^2} = [\rho \cos \psi - (-2h_0 \sin \delta)]^2 + (\rho \sin \psi - O)^2 + (O - 2h_0 \cos \delta)^2,$$
$$= \rho^2(\cos^2 \psi + \sin^2 \psi) + 4h_0\rho \cos \psi \sin \delta + 4h_0^2(\cos^2 \delta + \sin^2 \delta),$$
$$= \rho^2 + 4h_0^2 + 4h_0\rho \cos \psi \sin \delta.$$

As we have seen, the length of the reflected wave OQP is equal to $O'P = v_1 t$. Accordingly, we have

---

The trace $S'S$ is not necessarily the same as is shown in Figures 74 and 75. In this figure it would be the same if $\psi = 0$.

(1) $$(O'P)^2 = (v_1t)^2 = \rho^2 + 4h_0{}^2 + 4h_0\rho \cos \psi \sin \delta.$$

The angle between the direction of OP and that of $S'S$ is indicated by ϕ. It is the *apparent* dip of the plane p as measured in the direction of OP. It should be evident that

$$\angle O'OP = 90° + \phi.$$

Also,

$$O'P = v_1t,$$

$$O'O = 2h_0,$$

$$OP = \rho.$$

Using the law of cosines in triangle $O'OP$,

(2)
$$(O'P)^2 = (v_1t)^2 = \rho^2 + 4h_0{}^2 - 4h_0\rho \cos (90° + \phi),$$
$$= \rho^2 + 4h_0{}^2 + 4h_0\rho \sin \phi.$$

By reconciling this equation (2) with equation (1) above, we have

(3) $$\sin \phi = \cos \psi \sin \delta.$$

Now it should be evident by identifying equation (1), using equation (3), and equation (1) on page 50 that ϕ is the apparent angle of dip along the line of profile OP. *This is the angle between the direction of $S'S$ and OP* and, as such, would be the *dip measured if we used the assumption of the early lessons,* namely that our profile line of shooting was in the direction of dip.

Ex. 116: The apparent angle of dip, ϕ, is equal to the true angle of dip when, in equation (3), $\psi=0$. Discuss the meaning of this. When $\psi=90°$, what is the value of ϕ? Discuss the meaning of this.

*Ex. 117: For those who understand the use of direction cosines, find the relation (3) by using the direction cosines of

$$OP: (\cos \psi, \sin \psi, O)$$

and of

$$OO': (-\sin \delta, O, \cos \delta).$$

Find the direction cosines of $S'S$.

Answer:

$$\cos \psi \cos^2 \delta/(\cos^2 \psi \cos^2 \delta + \sin^2 \psi)^{1/2}, \ \sin \psi/(\cos^2 \psi \cos^2 \delta + \sin^2 \psi)^{1/2},$$

$$\cos \psi \sin \delta \cos \delta/(\cos^2 \psi \cos^2 \delta + \sin^2 \psi)^{1/2}$$

In the next lesson we shall discuss some more relations of fundamental importance before we proceed to the applications of the results.

---

* Examples which are indicated by asterisks may be omitted. They are inserted for the mathematically curious.

Lesson No. 27

REFLECTION FROM A SINGLE DIPPING INTERFACE—
FURTHER FUNDAMENTAL CONCEPTS

It may already have occurred to the reader that the concept of the emergence angle, which played such a fundamental role in the early Lessons, is not quite as simple in the three-dimensional problem.

In Figure 77, let s represent the plane of the surface of the earth. A plane wave front indicated by the area whose corners are each marked with a W is approaching the surface s. The point P is a point on s and on the wave front W. As the wave front W moves, it will occupy the position indicated by the section

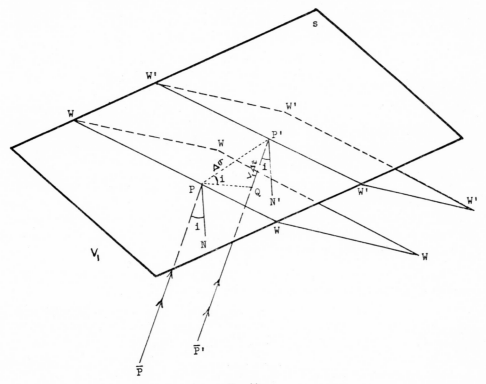

Fig. 77

marked by W' in each corner at some time, say Δt seconds, later. The point P' on s and on the wave front W' is such that *the line PP' is at right angles to the parallel traces of W and W' on s.*

The line $\overline{P}P$ indicates the wave *path* through P which is, of course, at right angles to all the positions of the wave fronts. Similarly, the line $\overline{P}'P'$ is the wave path or ray through P' which pierces the wave front W at right angles at some point Q.

139

The line PN is drawn perpendicular to PP' and in the plane of PQP', and similarly the line P'N' is perpendicular to PP' in the plane of PQP'.

It is this

$$\angle \overline{P}PN = \angle \overline{P}'P'N',$$
$$= \angle P'PQ,$$
$$= i,$$

which is defined as the emergence angle of the plane wave. It is to be noted that the emergence angle is equal to the dihedral angle formed by *s* and the plane of the wave front.

Ex. 118: Show that this definition of the emergence angle reduces to that defined on page 4 for a two-dimensional section.

Returning to Figure 77, let us indicate the velocity below the surface *s* by v_1. Further, let the distance *PP'* be indicated by $\Delta\sigma$. It must always be remembered that the direction of *PP'* will *not necessarily* be in line with that of the shooting profile. It is for that reason, in fact, that we have used another letter (σ in this case) rather than the customary *x* or ρ to indicate distance in the *PP'* direction. It is for this reason, too, that we must exercise caution in the use of emergence angles in the three-dimensional problem.

Another important corollary is that the lines *PN* snd *P'N'*, though both perpendicular to *PP'*, are *not* necessarily normal to *s*.

Ex. 119: Show that in Figure 77

$$\sin i = v_1(\Delta t/\Delta\sigma)$$

and that this reduces to the similar result of Lesson No. 1.

Finally, this definition must now be extended to wave fronts which are not plane wave fronts. Let *WW* in Figure 78 be the intersection of the surface of a wave front on the surface of the earth *s*, and let *P* be a point on this intersection. Let $\overline{P}P$ be the wave path through *P*, and *PT* the tangent line thereto at *P*. At *P* let *FF* be the tangent line to *WW*. Finally, let *PP'* be the perpendicular to *FF* at *P* in the plane *s*.

In the plane of *TPP'* draw *PN* at right angles to *PP'*. Then

$$\angle TPN = i$$

is the *emergence angle* of the wave at *P*.

Ex. 120: Show that this is the same as the preceding definition for a plane wave front and that by a "limiting process" this becomes the more general definition.

There is an important relation implied here which is a special case of what is known as the "equation of eikonal" and of which we shall make a great deal of

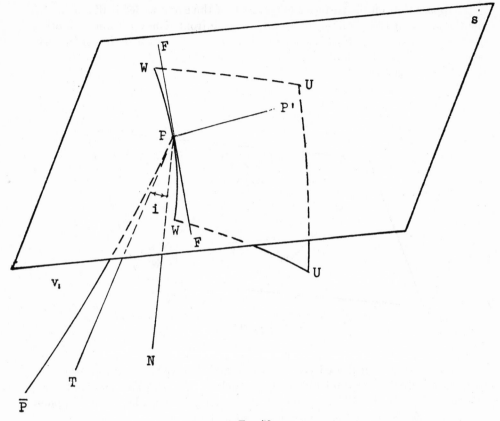

FIG. 78

use. To show this relationship we interpose the following

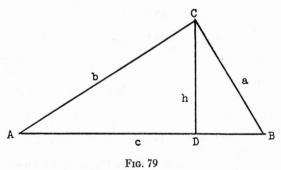

FIG. 79

Ex. 121: If h is the length of the altitude on the hypotenuse of a right triangle whose legs are a and b in length,

$$1/h^2 = 1/a^2 + 1/b^2$$

(See Figure 79).

Suppose that on the surface s (Figure 80) of the earth we let WW and $W'W'$ be the traces of two positions of a moving wave front removed from each other in time by Δt seconds. If Δt is small enough, the two traces WW and $W'W'$ will not be too far from each other in space, and, in fact, if the area of s under consideration is also restricted in size we may assume these two traces to be essentially *straight line* segments.

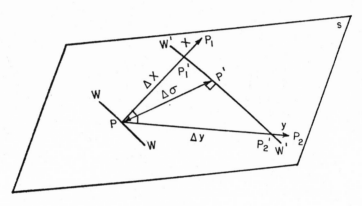

FIG. 80

Suppose that on WW we have a pickup P and that we have pickups also along any two mutually perpendicular lines through P; *viz.*, PP_1 and PP_2. Let these two lines intersect $W'W'$ in P_1' and P_2', respectively. Finally, let P' be that point on $W'W'$ such that PP' is perpendicular to $W'W'$.

Now, if we call the directions of PP_1 and PP_2 the x- and y-directions and, furthermore, if we let

$$PP_1' = \Delta x,$$

$$PP_2' = \Delta y,$$

and

$$PP' = \Delta \sigma,$$

then, by Exercise 121:

(1) $$(1/\Delta\sigma)^2 \cong (1/\Delta x)^2 + (1/\Delta y)^2.$$

Since P_1', P', and P_2' are all on the same wave front, the pickups there will record the arriving seismic event all at the same time; that is, Δt seconds after its arrival at P. If then we multiply equation (1) through by $(\Delta t)^2$, we have

(2) $$(\Delta t/\Delta\sigma)^2 \cong (\Delta t/\Delta x)^2 + (\Delta t/\Delta y)^2$$

We now let $\Delta t \rightarrow 0$, and have, as a result:

(3)
$$(dt/d\sigma)^2 = (dt/dx)^2 + (dt/dy)^2$$

The reciprocal of the left-hand side of this equation (not squared), namely

$$d\sigma/dt$$

is what we would naturally call the *apparent velocity* of the wave as the trace of its wave front moves along the surface s (see Ex. 119), and if we write this apparent velocity as $\bar{v}$, then equation (3) can be written

(4)
$$1/\bar{v}^2 = (dt/dx)^2 + (dt/dy)^2.$$

Notice that in the last result the *only* requirement on the directions of x and y is that they be mutually perpendicular.

REFLECTION FROM A SINGLE DIPPING INTERFACE—
FURTHER ANALYTIC PRELIMINARIES

We now return to the study of the fundamental and important analytic considerations which were begun in the last Lesson.

The lower part of Figure 81 is a repetition of Figure 76. For the sake of clarity, the basic necessary information is repeated:

OP represents a line along which a reflection profile is being shot, with
O, the shot-point and
P, the typical pickup at a distance
ρ from O. The angle
ψ is that between OP and the direction of true dip, so that, in value,

$$0° \leq \psi < 180°.$$

The amount of true dip is
δ, and the direction of that dip is taken as the positive
x-axis. This makes the
y-axis that of the strike direction, and the
z-axis is oriented positively downward.
The dipping plane
p is situated so that the (perpendicular) distance from O to it is
h_0. The foot of this perpendicular on p is indicated by
Q_0. Thus the image point of O with respect to p,
O', is on the extension of OQ_0 so that Q_0 bisects OO'.

The intersection

$S'S$ is that of p with the plane through OP perpendicular to p; *i.e.*, the plane
section of p with the plane
q containing the wave paths to OP.

If, then, the travel-time of a reflection from O to P is t and the velocity of propagation is v_1 , the relation existing is

(5) $$v_1{}^2t^2 = \rho^2 + 4h_0{}^2 + 4h_0\rho \cos \psi \sin \delta.$$

By identifying this relation with that of Lesson 11, *i.e.*, if we assume that we are shooting down (true) dip, we shoud conclude that our dip—which is now the *apparent* dip—is ϕ in which

(6) $$\sin \phi = \cos \psi \sin \delta.$$

In the direction of the true dip for which $\psi = 0$, this reduces to

$$\sin \phi = \sin \delta;$$

144

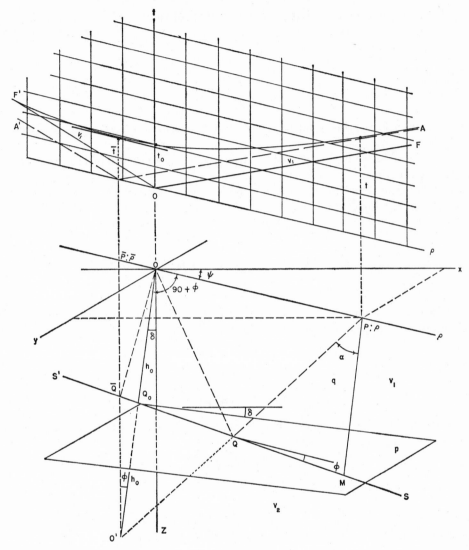

Fɪɢ. 81

i.e.,

$$\phi = \delta,$$

as, of course, it should.

In the upper part of Figure 81 we show the type of *time-distance* curve which would be obtained when shooting along OP. It is, in fact, the hyperbola defined by equation (5). On the t-axis, erected vertically at O, the travel-time t_0 is that of the wave from O reflected at p back to O. As is obvious, it represents the time for a wave to travel the distance

$$2OQ_o = 2h_o,$$

which is

(7) $$t_o = 2h_o/v_1.$$

On the other hand, this result is immediately apparent in equation (5) if we set $\rho = 0$.

In Figure 82 we have sketched in "true" scale the section shown as the "perspective shooting" section in Figure 81.

It must be remembered that this section of the subsurface is *not* a *vertical* section except for $\psi = 0$. It is, in fact, the section of Figure 81, in the plane q, similarly lettered and, as such, is inclined at an angle of ν with the vertical in which

(8) $$\sin \nu = \sin \psi \sin \delta/(\sin^2 \psi + \cos^2 \psi \cos^2 \delta)^{1/2}.$$

*Ex. 122: Prove this last result.

As P moves along the ρ-axis, the travel-time t changes with the changing ρ. The rate of change of t with ρ, as we know, is

$$dt/d\rho$$

as obtained from (5); *i.e.*,

(9) $$dt/d\rho = (\rho + 2h_o \cos \psi \sin \delta)/v_1^2 t.$$

We recall that this expresses the *slope* of the *time-distance* curve at any point. In particular, at the shot-point O, for which $\rho = 0$, the slope is

$$dt/d\rho \,|_o = 2h_o \cos \psi \sin \delta/v_1^2 t_o;$$

and since, for that point, the travel-time

$$t_0 = 2h_o/v,$$

we have the slope of the *time-distance* curve at O equal to

(10) $$\cos \psi \sin \delta/v_1 = \sin \phi/v_1,$$

in which ϕ is the apparent dip [see equation (6) above].

This last result is not surprising since it is a special case of the *emergence angle relations* of Lesson No. 1, which, in our present case, would read:

(11) $$\sin \alpha = v_1 dt/d\rho.$$

However, this angle α is the emergence angle *in the plane q*, only, and is *not* the actual emergence angle of the wave as described above, except for $\psi = 0$.

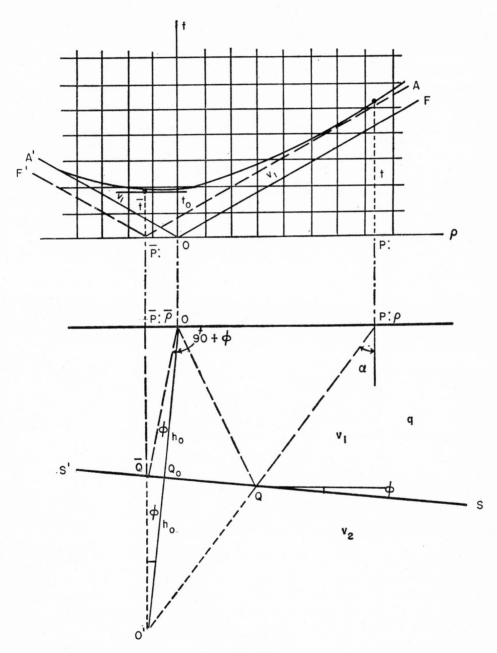

F<small>IG</small>. 82

At the origin O, this angle α is equal to ϕ, the apparent dip.

Ex. 123: What is the equation of the line representing the "first-kick" travel-times? Explain why this equation is independent of ψ.

Ex. 124: Show that as P recedes from O indefinitely ($\rho \rightarrow \infty$), the slope of the *time-distance* curve (equation 5) approaches $1/v_1$, independent of the value of ψ. Explain the significance of this fact.

Ex. 125: In any particular azimuth, the reflection of shortest path arrives at $\overline{P}$ at which the slope $dt/d\rho = 0$. Show that the position of P varies with ψ; in fact,

$$\bar{\rho} = -\, 2h_O \cos \psi \cdot \sin \delta.$$

Explain the minus sign. Explain why $\bar{\rho} = 0$ for $\psi = 90°$ and why $\bar{\rho}$ reaches its greatest numerical value for $\psi = 0°$. What is the corresponding travel-time $\bar{t}$? Show that the shortest reflection path of all possible ones occurs for $\psi = 0$ and $\bar{\rho} = -2h_O \sin \delta$, at which this shortest travel-time is $2h_O \cos \delta / v_1$.

REFLECTION FROM A DIPPING INTERFACE—THREE-DIMENSIONAL PROBLEM—APPLICATIONS.

Suppose that we have a section of a smooth curve C with limited curvature. The terms "smooth" and "limited curvature" imply concepts which, in the strict sense, require precise definition. Since, however, the considerable discussion to make these definitions precise would lead us astray, insofar as our purposes are concerned, we content ourselves in leaving the significance of these terms to our intuition.

This section of the smooth curve C is to be a portion of a *time-distance* curve of a seismic event for the straight-line interval indicated in Figure 83 as the x-axis between pickup positions $P_1:x_1$ and $P_2:x_2$.

We have often made use of the *slope* of the *time-distance* curve at a point corresponding to a pickup position $P:x_o$ midway between two others such as P_1 and P_2. Often, in fact, P_1 and P_2 are the positions of the *end* pickups of a spread

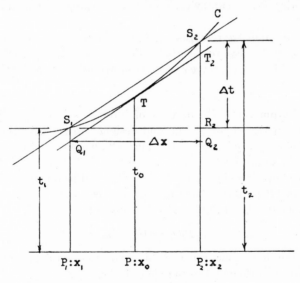

Fig. 83

straddling the shot-point P. We indicate the value of this slope at P by the symbol $(dt/dx)_P$. Now, it is obvious in Figure 83 that this slope, namely $(dt/dx)_P$, is equal to

$$\overline{Q_2T_2}/\overline{Q_1Q_2} = Q_2T_2/\Delta x,$$

in which Δx refers to the length of the interval P_1P_2; *i.e.*,

$$\Delta x = x_2 - x_1.$$

In practice, C is almost always drawn as the "best" straight-line segment through a set of points and has no analytic representation. The "first" of the points (at pickup position P_1) determining C is indicated by $S_1:(x_1, t_1)$, and the "last" by $S_2:(x_2, t_2)$. That is to say, the corrected travel-time for P_1, assumed to be t_1, is plotted at S_1; and similarly for P_2, the corrected travel-time t_2 is plotted at S_2. The difference in travel-times, *viz.*,

$$R_2S_2 = t_2 - t_1,$$

is represented by Δt:

$$R_2S_2 = \Delta t = t_2 - t_1;$$

and the slope of the *straight line* S_1S_2 is numerically equal to

$$\Delta t/\Delta x = (t_2 - t_1)/(x_2 - x_1).$$

It is the slope of this secant, S_1S_2, which, in practice, we take as being equal to the slope of the *time-distance* curve at T (*i.e.*, for pickup position P), and it can be shown that this accuracy is as much as we can expect with typical seismic data.

With these preliminary remarks as a background, which we should have made some time ago, we proceed to the applications of the considerations of the three-dimensional problem which have engaged our attention for some time.

* * *

Considered from the point of view of interpretation possibilities, the best pattern of pickup spreads on the ground designed to get reflection data from a (single) dipping interface is that of two mutually perpendicular spreads bisecting each other at the shot-point.

Let the two lines of pickup spreads on the ground be represented in Figure 84. The line segment P_1P_3 bisected at the shot-point O is to be considered as a spread of pickups of length 2ρ straddling the shot-point O:

$$P_1O = OP_3 = \rho.$$

Similarly, the line segment P_2P_4 is bisected at O and is to be considered, for the present at least, also equal to 2ρ in length; *i.e.*,

$$P_2O = OP_4 = \rho.$$

The angle between these two lines of pickup spreads is assumed to be 90°.

Travel-times are assumed to have been corrected for elevation and weathering. Let us assume, then, that under the plane surface of the ground on which are these two mutually perpendicular spreads straddling the shot-point O we have a medium in which the seismic velocity is v_1 bounded on its lower side by a reflecting plane.

A time-axis erected vertically at O will serve for the *time-distance* curves

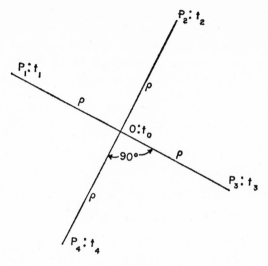

FIG. 84

along the two profiles P_1P_3 and P_2P_4. If the length ρ is small compared with the depth of the reflecting plane, we shall have as the refracted *time-distance* curves (*i.e.*, the so-called "first kick" curves), straight-line sections from O, all of them with slope equal to $1/v_1$ and whose equations therefore are

$$\rho = v_1 t.$$

In this last equation, ρ is taken as the "running" coordinate of the horizontal axis oriented *away from O*, to which is related the t-axis. It is believed that the context will usually make it clear and unambiguous which meaning of ρ—whether as the lengths OP_1, etc., or as denoting the "running" coordinate— is being used, quite as is the case with the more commonly used x.

Now, let the travel-times of the reflected event of the wave originating from the shot at O and reflected by the reflector back to the surface be

$$t_0$$

for the point O, and

$$t_1, t_2, t_3, t_4,$$

for the points

$$P_1, P_2, P_3, P_4,$$

respectively.

In general, for the solution of our problem, the data available consist of these travel-times, the distance ρ, and, we assume, the velocity v_1. From these data we seek the value of h_0 (the notation used is that described in Lesson No. 28) and the directions of dip and strike.

There are a few special cases of which we shall quickly dispose by a few remarks, the truth of which will become evident as we proceed.

The points P_1, P_2, P_3, and P_4 of Figure 84 are each at the same distance ρ from the shot-point O. If all four of the corrected travel-times, t_1, t_2, t_3, t_4, are equal, the reflecting plane p is horizontal; that is, parallel to the plane surface of the earth, s. Geometrically, this is evident when we consider the profile lines of Figure 84 placed on the surface s shown in Figure 85. The distances

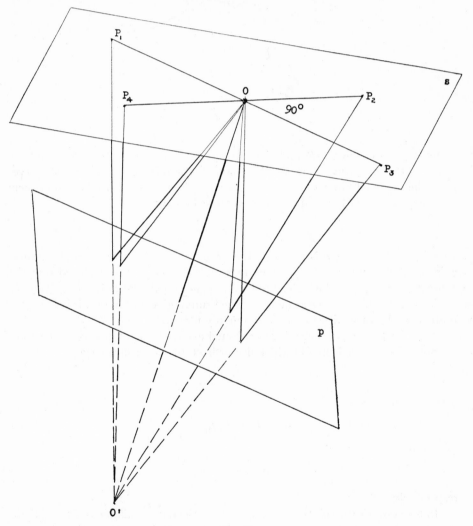

Fɪɢ. 85

$$O'P_1, \; O'P_2, \; O'P_3, \; O'P_4$$

are respectively equal to

$$v_1t_1, \; v_1t_2, \; v_1t_3, \; v_1t_4,$$

since O' is the image point of O with respect to p. If, then, $t_1 = t_2 = t_3 = t_4$, all these distances are equal, and

Ex. 126: The line $O'O$ is perpendicular to p and s, from which it follows that p is parallel to s.

Another special case is explained in

Ex. 127: If two of the travel-times are equal, say $t_1 = t_3$, and the other two, t_2 and t_4, are not equal, then the direction of P_1P_3 is that of the strike of p. The spread P_2P_4 is then along the dip of p, and the problem of computation reduces to that already discussed in the two-dimensional case.

Lesson No. 30

REFLECTION FROM A DIPPING INTERFACE—THREE-DIMENSIONAL PROBLEM—APPLICATIONS (*Continued*)

We now proceed to a discussion of the general case of our problem. It will become evident that the general case, in fact, includes the special cases already discussed.

Under the conditions which we have imposed thus far, namely, that the medium is one of constant seismic velocity, bounded by the horizontal plane of the earth and a dipping reflecting plane, there is a fact of basic importance:

The sum of the squares of the travel-times of a reflection from a central shot point to any pair of diametrically opposite points is constant; that is, this sum is the same whatever be the azimuth of the line joining the two points.

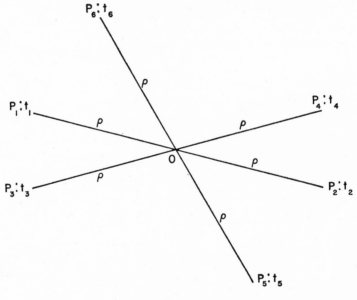

Fig. 86

If, in Figure 86, the distances from O to P_1, P_2, $\cdots$, P_6 are all equal and P_1P_2; P_3P_4; P_5P_6 form three pairs of diametrically opposite points with respect to the central shot point O; and if the travel-times of a reflection from O to each of these points is indicated by t with the corresponding subscript, then provided our conditions obtain:

$$t_1^2 + t_2^2 = t_3^2 + t_4^2 = t_5^2 + t_6^2.$$

154

Before proving this important fact, let us see what it signifies and how we can make use of it. In Figure 87, suppose

$$t_1 = 1.503,$$

$$t_2 = 1.478,$$

$$t_3 = 1.498.$$

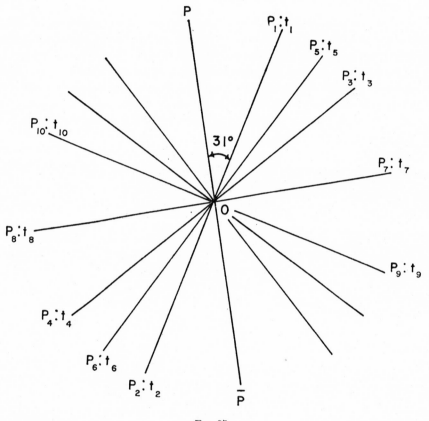

FIG. 87

What is the value of t_4?

The answer is obtained from the relation described, namely, that since P_1 and P_2 form a pair of diametrically opposite points, and so do P_3 and P_4,

$$t_1{}^2 + t_2{}^2 = t_3{}^2 + t_4{}^2;$$

i.e.

$$(1.503)^2 + (1.478)^2 = (1.498)^2 + t_4{}^2;$$

whence

$$t_4 = 1.483.$$

Ex. 128: If, in the same Figure 87, $t_5 = 1.501$, what is t_6? (Ans. $t_6 = 1.480$). Similarly, if $t_7 = 1.491$, what is t_8? From this last result, since $t_7 = t_8$, what can you say about the directions of strike and dip of the reflecting plane? Does this indicate possible methods of laying out cross-profiles for the determination of the direction of dip?

It becomes apparent that this property [that the sum of the squares of the travel-times of a reflection to any pair of diametrically opposite points is independent of azimuth and depends only on the length of the implied diameter (*i.e.*, the distance between the points of each pair)] may be used for purposes of correlating reflected events between two equal-length cross-profiles straddling a common central shot point. In fact, such correlation should be made, after surface corrections, before any further calculations are undertaken, since contradictions will arise if this situation does not obtain.

To be more specific, consider this example.

Suppose that the reflection discussed above is such that it is clearly discernible across P_3OP_4 and that we find

$$t_3 = 1.498 \quad \text{and} \quad t_4 = 1.483.$$

Suppose, too, that at the same time we shoot across P_1OP_2, but we are not sure to within a "cycle" as to whether

$$t_1 = 1.503 \quad \text{and} \quad t_2 = 1.478,$$

or whether

$$t_1 = 1.518 \quad \text{and} \quad t_2 = 1.494.$$

This question can be decided at once by noting that the *first* pair and *not* the second satisfies the relation

$$(1.503)^2 + (1.478)^2 = (1.498)^2 + (1.483)^2.$$

Consequently, it is the first pair which is to be used.

The proof of this last development is straightforward. Referring to equation (5) on page 144, the travel-time t_1 obeys the relation

$$v^2 t_1^2 = \rho^2 + 4h^2 + 4h\rho \cos \psi_1 \sin \delta,$$

provided that the distance $OP_1 = \rho$, that v is the velocity in the medium, that δ is the angle of dip, that h is the distance from O to the reflecting plane and, finally, that ψ_1 is the angle on the surface between the *direction* of OP_1 and the *direction* of dip.

Let P_2 be the diametrically opposite point to P_1. Then $OP_2 = \rho$, the quantities

v, h, δ remain as before, but the angle ψ_2 between the *direction* of OP_2 and that of the dip is such that

$$\psi_2 = \psi_1 + 180°.$$

Thus, for the travel-time t_2 we have

$$v^2 t_2{}^2 = \rho^2 + 4h^2 + 4h\rho \cos \psi_2 \sin \delta,$$
$$= \rho^2 + 4h^2 + 4h\rho \cos (\psi_1 + 180°) \sin \delta,$$
$$= \rho^2 + 4h^2 - 4h\rho \cos \psi_1 \sin \delta.$$

Adding this equation to the preceding, we find that

$$v^2 (t_1{}^2 + t_2{}^2) = 2(\rho^2 + 4h^2);$$

i.e.,

$$t_1{}^2 + t_2{}^2 = 2(\rho^2 + 4h^2)/v^2,$$

a result *independent* of ψ_1; from which fact our conclusion is drawn.

The two basic relations of our problem used in interpretation are

(1) $$v^2 t^2 = \rho^2 + 4h^2 + 4h\rho \cos \psi \sin \delta,*$$

and the derivative expression

(2) $$v^2 t\, dt/d\rho = \rho + 2h \cos \psi \sin \delta.†$$

Let the two cross-profiles $P_1 O P_2$ and $P_3 O P_4$ be at right angles (*Cf.* Figure 88). Our problem is to determine h, ψ, and δ in a practical manner, using the data obtained as a result of shooting along both profiles. We assume v to have been determined by some method or another and that

$$OP_1 = OP_2 = OP_3 = OP_4 = \rho.$$

The travel-times of the reflection from O to the points P_1, P_2, P_3 and P_4 are, respectively,

$$t_1, t_2, t_3 \text{ and } t_4,$$

for which

$$t_1{}^2 + t_2{}^2 = t_3{}^2 + t_4{}^2.$$

The travel-time of the same reflection back to O will be indicated by t_0, so that

(3) $$t_0 = 2h/v.$$

Ex. 129: Derive this last relation from equation (1) above.

---

* equation (5), page 144.
† equation (9), page 146.

It is customary to mark the reflection on the seismogram for a profile straddling the shot point by noting the travel-times on the end channels. As we have
discussed on pages 149 and 150, we will never be far afield in the practical sense
if we replace the *slope* of the *time-distance* curve *at O*, pertaining to the profile
P_1OP_2, by the slope of the straight line joining the end values t_1 and t_2, corresponding to P_1 and P_2.

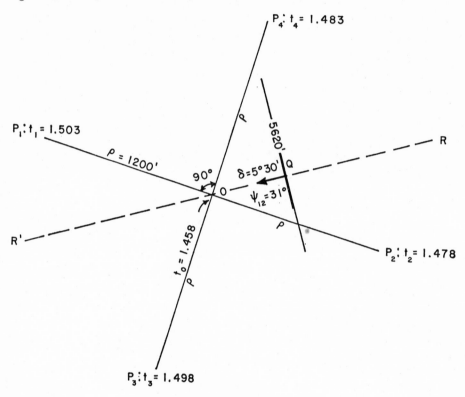

$P_4 : t_4 = 1.483$

$P_1 : t_1 = 1.503$

$P = 1200'$

$90°$

ρ

$5620'$

$\delta = 5°30'$ Q

R

$\psi_{12} = 31°$

$t_0 = 1.458$

R'

ρ

$P_2 : t_2 = 1.478$

ρ

$P_3 : t_3 = 1.498$

Fig. 88

Accordingly, the value of this derivative,

$$dt/d\rho \big|_{0,-P_1P_2},$$

which means the derivative at the shot point O along the profile P_1P_2, will be
written

(4)
$$(t_2 - t_1)/2\rho,$$
$$= (\Delta t)_{12}/2\rho,$$

since the distance $P_1P_2 = 2\rho$. As is implied, the symbol $(\Delta t)_{12}$ is used for the
difference

$$t_2 - t_1.$$

Equation (2), then , becomes, since $\rho=0$ at O,

(5)
$$(\Delta t)_{12}/2\rho = 2h \cos \psi_{12} \sin \delta/v^2 t_0,$$
$$(\Delta t)_{34}/2\rho = 2h \sin \psi_{12} \sin \delta/v^2 t_0,$$

in which equations, ψ_{12} is the angle between the direction of the line P_1OP_2 and that of dip.

Now: If $(\Delta t)_{12}=0$, $\psi_{12}=90°$ and P_3OP_4 is the direction of dip.

Ex. 130: Why is this last assertion true? Also show, similarly, that if $(\Delta t)_{34}=O$, P_1OP_2 is the direction of dip.

The down dip side is, of course, in the direction of the greater travel-times. For example, if $(\Delta t)_{12}=0$, the dip is toward P_3 if $t_3>t_4$ and toward P_4 if $t_4>t_3$. If, also, $t_3=t_4$, then $(\Delta t)_{34}=0$ and the reflecting bed is flat.

In the general case, $(\Delta t)_{12}\neq0$. In that case, the second of the equations (5) can be divided by the first with the result:

(6)
$$\tan \psi_{12} = (\Delta t)_{34}/(\Delta t)_{12}.$$

The importance of this result should be apparent. Let us apply it to our previous example, referring to Figure 88.

Ex. 131: Given

$$t_1 = 1.503, \qquad t_2 = 1.478,$$
$$t_3 = 1.498, \qquad t_4 = 1.483,$$
$$(\rho = 1,200).$$

(a) Check for consistency; *i.e.*, $t_1^2+t_2^2=t_3^2+t_4^2$.
(b) Show that

$$(\Delta t)_{12} = 0.025, \qquad (\Delta t)_{34} = 0.015,$$

and that

$$\tan \psi_{12} = 0.015/0.025 = 0.6,$$
$$\psi_{12} = 31°.$$

(c) Show in Figure 88 which way to draw $\psi_{12}=31°$ from P_1OP_2 (recall that ψ_{12} is the angle between the direction of P_1OP_2 and that of dip); *i.e.*, clockwise or counterclockwise, bearing in mind that the travel-time increases to a maximum in the direction of dip.

The next quantity, *h*, is readily obtained from equation (3):

$$t_0 = 2h/v.$$

Since v is assumed known and t_0 is obtained from the data,

$$h = vt_0/2.$$

Ex. 132: If in the numerical example being discussed, we assume $v = 7,750$ ft/sec and that $t_0 = 1.458$, show that $h = 5,650$ ft.

The final quantity to be determined is δ. This can be obtained from either of equations (5), since every quantity but δ is now known. We leave this as

Ex. 133: In our numerical example, in which, we recall, $\rho = 1,200$ ft, $v = 7,750$ ft/sec, and $h = 5,650$ ft, show that

$$\delta = 5°30',$$

from equation (5); namely

$$\sin \delta = (v^2 t_0/2h \cos \psi_{12}) \left[(\Delta t)_{12}/2\rho\right].$$

By simple use of simple formulas, then, we have solved our problem. Let us summarize:

Given two cross-profiles, P_1OP_2 and P_3OP_4 (Figure 88), such that

$$\rho = OP_1 = OP_2 = OP_3 = OP_4 = 1,200 \text{ ft}$$

and

$$\angle P_1OP_3 = 90°.$$

Given also that

$$t_1 = 1.503, \qquad t_2 = 1.478, \qquad t_3 = 1.498,$$

$$t_4 = 1.483, \qquad t_0 = 1.458,$$

and

$$v = 7,750 \text{ ft/sec.}$$

Our problem is to find the direction of dip, the amount of dip, depth of (the length of the normal from O to) the reflecting plane.

We have found

$$\psi_{12} = 31°, \qquad \delta = 5°30', \quad \text{and} \quad h = 5,650 \text{ ft.}$$

The final purpose is to plot the answers properly on the map or its equivalent in such manner that the result is amenable to contour. It should be apparent that "sections" cannot be made of subsurface dipping beds until the beds are contoured first. For that reason it is essential to get the information so that it may be contoured.

Along the direction of dip, then, which in Figure 88 is the line ROR', with R on the up-dip side, we mark off the distance

$$OQ = h \sin \delta = (5,650)(0.095),$$
$$= 530 \text{ ft.}$$

At Q the direction at right angles to ROR' is then the strike and is so contoured. The value of that contour—in subsurface depth—is, of course

$$h \cos \delta = (5,650)(0.995)$$
$$= 5,620 \text{ ft,}$$

as is shown in Figure 88.

Ex. 134: Justify the statements in the last paragraph.

Now the reader is asked to solve, similarly, the following problem, the solution to which is shown in Figure 89.

Ex. 135: Given

$$\rho = 1,200 \text{ ft,} \quad v = 8,510 \text{ ft/sec,}$$
$$t_1 = 1.791, \quad t_2 = 1.760,$$
$$t_3 = 1.780, \quad t_4 = 1.771,$$
$$t_o = 1.769.$$

Find ψ_{12}, h, and δ and so check the solution in Figure 89, for which $h = 7,150$ ft.

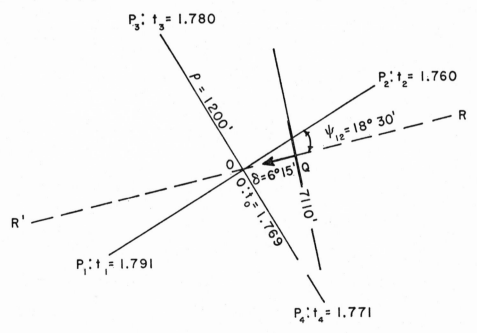

FIG. 89

It may have occurred to some readers that some developments in that discussion are amenable to graphical solutions. In particular, the result in equation (6), suggests a rectangular coordinate system, one axis of which carries $(\Delta t)_{12}$ and the other $(\Delta t)_{34}$, on which is superimposed a polar coordinate system concentric with the origin. Such a device is easily constructed and is recommended if much of this type of calculation is to be done.

To the Readers of the Lessons

With this Lesson, Part II comes to an end. The next series of Lessons will deal with the problem of reflections in a multi-layered earth. This will lead us to the so-called Theory of Curved Paths on the one hand, and, on the other hand, to a justification of the methods usually employed which are based on the concept of average velocity and which, as a consequence, make use of the interpretation devices already discussed as an approximation.

It is always a pleasant task to recall the friendly help of the many people who take part in making these Lessons. Mrs. Brantley, née Bodron, has left us, and this last Lesson and succeeding ones will be done by Miss Betty Stone, whose work, we are sure, will be of the same high caliber. To those who have written in suggestions, criticisms, and other kind letters, I am deeply grateful and I hope that the readers will continue to feel free to write.

M. M. Slotnick

The following method of determining the direction of strike and the magnitude of dip from the values of apparent dip in two given directions can be found in the literature. We propose first to indicate a simple proof of the method and then to show how it can be used in the determination of direction of strike and magnitude of dip from a seismic "four-way" set-up.

The method is as follows:

In the directions $\overrightarrow{OP_1}$ and $\overrightarrow{OP_2}$ (Figure I) let the measured angles of apparent dip be δ_1 and δ_2. In these directions, respectively, draw

$$OP_1 = k \tan \delta_1,$$

and

$$OP_2 = k \tan \delta_2,$$

where k is any suitable factor of proportionality (scale-factor). At P_1 draw P_1Q_1 perpendicular to OP_1 and at P_2 draw P_2Q_2 perpendicular to OP_2. Let the inter-

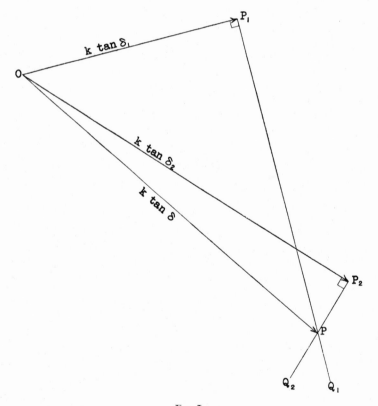

FIG. I

section of P_1Q_1 and P_2Q_2 be P. The direction of dip will then be that of $\overrightarrow{OP}$, and the length of OP will be

$$OP = k \tan \delta,$$

where δ is the amount of dip.

(Ex. Show the points O, P_1, P_2, P all lie on the circle defined by OP as a diameter.)

A simple trigonometric argument for this method is constructed in this manner. In Figure II, $OQRS$ represents the horizontal plane. A dipping plane Π has OQ as its direction of strike, and the angle of dip is δ. Choosing a suitable scale-factor, k, measure off on OR (at right angles to OQ) an amount

$$OP = k \tan \delta.$$

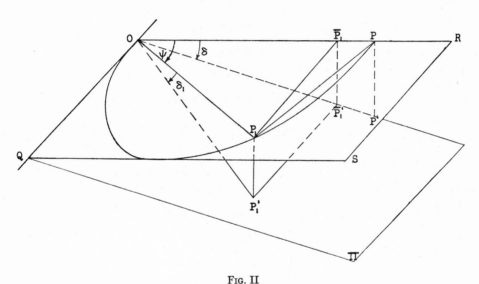

FIG. II

On OP as a diameter construct a circle in the horizontal plane, and let OP_1 be *any* line through O intersecting this circle at P_1. We designate the angle P_1OP by ψ. Then

$$OP_1 = OP \cos \psi$$

$$= k \tan \delta \cos \psi.$$

If PP' is the vertical through P intersecting Π in P', then

$$PP' = OP \tan \delta$$

$$= k \tan^2 \delta.$$

Similarly, if P_1P_1' is the vertical through P_1 intersecting Π in P_1', then

$$P_1 P_1' = OP_1 \tan \delta_1,$$

$$= k \tan \delta \cos \psi \tan \delta_1,$$

in which δ_1 in the angle of *apparent* dip in the direction of OP_1.

Now, let $\overline{P}_1$ be the foot of the perpendicular from P_1 on OR and let $\overline{P}_1'$ be the intersection of the vertical through $\overline{P}_1$ with II.

Then (exercise for the reader)

$$\overline{P}_1 \overline{P}_1' = P_1 P_1'.$$

But

$$\overline{P}_1 \overline{P}_1' = O\overline{P}_1 \tan \delta,$$

and

$$O\overline{P}_1 = OP_1 \cos \psi,$$

$$= k \tan \delta \cos^2 \psi.$$

Thus

$$P_1 P_1' = k \tan^2 \delta \cos^2 \psi.$$

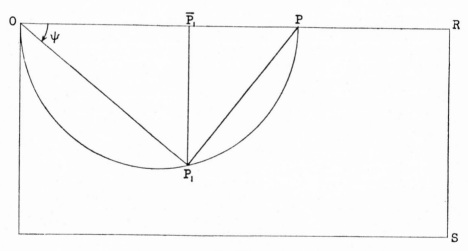

Fɪɢ. III

But we have shown that

$$P_1 P_1' = k \tan \delta \cos \psi \tan \delta_1.$$

If follows then that

$$\tan \delta_1 = \tan \delta \cos \psi$$

and that

$$OP_1 = k \tan \delta_1.$$

The interpretation of this last result is that the length of a chord through O in the circle drawn on OP as a diameter is proportional to the tangent of the angle of apparent dip in the direction of that chord.

Thus, given two directions OP_1 and OP_2, as in Figure I, with the lengths OP_1 and OP_2 drawn proportional to the tangents of the angles of apparent dip in those directions, the problem is simply to draw a circle through the points O, P_1 and P_2. The diameter through O defines the point P and OP will be the direction, of dip with its length proportional to the tangent of the angle of dip. Since, however, we usually desire only the point P rather than the whole circle, it is best obtained as the intersection of P_1Q_1, the perpendicular to OP_1 at P_1, with P_2Q_2, the perpendicular to OP_2 at P_2. (An angle inscribed in a semicircle is a right angle.)

We now proceed to use this result in reflection seismology interpretation technique.

Let our pickups be in line (P_1OP_2), with O the shot point and P_1 and P_2 the end pickups. A reflection which arrives at P_1 in travel-time t_1 and at P_2 in travel-time t_2 will indicate an apparent dip in this direction P_1P_2 of ϕ_{12}, in which

$$\Delta t_{12}/\Delta x = 2h_0 \sin \phi_{12}/v_1{}^2 t_0$$

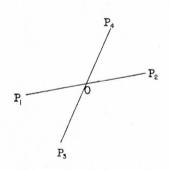

[See Lesson No. 28, in particular page 144, Equation (6), and page 146, Equation (9).]

In this relation,

$(\Delta t)_{12} = t_2 - t_1,$

$\Delta x = P_1P_2,$

h_0 is the length of the perpendicular from O to the reflecting plane,

t_0 is the travel-time of the reflection from O back to O, and

v_1 is the seismic velocity of the reflected wave.

We may write this last result:

$$\sin \phi_{12} = v_1{}^2 t_0 (\Delta t)_{12}/2h_0\Delta x.$$

In any other direction, P_3P_4, the angle of apparent dip will be defined by the relation

$$\sin \phi_{34} = v_1{}^2 t_0 (\Delta t)_{34}/2h_0\Delta x,$$

provided that $P_3P_4 = P_1P_2 = \Delta x$, that O bisects both spreads, and that $(\Delta t)_{34}$ is the difference in the travel-time of the reflection to P_3 and to P_4. (The greater travel-time in each pair, t_1, t_2 and t_3, t_4, indicates, of course, the "down-dip" end.)

Now, if the two angles ϕ_{12} and ϕ_{34} are small enough—and with the customary degree of precision in seismograph work, this means that each is less than about 10°—we may replace the sines by the tangents; *i.e.*, we may write

$$\tan \phi_{12} \cong K(\Delta t)_{12}$$

and

$$\tan \phi_{34} \cong K(\Delta t)_{34};$$

or, better,

$$(\Delta t)_{12} \cong \sigma \tan \phi_{12}$$

and

$$(\Delta t)_{34} \cong \sigma \tan \phi_{34}.$$

That is to say, if the measured angles of apparent dip on a "four-way" reflection shot are each less than about 10°, the corresponding Δt's *across* the shot point (the spreads being equal) are substantially *proportional* to the tangents of the angles of apparent dip. We may, therefore, use any scale-factor and proceed to get the direction of dip (and the corresponding Δt) in that direction by the method explained previously. This can be done mechanically in several ways, one of which is by use of an instrument called a "dip-strike resolver."

Whatever be the values of the angles of apparent dip, the method outlined in Lesson No. 30 is applicable. Only when these angles are less than 10° can the method above be used, because only for such small angles can their sines be replaced by the tangents within the usual accuracy of seismic data.

LESSONS
IN
SEISMIC COMPUTING

PART III

THE MULTI-LAYERED PROBLEM. INTRODUCTORY DISCUSSION

The discussion has been restricted, heretofore, to the case of a single isotropic medium in which the seismic velocity is assumed to be constant. Generally speaking, the sedimentary beds with which the petroleum seismologist is concerned are neither ideally uniform as our theoretical requirements demand, nor is the subsurface of one medium. Still another item that must constantly be kept in mind is that the bedding in the subsurface studied from the geological standpoint is, at times, quite different when studied from the seismic standpoint. However, for the most part, these two aspects of bedding are generally quite conformable or parallel to one another, and, in fact, often coincidental. It is this fortuitous situation which makes it possible to apply seismological methods in petroleum exploration.

It is conceivable that, with the data of sufficiently high precision and of the proper type and with the application of the appropriate mathematical procedures, a complete delineation of the subsurface bedding—seismically considered—could be accomplished. It is doubtful whether precision of this degree in our data could ever be attained.

Experience has amply shown—and proof of a quantitative nature can be provided—that the complicated problem of interpreting the seismic data pertaining to the more or less complicated subsurface can be distilled and reduced, for the most part, to the type of problem heretofore discussed, *i.e.*, to the single-layer problem. Particularly is this true for the reflection techniques as contrasted with the refraction techniques.

In reflection seismology the *surface* distances between shot-point and receiving, *i.e.*, pickup, points are generally small compared with the depths being investigated. This means that we approximate the situation in which the shot-point and pickup point are at the same location. This, as we have seen, presents us with a simpler problem for the single-layer case, and, as we shall see, the same is true for the more general case.

In almost all interpretation work, an assumption brought into play is that, locally, the bedding is such that between the surface and each interface the totality of all the intervening media can be lumped into a single medium in which the seismic velocity is constant, its value being called the *average velocity*. From the mathematical viewpoint and for the most general cases, this seems to be a most startling type of *averaging*, since the average velocity to any particular reflecting surface—or as we sometimes say, horizon—will probably change from each location to the next and at an uncomfortable rate. However, and fortunately, the errors in depth computations by such average-velocity devices, though generally cumulative from location to location, are such that their possible disastrous effects are most often ameliorated either by the use of other types of data, additional well-velocity surveys, or even compensating inaccuracies. Nonetheless, it is well always to be consciously aware that this source of error—the use of average velocities—may lead to serious discrepancies in depth calculations, and all means at one's disposal should be used to lessen the magnitudes of these discrepancies.

One attempt to accomplish this end has been to evade depth determinations by maintaining resultant maps and sections in terms of travel-times rather than depths. We feel that this device does not solve the implied problem, especially in areas of steep dip, and ultimately is of no value except that maps and sections based on such time data form convenient filing systems for the data; they do not constitute a satisfactory interpretation of the data.

Particularly is this a matter of consequence, as we have said, in areas of steep dip. It is impossible to indicate the proper disposition of a dipping reflecting bed even in the simplest case of a single intervening medium between that bed and the surface (as discussed in Lesson No. 30) without the use of velocity data. To plot the sections in time alone will lead to situations such as are described in Lesson No. 14.

Now it is the purpose of these Lessons to try and help the reader to understand the basis of interpretation techniques—the underlying assumptions and the implications and conclusions resulting from these assumptions. Except for numerical examples inserted for the purpose of clearness, it is not our purpose—at least, not yet—to discuss the details of record reading or to suggest processes and systems for the necessary routine tasks of the seismic computer. In short, we feel that if the computer understands his problem and has at his command the tools for the solution, the rest will come readily; and over all he will have the confidence in his work without which nothing much of consequence can be done.

To return to our original discussion, then:

Velocity studies in areas to be investigated are of basic importance. In some areas the highest accuracy attainable is necessary. It is true that there are problems in which high precision is not too urgent, particularly where absolute depths are not of any great importance. Amount of closure of structures, amount of throw in faults—these may be of greater importance than depths, and these may be computed with velocity information of limited accuracy. But surely it is evident that it is never wrong to have the best velocity data obtainable.

There are various ways in which velocities are used and each of these leads to one or another type of *average velocity*, but, basically, the average velocity of a wave in a medium is the ratio of the distance traveled by the wave to the time of travel.

Thus it is, then, that for the most part, in dealing with the multilayered problem we restrict ourselves to the easiest problem: that for which all beds are bounded by horizontal planes or that for which the true velocity varies with depth alone. In the case of *refraction* interpretation of the problem of a multilayered earth we admit the case of dipping interfaces but assume that the profiling is done in the direction of dip. Adjustment for the deviation of the profile azimuth from the direction of dip is usually made after the "standard" interpretation is accomplished.

We shall therefore spend a short while on the problem of reflection for the two-layer problem, both interfaces being planes parallel to the plane surface of the earth. This will be followed by the generalization to more layers. It will then be a relatively simple matter to go into a problem of having the velocity vary continuously with depth, that is, to the so-called "curved path theory." As is well-known, the latter is a most useful concept in interpretation, whose value has amply proved itself.

Though the treatment will be mathematical, it should not prove too difficult a matter to follow. The elements of the differential and integral calculus will enter—evading them seems to be impossible.

We shall attempt to show how the theory we evolve can best be put into practice in exploration work and in well-velocity surveys.

Lesson No. 32

INTRODUCTION OF PARAMETRIC FORM OF THE TIME-DISTANCE REFLECTION CURVE

Let Figure 90 represent the vertical section of the subsurface, with Ox being the line of pickup locations, so that, as usual, x represents the algebraic distance on the surface between the shot-point O and the typical pickup location P. The horizontal lines $S_1'S_1$ and $S_2'S_2$ represent the traces of two horizontal plane interfaces, the first of which forms the lower boundary of a medium of thickness, h_1, in which the seismic velocity is v_1. Immediately below this medium is a second medium of thickness, h_2, in which the velocity is v_2 and which is bounded by the planes whose traces are $S_1'S_1$ and $S_2'S_2$.

It is sometimes valuable to introduce a "depth" axis through the shotpoint O, oriented vertically downward. This will be indicated as the h-axis. With respect to a coordinate system referred to this axis and the x-axis, the traces $S_1'S_1$ and $S_2'S_2$ have the equations

$$h = h_1$$

and

$$h = h_1 + h_2$$

respectively.

As before, we construct a vertical time- (t-) axis through O, with respect to which we shall consider the time-distance curves we should expect to obtain under ideal conditions over the subsurface situation described.

The *time-distance* curves, relating to reflections and refractions from the first interface, $S_1'S_1$, were discussed in Lesson No. 19. The situation is represented in Figure 60, on page 92, and is repeated as part of Figure 90. In may be advisable to repeat some of the facts already discussed.

In Figure 90, then, the line OD is the *time-distance* curve of the refracted (surface) wave running along the surface Ox with a velocity v_1, whose equation, therefore, is

$$t = x/v_1.$$

This event is the "first-kick" event for all pickup positions from the shot-point O to the pickup at P_2. From this point on, the "first-kicks" are those of the refracted wave from the interface $S_1'S_1$ (we assume $v_2 > v_1$ for the present) whose *time-distance* curve is the straight line MT. Beyond P_2, in fact, the line MD, which is the extension of OM, represents the arrivals of the surface wave as "secondaries."

The point Q is that at which the emergence angle of the *reflected* wave is precisely equal to the critical angle ϕ for the two beds:

$$\sin \phi = v_1/v_2.$$

174

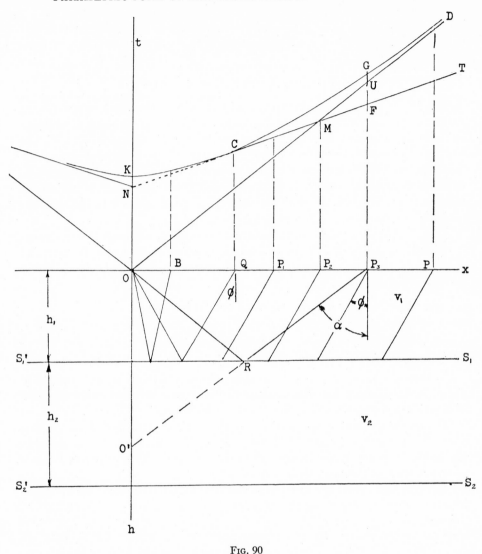

Fɪɢ. 90

Therefore, as we have seen, the point C on the *time-distance* curve for the reflections from $S_1'S_1$ must also be on the extension (to the left) of MT. We could
get a refracted event from $S_1'S_1$ beginning at point Q, and CM would be the
section of the *time-distance* curve for which this refracted wave arrives as a
"secondary" refraction event.

We recall that the line CMT is *tangent* to the *time-distance* curve of the reflections from $S_1'S_1$ at the point C corresponding to the pickup Q. The equation
of CMT has been found to be (*cf.* Ex. 81, page 95)

$$t = x/v_2 + 2h_1(v_2{}^2 - v_1{}^2)^{1/2}/v_1v_2.$$

The equation of the *time-distance* curve of the reflection from $S_1'S_1$ may be written in the form

$$v_1{}^2t^2 = x^2 + 4h_1{}^2,$$

which is that of a hyperbola whose asymptote on the right hand side is the line OD

$$t = x/v_1,$$

and the tangent to which at C is CT.

Finally, we must also recall that the relation between the emergence angle and slope of the *time-distance* curve for the two-dimensional (vertical section along dip) situation always obtains:

$$dt/dx = \sin \alpha/v_1.$$

In particular, at the point Q:

$$dt/dx = \sin \phi/v_1$$

$$= 1/v_2,$$

since, at that point, $\alpha = \phi = \sin^{-1}(v_1/v_2)$, the critical angle.

Thus, at a point such as P_3, we have three events to consider if we are restricted to the first medium and the first interface $S_1'S_1$ for which

$$v_2 > v_1.$$

These are:

(1) The first arrival (in time, P_3F) of the refracted wave from $S_1'S_1$ arriving at emergence angle $\phi[\sin^{-1}(v_1/v_2)]$. The slope on the corresponding *time-distance* curve is thus

$$dt/dx = \sin \phi/v_1 = 1/v_2,$$

a constant, indicating that the *time-distance* curve is a straight line (MT).

(2) The next event is the surface refracted wave. Its emergence angle is $90°$ (and arrives in time P_3U). The slope of this time-distance curve is

$$dt/dx = \sin 90°/v_1 = 1/v_1,$$

also a constant, indicating that this *time-distance* curve is also a straight line (OD). This refracted event arrives as a "secondary" in the neighborhood of P_3.

(3) Finally the reflected wave ORP_3 arrives. It will be recalled that the reflecting point R is the intersection of the interface $S_1'S_1$ with $O'P_3$, O' being the image point of O with respect to $S_1'S_1$. This wave arrives in time indicated by $P_3G = t$, whence

$$t = (OR + RP_3)/v_1,$$

$$= O'RP_3/v_1,$$

$$= (\overline{OO'}{}^2 + \overline{OP_3}{}^2)^{1/2}/v_1,$$

$$= [(2h_1)^2 + x^2)]^{1/2}/v_1; \qquad (OP_3 = x),$$

or better

$$v_1{}^2 t^2 = 4h_1{}^2 + x^2.$$

The value of the angle of emergence of this wave, indicated by α in Figure 90, can be obtained by differentiation of the equation of the *time-distance* curve (hyperbola, in this case) and using the relation

$$dt/dx = \sin \alpha / v_1;$$

or, conversely, since it is apparent in Figure 90 that

$$\sin \alpha = x/v_1 t,$$

we can find the slope of the *time-distance* curve:

$$dt/dx = (x/v_1 t)/v_1$$
$$= x/v_1{}^2 t.$$

So much, then, by way of review.

In anticipation of the problems to follow, we now proceed to solve the elementary reflection problem in a different manner, but one which has many advantages, as will become evident.

Consider again the situation at the shot-point O at the surface of the upper medium in which the velocity is v_1. The wave fronts are spheres—or, in the case of our vertical section, circles concentric with O. Correspondingly, the rays are the totality of straight lines emanating from O. Of all these rays, any particular one can be defined by the angle α* made by that particular ray and the vertical OH. We shall restrict ourselves to non-negative values of α, leaving it to the reader to extend the meanings of the results to negative values of α.

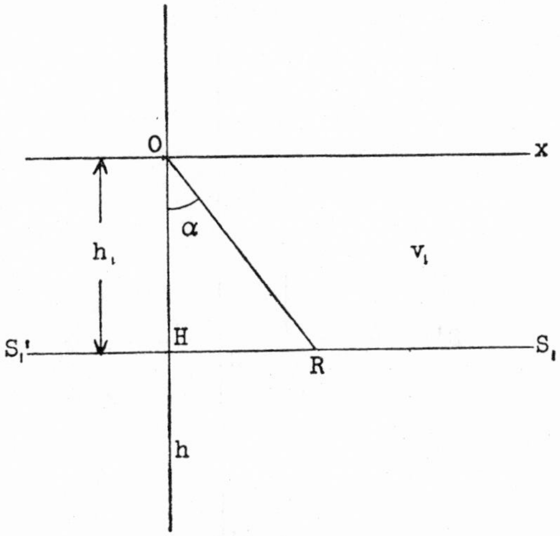

The ray emanating from O, characterized by a particular value of α, will strike the interface $S_1'S_1$ (see Figure 91) at a point R. For each value of α there will be only one point R on $S_1'S_1$ and, conversely, for each point R on $S_1'S_1$ there is a corresponding value of α. Numerically, α must lie between $0°$ and $90°$:

$$0° \leq \alpha \leq 90°,$$

Fig. 91

* The use of α in this connection will not be confusing since, as will become evident, it will be intimately related to the emergence angles for which we have also used the letter α.

the minimum value corresponding to the vertical ray and the maximum to the surface ray in the right hand direction ($+x$-axis). As α varies from $0°$ to $90°$, the point R will move from H outwardly (to the right) and indefinitely along $S_1'S_1$.

Now any particular ray OR, corresponding to a specified value of α, is partly reflected back to the surface to a point P. This reflected part will be represented by the ray RP (Figure 92) having an emergence angle also equal to α.

Ex. 136. Show that the emergence angle of this reflected ray RP is equal to α, the angle between the vertical and OR.

To each value of α, there will correspond one and only one point P on Ox. To have the reader appreciate this fact and its implications we suggest the following:

Ex. 137. Draw Figure 92, for which $\overline{OH} = 6{,}150$ ft. Draw the rays and reflection paths for

$$\alpha = 0°,\ \pm 5°,\ \pm 10°,\ \pm 15°,\ \pm 20°,\ \pm 25°,\ \cdots,$$

For each of these paths, scale off the corresponding value for the distances HR and OP. Show that

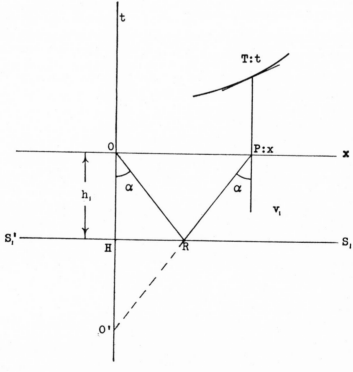

Fig. 92

$$OP = 2HR = 2h_1 \tan \alpha.$$

The distance OP will be indicated by x, the horizontal coordinate of the point P. Then

$$x = 2h_1 \tan \alpha.$$

Ex. 138. The travel-time for the reflection ORP is

$$t = (\overline{OR} + \overline{RP})/v_1 = 2\overline{OR}/v_1$$

$$= 2h_1/v_1 \cos \alpha.$$

Consider now these last two results:

(1)
$$x = 2h_1 \tan \alpha,$$

$$t = 2h_1/v_1 \cos \alpha.$$

For each value of α there is one value, and only one, for each of x and t. If we plot, on the (x, t)-coordinate system of Figure 92, the point (x, t) corresponding to each value of α, we shall have a curve—the *time-distance* curve—for the reflection event. The equation so expressed in terms of α is said to be *parametrically* represented, the angle α being the *parameter*.

Ex. 139. Referring to Ex. 137 and letting $v_1 = 7{,}280$ ft/sec, find values for x and t in equation (1) for the values of α suggested in Ex. 137.

Ex. 140. Show that in equations (1), the parameter α can be eliminated (using trigonometric identities) with the result that

(2)
$$v_1{}^2 t^2 = x^2 + 4h_1{}^2,$$

the equation of the hyperbola, which was to be expected.

Putting the equation of our hyperbola (2) into the parametric form (1) has many advantages, as we shall see. One advantage immediately apparent is that each position of the pickup (x) and the corresponding travel-time (t) of the reflection are associated with the specific ray pertaining thereto, described by the corresponding value of α, and this value of α is precisely the emergence angle of the corresponding wave path.

It turns out to be more convenient to replace the parameter α by another one in the following manner. Set

(3)
$$p = \sin \alpha/v_1.$$

For each value of α, there is a corresponding value p, and conversely.

Ex. 141. Let $v_1 = 7{,}280$ ft/sec. Compute the values of p corresponding to

$$\alpha = 0°, \pm 5°, \pm 10°, \cdots, \pm 90°.$$

Ex. 142. As α varies from $-90°$ to $+90°$ how does p vary? Numerically (that is, disregarding the sign $\pm$) the least value of p is 0 and the largest is $1/v_1$; *i.e.*,

$$0 \leq p \leq 1/v_1.$$

To what ray does the value $p=0$ correspond? To what ray does the value $p=1/v_1$ correspond? In Exs. 137 and 139, find the values of p for $\alpha=0°$, 30°, 45°, 60°, 90°.

Ex. 143. From equation (3) show that, in terms of p,

(4)
$$\cos \alpha = (1 - p^2 v_1^2)^{1/2},$$
$$\tan \alpha = p v_1/(1 - p^2 v_1^2)^{1/2}.$$

Ex. 144. From (1) and (4) show that, in terms of p as parameter, equations (1) are

(5)
$$x = (2h_1 p v_1)/(1 - p^2 v_1^2)^{1/2},$$
$$t = 2h_1/v_1(1 - p^2 v_1^2)^{1/2}.$$

Ex. 145. Let

$$h_1 = 6{,}150 \text{ ft (as in Ex. 137)}$$

and

$$v_1 = 7{,}280 \text{ ft/sec (as in Ex. 139)}.$$

Starting from $p=0$ and letting p increase to its maximum value (what is this value?) in a few stages, plot the corresponding values of x and t, using equations (5). Show that all these points lie on the hyperbola

$$(7{,}280t)^2 = x^2 + 4 (6{,}150)^2.$$

Why?

Returning to equations (5), in which x and t are expressed in functions of the parameter p, it can be shown that the slope of the curve so expressed can be obtained from the relation

(6) $$dt/dx = (dt/dp)/(dx/dp).$$

Ex. 146. Show that, in equations (5),

$$dt/dp = (2h_1 p v_1)/(1 - p^2 v_1^2)^{3/2},$$

and

$$dx/dp = (2h_1 v_1)/(1 - p^2 v_1^2)^{3/2},$$

and that, consequently, using (6),

$$dt/dx = p.$$

The significance of the result in this exercise is that the *slope* of the *time-distance* curve at the point of an emerging ray is equal to the value of the parameter p for that ray. In fact, if the last result is compared with (3) and if, further, we recall that, for any emergent ray, its angle of emergence and the slope of the *time-distance* curve at the corresponding point are related to one another by the equation

$$v_1(dt/dx) = \sin \alpha,$$

the conclusion we have reached is seen to be quite an apparent one. We must, of course, bear in mind that the emergence angle of the ray, from considerations of symmetry, is equal to the angle at which its first branch left the shot-point.

The basic facts to remember are: that the equation of the *time-distance* hyperbola of Lesson No. 6 for the travel-times of the waves reflected from the first (horizontal) interface, namely

$$v_1^2 t^2 = x^2 + 4h_1^2,$$

can be written in the parametric form

$$x = 2h_1 p v_1/(1 - p^2 v_1^2)^{1/2},$$
$$t = 2h_1/v_1(1 - p^2 v_1^2)^{1/2};$$

that each value of the parameter, p, defines the particular ray arriving at distance x in travel-time t; and that, at the corresponding point in the *time-distance* curve, the slope is equal to this value of the parameter p.

Ex. 147. Show that the reflected ray emerging at the point Q in Figure 90 corresponds to the parametric value, $p = 1/v_2$.

Lesson No. 33

THE TWO-LAYER REFLECTION TIME-DISTANCE CURVE

In Figure 93, we repeat the section described in the discussion of the previous Lesson which pertains to Figure 90,

The transmission of the energy in wave form from shot-point O is represented by the rays emanating therefrom. Some of this energy is reflected at the first interface, $S_1'S_1$, back to the surface Ox.

One such typical path is shown as OR_1P, for which the emergence angle is denoted by α_{11}. The *time-distance* curve corresponding to reflections from this interface may be parametrically represented by the equations

(1)
$$x = 2h_1 \tan \alpha_{11},$$
$$t = 2h_1/v_1 \cos \alpha_{11},$$

in which we consider α_{11} as a parameter: to each value of α_{11} $(0° \leq \alpha_{11} \leq 90°)$ there corresponds one and only one ray from O reflected by $S_1'S_1$. The corresponding reflected ray arrives at some definite point $P:x$ and its travel-time is t (PT_1 in Figure 93). There is one and only one point P and a corresponding travel-time t determined by each value of α_{11}.

If we replace the parameter α_{11} by another parameter p, such that

(2)
$$p = \sin \alpha_{11}/v_1,$$

then equations (1) may be rewritten:

(3)
$$x = (2h_1pv_1)/(1 - p^2v_1^2)^{1/2},$$
$$t = 2h_1/v_1(1 - p^2v_1^2)^{1/2}.$$

These two together constitute the parametric equations defining the *time-distance* hyperbola $W_1CT_1E_1$ of Figure 93,

$$v_1^2t^2 = x^2 + 4h_1^2.$$

The slope of this curve at any point is

(4)
$$dt/dx = p = \sin \alpha_{11}/v_1,$$

which gives further significance to the parameter p.

Ex. 148. Let C be the point of the hyperbola at which the slope is

$$\sin \theta_{12}/v_1,$$

where θ_{12} is the critical angle for the velocities v_1 and $v_2(v_2 > v_1)$ of the two media. The value of p corresponding to this point of the *time-distance* curve is $1/v_2$.

(The reader is asked to meditate on the meaning of the parameter p, particularly as to how each of its values characterizes a particular reflection path.)

182

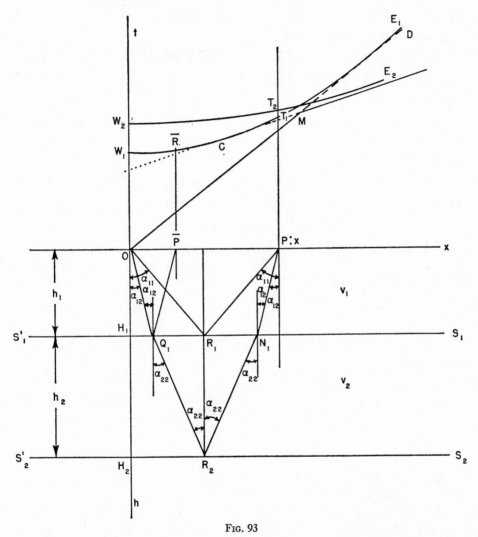

FIG. 93

Returning to Figure 93, a ray OQ_1 emanating from O at an angle α_{12} will strike $S_1'S_1$ at some point Q_1 at the same angle. Part of the energy will be reflected to the surface to a point $\overline{P}$ and will give us a reflected event of travel-time corresponding to the point $\overline{R}$ on the hyperbola $W_1CT_1E_1$. Some of the energy is then refracted into the lower medium and the transmission of this energy, as we have seen in Lesson No. 16, is such that the rays in this second medium are straight lines also. In fact, OQ_1 will "refract" into a ray such as Q_1R_2, which is at some angle α_{22} with the vertical, which, according to Snell's Law, has a value determined by:

(5) $$\sin \alpha_{22}/\sin \alpha_{12} = v_2/v_1.$$

Some of the energy is reflected at the second interface, $S_2'S_2$, and this is indicated by the ray Q_1R_2 being reflected at R_2. Since the angle of incidence equals the angle of reflection, geometrical considerations show these angles each to be equal to α_{22}. We trace the reflected ray back to N_1 on $S_1'S_1$ and from there, again by refraction according to Snell's Law, to a point $P:x$ on Ox.

Now, if the distance $OP=x$ and if the travel-time along $OQ_1R_2N_1P$ be indicated by t,

Ex. 149: Show that

$$x = 2(h_1 \tan \alpha_{12} + h_2 \tan \alpha_{22}),$$

(6) $$t = 2(h_1/v_1 \cos \alpha_{12} + h_2/v_2 \cos \alpha_{22}),$$

$$\sin \alpha_{12}/\sin \alpha_{22} = v_1/v_2.$$

If, in the last equation of this example, we set $\alpha_{12}=0°$, we find α_{22} to be indeterminate at first glance. It should be obvious, from physical considerations (and it will become apparent later from the mathematical standpoint) that $\alpha_{22}=0°$ also. Then equations (6) yield, for this ray ($\alpha_{12}=\alpha_{22}=0°$),

$$x = 0,$$

(7)

$$t = 2(h_1/v_1 + h_2/v_2).$$

This result pertains to the *vertical* ray reflected back to O from the second interface, yielding the travel-time point W_2 in Figure 93.

As α_{12} in equations (6) increases from $0°$, so does α_{22}, as is evident from the third of equations (6). It is also evident that, since $v_2>v_1$, $\alpha_{22}>\alpha_{12}>0°$; and, therefore,

$$\sin \alpha_{22} > \sin \alpha_{12}.$$

Now the largest value $\sin \alpha_{22}$ can assume is 1, corresponding to which $\alpha_{22}=90°$. Thus as α_{22} increases from $0°$ to this maximum value of $90°$, $\sin \alpha_{22}$ increases from 0 to 1. What happens meanwhile to $\sin \alpha_{12}$? $\cdots$ and α_{12}? Clearly, $\sin \alpha_{12}$ increases from 0 to v_1/v_2; and α_{12} increases from $0°$ to $\sin^{-1} (v_1/v_2)$, the latter of which we had been indicating by θ_{12}, the critical angle for the two velocities v_1 and v_2. Thus, insofar as reflections from the second interface are concerned, they will exist only for the rays within the cone whose vertex is at O and whose half-angle, so to speak, is θ_{12}. In Figure 94, we indicate some of the rays refracted into the lower medium. For rays whose angle with the vertical at O is greater than θ_{12} we have total reflection, none of the energy pertaining to those rays being refracted into the lower medium. A typical path of this sort is OQ.

By introducing a parameter, p, in a manner similar to that used in Lesson No. 32, the three equations (6) are reduced to two which assume very convenient forms.

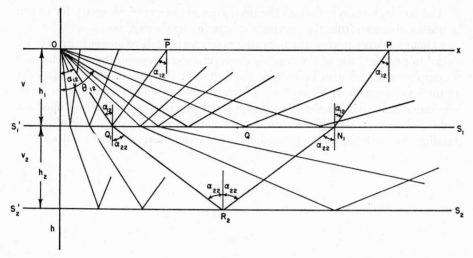

FIG. 94

In the third of equations (6), let the constant of proportionality between the sines of the angles and the corresponding velocities be p; *i.e.*, let this equation be written:

$$\sin \alpha_{12} = pv_1,$$

and

$$\sin \alpha_{22} = pv_2.$$

Ex. 150: Show that

$$\cos \alpha_{12} = (1 - p^2v_1^2)^{1/2},$$
$$\tan \alpha_{12} = pv_1/(1 - p^2v_1^2)^{1/2};$$

and write the corresponding results for $\cos \alpha_{22}$ and $\tan \alpha_{22}$.

Ex. 151: What is the range of numerical values for this parameter p?

With these results, equations (6) now assume the forms

(8)
$$x = 2[h_1pv_1/(1 - p^2v_1^2)^{1/2} + h_2pv_2/(1 - p^2v_2^2)^{1/2}],$$
$$t = 2[h_1/v_1(1 - p^2v_1^2)^{1/2} + h_2/v_2(1 - p^2v_2^2)^{1/2}].$$

These equations are the *parametric equations* for the *time-distance* curve of the reflections from $S_2'S_2$, which is shown as the curve $W_2T_2E_2$ in Figure 93.

In theory—but very difficult in practice—one could eliminate the parameter p from the equations (8) and obtain the equations of the *time-distance* curve in the usual form. Obviously, this curve would *not* be a hyperbola. It would, in fact, be an algebraic curve of a high order.

The fact is, however, that all the properties of the curve necessary for us can be readily obtained from the parametric form (8), as we shall see.

(Though a large part of the following mathematical developments are not essential to practical use of the results, we nevertheless develop them for the sake of completeness and also because of the fact that the results are necessary for future developments which are basic. A reasonably complete discussion is therefore undertaken, but we shall retain our usual practice to emphasize important results. Thus even though the reader may not feel equal to the task of understanding the analysis, he should understand the significance of the results.)

Lesson No. 34

THE TWO-LAYER REFLECTION TIME-DISTANCE CURVE
(*Continued*)

We start with a matter of notation. For the sake of brevity, the sum of a number of terms, each of which is of the same form, is often abbreviated by writing only one term of that form and prefixing it by a capital sigma, Σ, suitably inscribed. For example, the expression

$$x_1{}^2 + x_2{}^2 + x_3{}^2 + x_4{}^2$$

is written as

$$\sum_{i=1}^{4} x_i{}^2,$$

which means, "the sum of terms each of which is of the form $x_i{}^2$, with i assuming the values 1, 2, 3, 4, consecutively." For brevity, too, the expression is read, "*Sigma* $x_i{}^2$, i running from 1 to 4."

Another example is

$$\sum_{i=1}^{n} h_i \tan \alpha_i;$$

which is an abbreviated way of writing

$$h_1 \tan \alpha_1 + h_2 \tan \alpha_2 + \cdots + h_n \tan \alpha_n,$$

and which is read, "*Sigma* $h_i \tan \alpha_i$, i running from 1 to n."

Once this symbolism is understood, there should be no difficulty in operating with it.

Consider, in fact, the equations (8) of the last lesson (Lesson No. 33) which express, in parametric form, the *time-distance* curve of the reflection arrivals from the bottom of the second of two horizontal planes, the velocities in the intervening beds being v_1 and v_2 and the thicknesses of which are h_1 and h_2. We repeat these equations:

(1)
$$x = 2[h_1 p v_1/(1 - p^2 v_1{}^2)^{1/2} + h_2 p v_2/(1 - p_2 p v_2)^{1/2}],$$
$$t = 2[h_1/v_1(1 - p^2 v_1{}^2)^{1/2} + h_2/v_2(1 - p^2 v_2{}^2)^{1/2}].$$

Ex. 152: Show that, using the summation notation, the equations (1) assume the forms

(2)
$$x = 2 \sum_{i=1}^{2} h_i p v_i/(1 - p^2 v_i{}^2)^{1/2}, \qquad = 2p \sum_{i=1}^{2} h_i v_i/(1 - p^2 v_i{}^2)^{1/2},$$
$$t = 2 \sum_{i=1}^{2} h_i/v_i(1 - p^2 v_i{}^2)^{1/2}.$$

Before continuing, let us recall that for the present we are considering the case for which

$$v_2 > v_1.$$

The denominators of the two terms of both of equations (2) are meaningful only when each of the terms of the form

$$(1 - p^2 v_i^2)$$

is *positive* since the expressions $(1 - p^2 v_i^2)^{1/2}$ are involved. This means that the value of the parameter p is restricted in value so that

$$0 \leq p^2 v_i^2 < 1;$$

and that, therefore,

$$-1/v_i < p < 1/v_i,$$

for both $i = 1$ and $i = 2$.
Since, however,

$$v_2 > v_1,$$

$$1/v_1 > 1/v_2,$$

and so

$$-1/v_2 < p < 1/v_2.$$

The negative values of p, we have seen, pertain to the negative x-direction (see, *e.g.*, Figure 95), and the *time-distance* curve is symmetrical with respect to the t-axis (see Ex. 154, below). Consequently, we continue to discuss the case only for positive values of p; that is to say, we shall for the present consider only

$$0 \leq p < 1/v_2.$$

Substituting the lower value for p, $p = 0$, into equations (2), we have

$$x = 0$$

(3) $$t = 2 \sum_{i=1}^{2} h_i/v_i = 2(h_1/v_1 + h_2/v_2).$$

On the *time-distance* curve this is the point on the t-axis corresponding to the vertical reflection, and, in Figure 95, is indicated by the point W_2.

Physically, it should be evident, too, that as p increases from the value O, both x and t increase. In fact,

Ex. 153: Using equations (2), show that x and t increase as p increases from O; and that as p approaches its maximum value, $1/v_2$, x and t increase indefinitely. Explain the corresponding meaning in Figure 95 in terms of wave paths and travel times.

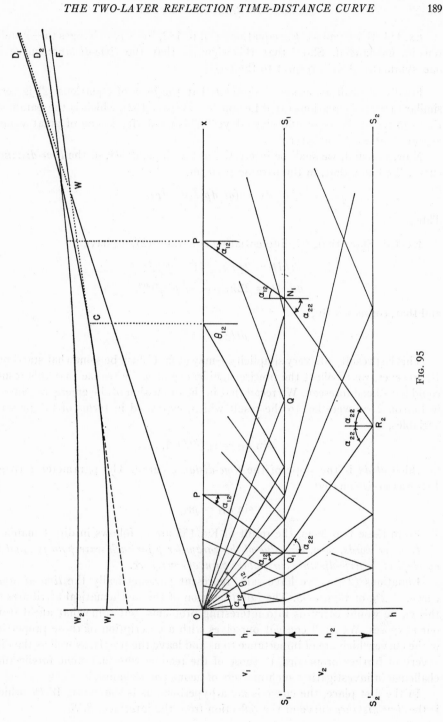

Fig. 95

Ex. 154: If we replace p in equations (3), p. 182, by $-p$, x changes to $-x$ and t remains unchanged. Show that this signifies that the *time-distance* curve is one symmetrical with respect to the t-axis.

Finally, we call attention to the fact that the *form* of equations (2) is very similar to that of equations (3) of Lesson No. 33 (page 182), which is the parametric form for the case of the single-layer. This similarity is one of great value, as will become evident later.

Now, as usual, we shall be interested in the slope, dt/dx, of the *time-distance* curve. We know that, in the parametric form,

$$dt/dx = (dt/dp)/(dx/dp).$$

Thus,

Ex. 155: Show that, by differentiating equations (2), we have

$$dt/dp = 2p\Sigma h_i v_i/(1 - p^2 v_i^2)^{3/2},$$
$$dx/dp = 2\Sigma h_i v_i/(1 - p^2 v_i^2)^{3/2},$$

and that, consequently,

$$dt/dx = p.$$

This last result—its very simplicity—may at first blush be somewhat startling. If, however, we recollect the precise significance of p, we realize that this result could have been foreseen. We recall that in the discussion of the emergence angles in Lesson 2 we were led to the result which, expressed in terms of the present variables, is

$$\sin \alpha_{12} = v_1 (dt/dx),$$

in which dt/dx is the slope of the *time-distance* curve. The parameter p (page 182) was so chosen that

$$\sin \alpha_{12} = pv_1.$$

From these two facts, the result of Ex. 155 above follows in direct manner. *In other words, then, the value of the parameter p for each wave path is equal to the slope of the time-distance curve at the point of emergence.*

Equations (2), as we have said, represent parametrically the *time-distance* curve, $W_2 D_2$, of Figure 95. The full discussion of the mathematical attributes of this curve would carry us into interesting problems, but somewhat afield from our purposes. We shall content ourselves with a description of those properties of the curve which are of importance to us and leave the proofs, as well as the discovery of further properties, to those of the readers who find some intellectual challenge in investigating such matters of geometric elegance.

In the first place, the curve is *not* a hyperbola, as is the curve, $W_1 D_1$, which is the *time-distance* curve of the reflection from the interface, $S_1' S_1$.

It is, however, a curve which has properties quite similar to the hyperbola.

(1) The curve is symmetric with respect to the vertical axis [changing p to $-p$ changes x to $-x$ but leaves t unaltered, in equations (2)].

(2) The curve approaches the line MF (Figure 95) asymptotically. It will be recalled that the line MF is the refraction *time-distance* curve pertaining to the interface, $S_1'S_1$, that it has the slope $1/v_2$, and that it is tangent to the curve W_1D_1 at the point C (where the slope is $1/v_2$) which is the point at which the reflection from $S_1'S_1$ arrives at the critical angle $\theta_{12} = \sin^{-1}(v_1/v_2)$.

Ex. 156: From equations (2), show that the line MF is an asymptote to the curve W_2D_2 by examining the properties of the curve as $p \rightarrow 1/v_2$.

Lesson No. 35

EXTENSION TO THE MULTI-LAYERED PROBLEM—
AVERAGE VELOCITIES

We are now in a position to extend our results to the problem of many layers.

Suppose that underlying the plane surface of the earth we have a series of n layers, each of which is bounded above and below by planes parallel to the surface. Beginning at the surface, the *thicknesses* of the beds are consecutively h_1, h_2, h_3, $\cdots$, h_n, and the seismic wave velocities in these beds are denoted by v_1, v_2, v_3, $\cdots$, v_n, respectively. For the present we shall add a further restriction by requiring the velocities to increase with depth; *i.e.*,

$$v_1 < v_2 < v_3 < \cdots < v_n.$$

Now, consider the illustration in Figure 96. The wave path from O reflected from the bottom of the nth layer at R_n back to the surface to the typical pickup position on the surface $P:x$ is such that its first half consists of:

$$OR_1R_2R_3 \cdots R_{i-1}R_i \cdots R_{n-1}R_n.$$

Its second half, back to the surface, is the portion symmetric to the first half with respect to the vertical through R_n.

The distance $OP = x$ is obviously equal to $2\overline{OC}$ and, in turn, $\overline{OC}$ is equal to the sum of the horizontal components:

$$OC = OT + R_1T_1 + \cdots + R_{i-1}T_{i-1} + \cdots + R_{n-1}T_{n-1}.$$

If we indicate the angle made by the ith section of the wave path, namely $R_{i-1}R_i$, with the vertical by $\alpha_{i,n}$, then

$$R_{i-1}T_{i-1} = h_i \tan \alpha_{i,n}.$$

Thus,

$$OP = 2\overline{OC} = x,$$

where

(1)
$$x = 2[h_1 \tan \alpha_{1,n} + h_2 \tan \alpha_{2,n}, + \cdots$$
$$+ h_i \tan \alpha_{i,n}, + \cdots + h_n \tan \alpha_{n,n}];$$

i.e.,

(2)
$$x = 2 \sum_{i=1}^{n} h_i \tan \alpha_{i,n},$$

Now consider the travel-time along this wave path:

$$t = 2[OR_1/v_1 + R_1R_2/v_2 + \cdots + R_{i-1}R_i/v_i + \cdots + R_{n-1}R_n/v_n].$$

192

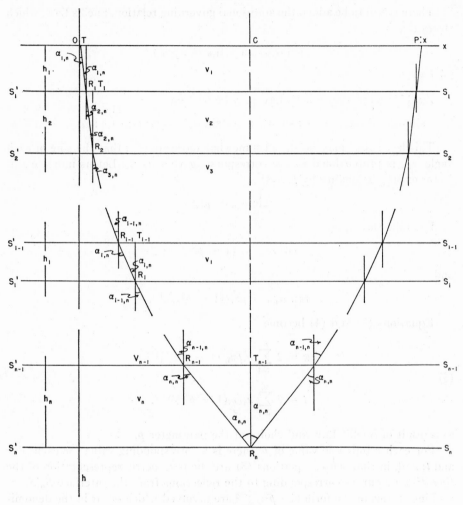

FIG. 96

Since

$$R_{i-1}R_i = h_i/\cos \alpha_{i,n},$$

the result may be written

(3)
$$t = 2[h_1/v_1 \cos \alpha_{i,n} + h_2/v_2 \cos \alpha_{2,n} + \cdots \\ + h_i/v_i \cos \alpha_{i,n} + \cdots + h_n/v_n \cos \alpha_{n,n}];$$

i.e.,

(4)
$$t = 2 \sum_{i=1}^{n} h_i/v_i \cos \alpha_{i,n}.$$

There is still to be added the additional governing relation, Snell's Law, which states that

$$\sin \alpha_{i,n}/\sin \alpha_{i+1,n} = v_i/v_{i+1}$$

for $i = 1, 2, 3, \cdots, n-1$.

Ex. 157: Show that Snell's Law may be written

$$\sin \alpha_{1,n}: \sin \alpha_{2,n}: \cdots : \sin \alpha_{i,n}: \cdots \sin \alpha_{n,n} = v_1: v_2: \cdots : v_i: \cdots v_n.$$

This last result may be stated somewhat more simply: that the sine of each angle $\alpha_{i,n}$ is proportional to the corresponding velocity v_i. Let us indicate this factor of proportionality by p, so that

$$\sin \alpha_{in} = pv_i.$$

Ex. 158: Show that

$$\cos \alpha_{i,n} = (1 - p^2 v_i^2)^{1/2}$$

and

$$\tan \alpha_{i,n} = pv_i/(1 - p^2 v_i^2)^{1/2}.$$

Equations (2) and (4) become

(5)
$$x = 2 \sum_{i=1}^{n} h_i pv_i/(1 - p^2 v_i^2)^{1/2},$$

$$t = 2 \sum_{i=1}^{n} h_i/v_i(1 - p^2 v_i^2)^{1/2},$$

as a result of Snell's Law and choice of the parameter p.

For each admissible value of p, there is a corresponding value for each of x and t; and, in that sense, equations (5) are the parametric representation of the *time-distance* curves corresponding to the reflections from the interface $S_n'S_n$.

Since terms of the form $(1 - p^2 v_i^2)^{1/2}$ are involved which occur in the denominators, we must require that

$$0 \le p^2 v_i^2 < 1$$

for all v_i's.

Ex. 159: From the demand that the greatest of the v_i's is v_n, the range of values for p is

$$-1/v_n < p < 1/v_n.$$

Thus, as p runs through the values in this range, x and t are determined by equations (5) and define the *time-distance* curve which is obviously symmetrical in the vertical (t-) axis.

Ex. 160: Prove this last assertion.

It can be shown that the *time-distance* curve approaches asymptotically the refraction straight line pertaining to the interface $S'_{n-1}S_{n-1}$.*

It can be further shown that this refraction straight line is the tangent line to the *time-distance* curve corresponding to reflections from $S'_{n-1}S_{n-1}$ whose slope is $1/v_n$.*

Finally, it is well to note the similarity in form between equations (5) for n layers to equations (2) of Lesson No. 34 for the two-layer case. In fact, we suggest now:

Ex. 161: Show that the slope of the curve defined by equations (5) is

$$dt/dx = p$$

and explain the reason for this result.

We further suggest:

Ex. 162: Discuss the mathematical aspect to this problem if included among the velocities $v_1, v_2, \cdots, v_n$, there is one slower than the preceding. This amounts to discussing the problem in which

$$v_n < v_{n-1},$$

but that

$$v_1 < v_2 < \cdots < v_{n-1}.$$

As a matter of fact, if one were to go over the preceding arguments he would notice that the restriction that the velocities increase with depth is not necessary for the purposes in hand. It is of interest primarily in refraction theory. Consequently, and for emphasis, we now state our results as follows:

Given n beds each of which is bounded above and below by plane interfaces parallel to the plane surface of the earth, the thickness of the ith bed being h_i and the velocity in that medium being v_i, a ray from the shot point will emerge to the surface after reflections from the bottom of the nth layer at a distance x from the shot point in travel-time t at an angle $\alpha_{1,n}$ where

(6)
$$x = 2 \sum_{i=1}^{n} h_i p v_i/(1 - p^2 v_i^2)^{1/2},$$

$$t = 2 \sum_{i=1}^{n} h_i/v_i(1 - p^2 v_i^2)^{1/2},$$

and

$$\sin \alpha_{i,n} = p v_i.$$

* Suggested as an exercise of mathematical interest.

The slope of the *time-distance* curve along the profile joining the shot point to this pickup point at this pickup point, *i.e.*, dt/dx at this point, is equal to the value of the parameter p for the corresponding path.

Here we pause a moment to point out that if we keep the hypothesis of the velocities increasing with depth, a number of interesting geometrical relations result from considering the asymptotic properties of the *time-distance* curves from the bottoms of each bed as related to the complete set of refraction *time-distance* line segments. These refraction line segments are tangent to the *time-distance* reflection curves from the interface immediately above at the point where the ray emerges at the "critical angle." The mathematically-inclined reader is urged to study these interrelationships which he will find elegant and rewarding.

We return to our problem to re-introduce a concept of the utmost importance in practical work.

In practice, the distance of the outermost pickup from the shot point is in general not too large compared with the depth of the reflection horizons. This, in turn, means that all the angles $\alpha_{i,n}$ (Figure 96) are quite small.

Suppose, then, we return to equations (6) and consider the *vertical* ray only —which, of course, means that all the angles $\alpha_{i,n}$ are, for practical purposes, equal to 0. This means that $p=0$, and this, in turn, reduces equations (6) to

(7)
$$x = 0,$$
$$t = 2 \sum_{i=1}^{n} h_i/v_i.$$

Now, the total depth to the bottom of the nth layer is obviously

(8)
$$h = h_1 + h_2 + h_3 + \cdots + h_n.$$

The travel-time for the reflected wave is, as we have seen,

$$t = 2 \sum_{i=1}^{n} h_i/v_i = 2[h_1/v_1 + h_2/v_2 + h_3/v_3 + \cdots + h_n/v_n].$$

Since the wave had traveled this total distance in this time, the *average velocity* V is then defined by writing:

$$V = 2[h_1 + h_2 + h_3 + \cdots + h_n]/2[h_1/v_1 + h_2/v_2 + h_3/v_3 + \cdots + h_n/v_n]$$
$$= \sum_{i=1}^{n} h_i \bigg/ \sum_{i=1}^{n} (h_i/v_i).$$

For the deep reflections received close to the shot point, the use of this average velocity concept is obviously justifiable and definitely practical. It is used quite generally, however, with errors which may at times be sizeable. We expect to discuss such matters as time goes on. For the present we suggest this lengthy exercise:

Ex. 163: Given a subsurface in which

$$h_1 = 4{,}500 \text{ ft}, \qquad h_2 = 3{,}000 \text{ ft}, \qquad h_3 = 5{,}200 \text{ ft},$$
$$v_1 = 5{,}800 \text{ ft/sec}, \qquad v_2 = 8{,}600 \text{ ft/sec}, \qquad v_3 = 11{,}500 \text{ ft/sec}.$$

Construct the refraction *time-distance* curve and the three reflection *time-distance* curves

Calculate the reflection *time-distance* curves of the lower two interfaces using average velocities and so assuming these curves to be hyperbolas.

LESSONS
IN
SEISMIC COMPUTING

PART IV

Lesson No. 36

INTRODUCTION TO THE THEORY OF CURVED PATHS

The purpose of the mathematical developments of the preceding five lessons was two fold. The material developed was, on the one hand, intrinsically valuable. The mathematical discussions—particularly those concerning the parametric representations of the *time-distance* curves for the parallel layers—were necessary and will be useful in developing our interpretation methods. We were, in fact, led anew to that much-used and oft-abused *average velocity* concept which plays such an important role in all depth-determination techniques of the reflection seismograph method. On the other hand and most importantly, we are now in a position to outline the mathematical developments of the so-called "curved-path" theory in its general aspects. We shall then be ready to apply the results particularly to the widely-used case in which the velocity is assumed to vary linearly with depth.

Let us assume that below the horizontal plane representing the surface of the earth, we have the velocity of seismic propagation depending only on the depth below the surface. In mathematical parlance, this is expressed by saying that this velocity, v, is a function of depth below surface, h, alone; and we write,

$$v = v(h).$$

The mathematical developments to follow demand that this function, $v(h)$, be integrable in the Riemannian sense. This means that the function be "piecewise" continuous with at most a finite number of discontinuities. In lay language, we say that the velocity, $v(h)$, shall be constant or a "smoothly changing" function or a succession of such functions. For practical purposes, this requirement always obtains; that is, the mathematical needs are fully satisfied insofar as seismic prospecting interpretation is concerned.

The seismic paths in such a medium can be "approximated" by considering this medium to be divided into a "large" number of beds bounded by plane interfaces parallel to the surface. Each bed is to be of "small" thickness and in each the seismic velocity is assumed constant and equal to some mean value between its maximum and its minimum values in that thin bed.

The reader will note that we are using the fundamental concepts of the integral calculus here. We do so briefly and, perhaps, hurriedly, simply outlining the procedure so that we attain our goal in a somewhat heuristic manner.

Through the shot-point, O (Figure 97), then, on the plane surface, $S'S$, of the earth, we erect a vertical h-axis. We then divide the subsurface to some given depth, h, into a large number, n, of beds by planes parallel to the surface and of limited thickness. The typical bed, the ith one, is the bed which is bounded by the planes

$$h = h_{i-1}$$

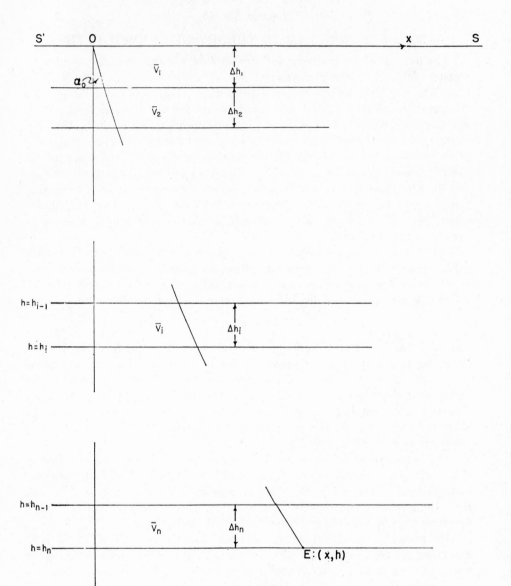

Fɪɢ. 97

and

$$h = h_i = h_{i-1} + \Delta h_i,$$

so that its thickness is Δh_i. With our restrictions on the function, $v(h)$, this thickness can always be made small enough, if need be, so that in this ith bed the velocity has no discontinuities. Thus, it has a maximum value and a minimum value (which, in the case of constant velocity, are both equal), which are not too far apart. Any suitable mean value of this velocity, which would lie between these extreme values, would serve as a good approximation for an average velocity for this thin bed—if, as we assume, it is thin enough. Let this mean value, in fact, be indicated by

$$\bar{v}_i = v(\bar{h}_i)$$

in which, of course,

$$h_{i-1} \leq \bar{h}_i \leq h_i.$$

Now, a wave path, starting at O at an angle α_0 with the vertical, traveling to the point $E: (x, h)$ in the medium defined by the totality of these thin beds, would be described by (see equations 5, page 194)

$$x = \sum_{k=1}^{n} p\Delta h_k v(\bar{h}_k)/[1 - p^2 v^2(\bar{h})_k]^{1/2},$$

(1)
$$h = \sum_{k=1}^{n} \Delta h_k,$$

$$t = \sum_{k=1}^{n} \Delta h_k/v(\bar{h}_k)[1 - p^2 v^2(\bar{h}_k)]^{1/2}.$$

Here, p is defined by the relation

$$\sin \alpha_0 = pv(0),$$

α_0 being the angle of the wave path with the vertical at $h=0$; the summations are taken over the vertical section from the surface at the point O to the point E, and t is the travel-time of the wave from O to E.

The method to set up these equations is that used in Lesson No. 35, *with the difference, however, that we are not now* considering the wave as being reflected back to the surface, but rather as traveling, as we have said, from O to E.

Of these three equations, one might say that the middle one is somewhat superfluous—and, in a sense, it is, if the depth h of the point E is considered fixed. In that case, the first equation expresses the horizontal coordinate, x, of the point E in terms of the parameter p as E moves along a horizontal line at depth h with changing values of this parameter p. On the other hand, we may think of the first equation as that of the "curve" of the wave path leaving O at an angle $\alpha_0 [= \sin^{-1} pv(O)]$ on the (x, h)-plane.

It is important for the reader to understand these considerations if he is to comprehend fully the discussions which follow. We shall continue to indicate the meanings of each result as it is obtained, even at the risk of constant repetition.

In fact, let us repeat: Our medium is one in which the velocity v depends on h alone; *i.e.*,

$$v = v(h).$$

We subdivide it by a large number, n, of parallel planes, each of limited thickness, that of the ith being Δh_i. To each of these thin beds we ascribe an average velocity of propagation $\bar{v}(h_i)$ which is a value lying between the greatest and least value of the velocity in this bed. The equations (1) are then a good approximation to the wave path, defined by an assigned value of the parameter p, in the (x, h)-plane, and the time of travel from O along this path to the point (x, h) is defined by the third of these equations (1).

Now, let the number of these thin beds, n, increase indefinitely in such a way that the greatest thickness is allowed to approach zero (max $\Delta h_i \rightarrow 0$). Equations (1) will then become in the limit, respectively,

$$x = \int_0^h pv(h)dh/[1 - p^2v^2(h)]^{1/2},$$

(2)
$$h = \int_0^h dh,$$

$$t = \int_0^h dh/v(h)[1 - p^2v^2(h)]^{1/2}.$$

These are the fundamental equations for "curved path" theory which we are going to develop in the next Lesson for the case of "Linear Variation of Velocity with Depths."

Let us summarize the significance of these relations.

Given a velocity distribution $v(h)$. The first equation:

$$x = \int_0^h pv(h)dh/[1 - p^2v^2(h)]^{1/2},$$

in which the upper limit h of the integral is variable, expresses the *equation* in the (x, h)-plane of the curved paths, each of the paths being characterized by a corresponding value of the parameter p.

The equation

$$t = \int_0^h dh/v(h)[1 - p^2v^2(h)]^{1/2}$$

is the travel-time of the wave from the source to the point at a depth h on the wave path characterized by the parameter p.

Lesson No. 37

LINEAR DISTRIBUTION OF VELOCITY—I

Experience has shown that the velocity of seismic wave propagation in Tertiary basins can be closely approximated by expressing it as a linear function of depth. It is for that reason that this hypothesis is widely used, even where, at times, its use is hardly justifiable.

For our purposes we write the relation in the form

$$(1) \qquad\qquad v = v_o + ah,$$

in which the dimensions of v and v_o are feet (or meters) per second and those of h are feet (or meters). This implies that the dimensions of a are (seconds)$^{-1}$, or, perhaps better stated, feet per second per foot (or meters per second per meter). It is thus seen that the value of a is the same whether feet or meters are used, and, as a matter of fact, the value of a is the increase in velocity per unit of depth.

Some writers have preferred to write (1) in the alternative form

$$(2) \qquad\qquad v = v_o(1 + kh).$$

The dimensions of k are seen to be (feet)$^{-1}$ [or (meters)$^{-1}$]. To reconcile the conclusions reached by using the one form with those from the other we need only bear in mind that

$$(3) \qquad\qquad a = v_o k.$$

It is a curious, interesting, and important observation and a good rule-of-thumb, which applies generally in all areas for which the use of (1) is indicated, is that

$$v_O = 6{,}000 \text{ ft/sec} \quad \text{and} \quad a = 0.6 \text{ ft/sec/ft.}$$

Thus, for example, in a normal section of the Gulf Coast of Texas and Louisiana, or in the San Joaquin Valley of California, or the Maturin Basin of Venezuela and other similar places, one can safely assume that the velocity at a depth of about 5,000 feet is approximately

$$v_{5,000} = 6{,}000 + (0.6)\ (5{,}000),$$
$$= 9{,}000 \text{ ft/sec.}$$

This linear relationship cannot hold, obviously, for unlimited depths. Generally, it is true to about that depth for which the velocity is 18,000 ft/sec. Thus, in the rule-of-thumb used above, we find that this velocity is attained at a depth h_{max} for which

$$18{,}000 = 6{,}000 + (0.6)\ (h_{max.})$$

That is to say,

$$h_{max} = 20{,}000 \text{ ft,}$$

which is about the greatest depth for which the linear relationship and the rule-of-thumb should be used.

We shall proceed with the mathematical arguments which stem from the hypothesis of this linear distribution of velocity in a slow—and, we hope—methodical way. It is our feeling that a good understanding of these arguments will lead to a more intelligent use of the method and its consequences.

Other assumptions of velocity distribution could be used. However, except for the use of constant (or average) velocity, no other assumption has attained the wide usage of the linear hypothesis, since, in general, "closer approximation" by other assumptions is a meaningless term in a practical sense.

We now repeat the summary of the results of page 204.

We establish an x-axis on the horizontal surface of the earth. Through the shot point O which is used as an origin, we set up an h-axis oriented positively downward. Further, if the velocity of seismic propagation is assumed to be

$$v = v(h),$$

the wave paths from O are defined by

$$(4) \qquad x = \int_0^h pv(h)dh/[1 - p^2v^2(h)]^{1/2},$$

in which p is the parameter of the family of these curves. For each value of p (in a properly limited range) there is defined a curve—wave path. The physical significance of p may be guessed from previous results but it will become apparent again in the course of the argument.

Along the wave path corresponding to a value of the parameter p, the travel-time from O to point (x, h) is given by

$$(5) \qquad t = \int_0^h dh/v(h)[1 - p^2v^2(h)]^{1/2}.$$

Now, in particular, we write

$$(6) \qquad v = v(h) = v_o + ah.$$

Then, equations (4) and (5) become, respectively,

$$(7) \qquad x = \int_0^h p(v_o + ah)dh/[1 - p^2(v_o + ah)^2]^{1/2}$$

and

$$(8) \qquad t = \int_0^h dh/(v_o + ah)[1 - p^2(v_o + ah)^2]^{1/2}.$$

We proceed to integrate these expressions. By an obvious change of variable from h to v:

$$v = v_o + ah,$$

these become, respectively,

(9)
$$x = 1/a \int_{v_o}^{v} pv dv/(1 - p^2 v^2)^{1/2},$$

and

(10)
$$t = 1/a \int_{v_o}^{v} dv/v(1 - p^2 v^2)^{1/2}.$$

A further simplification can be effected by staying on any particular wave path; that is, by holding p constant, and setting

(11)
$$pv = S.$$

Then,

(12)
$$x = 1/ap \int_{pv_o}^{pv} S dS/(1 - S^2)^{1/2}.$$

and

(13)
$$t = 1/a \int_{pv_o}^{pv} dS/S(1 - S^2)^{1/2}.$$

These, now, integrate directly into

(14)
$$x = (-1/ap) \left[(1 - S^2)^{1/2}\right]_{pv_o}^{pv}$$

and

(15)
$$t = (-1/a) \left[\log \left\{(1/S)\left[1 + (1 - S^2)^{1/2}\right]\right\}\right]_{pv_o}^{pv}.*$$

When we insert the limits of integration, we find that

(16)
$$x = (1/ap)\left[(1 - p^2 v_o^2)^{1/2} - (1 - p^2 v^2)^{1/2}\right]$$

and

(17)
$$t = (1/a) \log \left\{[1 + (1 - p^2 v_o^2)^{1/2}]pv/[1 + (1 - p^2 v^2)^{1/2}]pv_o\right\}.$$

Finally, we return to our original variable, h, using the relation

$$v = v_o + ah,$$

and we have:

(18)
$$x = (1/ap)\left\{[(1 - p^2 v_o^2)^{1/2}] - [1 - p^2(v_o + ah)^2]^{1/2}\right\}\dagger$$

---

* Here, of course, logarithms to the "natural" base e are indicated.

† We have gone through the process of integration formally to arrive at these results. Actually,

and

(19) $t = (1/a) \log \left[(v_0 + ah)\left[1 + (1 - p^2 v_0^2)^{1/2}\right]/v_0\left\{1 + \left[1 - p^2(v_0 + ah)^2\right]^{1/2}\right\}\right].$

The first consequence of the greatest importance follows from the first of these two equations. This equation (18) can be written as

(20) $\qquad [x - (1 - p^2 v_0^2)^{1/2}/ap]^2 + (h + v_0/a)^2 = 1/a^2 p^2.$

Ex. 164: Transform equation (18) into this last relation (20).

This is the equation of a *circle* of radius $1/ap$, whose center is at the point with the coordinates

(21) $\qquad x = (1 - p^2 v_0^2)^{1/2}/ap, \qquad h = - v_0/a.$

Note that the h-coordinate of the center is independent of the parameter p.

Ex. 165: Show that the circle (20) passes through the origin (shot point) O whatever the value of the parameter p.

The last result is of such basic importance that it is worthwhile to have it very specifically stated:

In a medium in which the velocity increases linearly with depth,

$$v = v_0 + ah,$$

the wave paths are arcs of circles whose centers lie at a distance v_0/a "above" the surface. In particular, in a vertical section through a shot point through a line (of pickups) on the surface, the wave paths are circular arcs through the shot point whose centers lie on the line parallel to and at a distance v_0/a "above" the line on the surface.

In Figure 98 we show schematically a few of these wave-paths numbered 1, 2, 3, $\cdots$, and the centers of the circles, of which these paths are arcs, lettered $C_1, C_2, C_3, \cdots$.

In Figure 99 we show, in more detail, one of these circular wave paths pertaining to the particular value p for the parameter. The circle has its center at

(22) $\qquad C: [(1 - p^2 v_0^2)^{1/2}/(ap, - v_0/a)].$

Its radius is equal to

$$1/ap$$

---

however, these results are valid only as long as $|pv| < 1$, since the situation when $|pv| = 1$ demands further attention, as can be seen from the form of the integrands in (4) and (5).

As we shall see, this means that the results are valid as long as we do *not* go beyond the *lowest* point on any of the wave paths; in other words, as long as we are still going "deeper" into the medium. The integrations will have to be examined further (in the next Lesson) for the "upward" parts of, and the complete, wave paths.

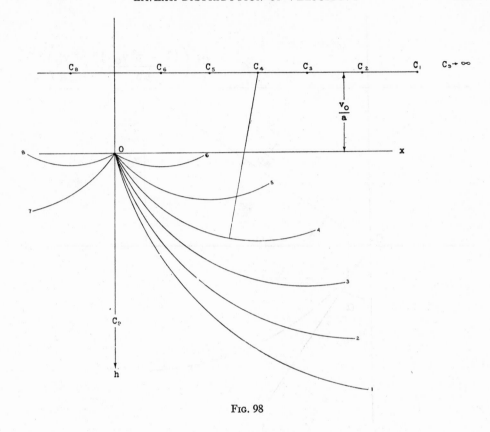

Fig. 98

and it passes through the shot point (origin) O.

Ex. 166: From the geometry of Figure 99, show that the radius of the circle being $1/ap$, its center being on the line

$$h = - v_0/a,$$

and passing through O, the x-coordinate of its center (C) must be that indicated in (22).

Ex. 167. Assuming the rule-of-thumb described on page 205, draw a few of the circular paths to scale.

In Figure 99, the wave path shown is emerging at the surface (it should be apparent that the emergence angle "law" for wave paths holds whether the wave is immerging into the medium from the surface or emerging therefrom at the surface) at an angle α.

Ex. 168. From the geometry implied in Figure 99, show that the angle of

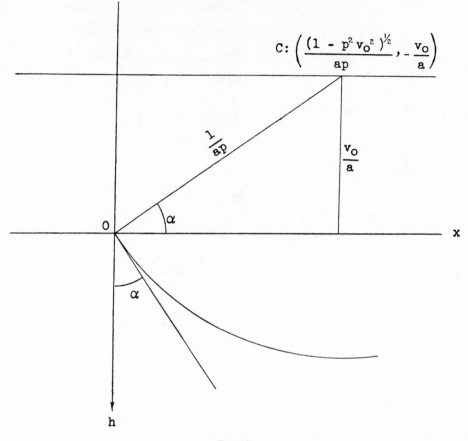

$$C: \left(\frac{(1 - p^2 v_0^2)^{1/2}}{ap} , -\frac{v_0}{a} \right)$$

FIG. 99

emergence α is equal to the angle made by the radius of the wave path through O (*i.e.*, CO) with the x-axis.

Thus, it follows that

(23) $$\sin \alpha = (v_0/a)/(1/ap) = p v_0;$$

i.e.,

(24) $$p = \sin \alpha / v_0.$$

Ex. 169. Referring again to Figure 99, show that the maximum penetration of the wave path shown is

$$h_{max}(p) = (1/ap) - (v_0/a) = (1 - p v_0)/ap.$$

Ex. 170. Again, using the rule-of-thumb

$$v_0 = 6,000 \text{ ft/sec} \quad \text{and} \quad a = 0.6,$$

draw to scale the wave paths through O emerging at distances of

$$10,000 \text{ ft;} \qquad 15,000 \text{ ft;} \qquad 20,000 \text{ ft.}$$

How deep has each of these paths penetrated?

LINEAR DISTRIBUTION OF VELOCITY—II.
THE REFRACTION TIME-DISTANCE CURVE

To remove the difficulties mentioned in the second footnote on page 207 and 208, and, at the same time, to give further meaning to the mathematical developments and results which are of basic importance, we shall begin by examining in yet another way the initial problems implied in the integrations of the preceding Lesson.

From the meaning of the parameter p and the discussions leading to equations (2) on page 204, it is apparent that, at a point Q at depth h (see Figure 100), at which depth the seismic velocity is, of course, $v(h)$, the angle α between the direction of the wave-path through Q and the vertical is such that

$$\sin \alpha = pv(h).$$

A confirmation of this fact is directly obtained by differentiating the first of these aforementioned equations and recalling that

$$dx/dh = \tan \alpha.$$

Specifically, in the linear case, we have $\sin \alpha = p(v_o + ah)$ as defining the angle α

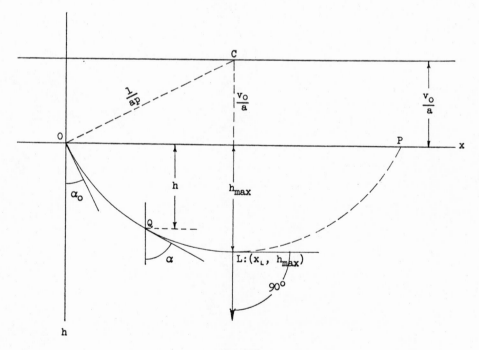

Fig. 100

212

which the circular wave path at any point makes with the vertical.

At the "lowest" point of this circular wave path; that is, at the point of deepest penetration, the angle α is equal to 90° (as shown at the point L in Figure 100). At this point of deepest penetration, the depth of which we might indicate by $h_{\max}$, we have

(1) $$\sin \alpha = \sin 90° = 1 = p(v_o + ah_{\max}),$$

from which we conclude that, given the value of the parameter p pertaining to a particular wave path, the depth of penetration of that wave path will occur at

(2) $$h_{\max} = (1 - pv_o)/ap.$$

(Compare this result with that of Exercise 169.)

Ex. 171. Using the fact that $pv_0 = \sin \alpha_0$, show that (2) may be written as

(3) $$h_{\max} = (v_0/a)(1 - \sin \alpha_0)/\sin \alpha_0$$

where α_0 is the angle of emergence of the wave-path.

To determine the x-coordinate (x_L) of this point L and the travel-time (t_L) of the wave from O to L, we use the integrals (12) and (13) on page 207 with the upper limit

(4) $$pv = p(v_o + ah_{\max}) = 1:$$

i.e.,

(5) $$x_L = 1/ap \int_{pv_o}^{1} SdS/(1 - S^2)^{1/2},$$

and

(6) $$t_L = 1/a \int_{pv_o}^{1} dS/S(1 - S^2)^{1/2},$$

provided these integrals converge as S *increases* towards the limit 1.

This is indeed the case (as is obvious from integration) and we have

(7) $\quad x_L = (1/ap)\left[-(1 - S^2)^{1/2}\right]_{pv_o}^{1} = (1/ap)(1 - p^2v_o^2)^{1/2} = (v_0/a) \cot \alpha_0$

and

(8)
$$t_L = (- 1/a)\left[\log\left\{(1/S)\left[1 + (1 - S^2)^{1/2}\right]\right\}\right]_{pv_o}^{1},$$
$$= (1/a) \log\left\{(1/pv_0)\left[1 + (1 - p^2v_0^2)^{1/2}\right]\right\},$$
$$= (1/a) \cosh^{-1}(1/pv_0).{}^{*}$$

Ex. 172. Show that the results (2) and (7) above can be obtained directly from

---

* For this last result, see Appendix beginning on page 217.

the geometry in Figure 100, using the facts already known concerning the radii and centers of the circular wave paths.

At the risk of repetition, let us summarize the results just obtained.

The wave path leaving the shot-point O at an angle α_0 with the vertical is that for which the parameter p has the value

$$p = \sin \alpha_0/v_0.$$

It is the arc of the circle whose center is on the line

$$h = - v_0/a,$$

and whose radius is

$$1/ap = (v_0/a) (1/\sin \alpha_0.)$$

Accordingly, the coordinates of its center C are

$$[(1 - p^2 v_0^2)^{1/2}/ap, - v_0/a];$$

i.e.,

$$[(v_0/a) \cot \alpha_0, - v_0/a].$$

The angle at depth h between the path and the vertical is α, where

$$\sin \alpha = p(v_0 + ah).$$

The point of deepest penetration L has the coordinates

$$[(1 - p^2 v_0^2)^{1/2}/ap, (1 - pv_0)/ap];$$

i.e.,

$$[(v_0/a) \cot \alpha_0, (v_0/a) (1 - \sin \alpha_0)/\sin \alpha_0],$$

since at that point $\alpha = 90°$.

The travel-time of the wave from O to L is

$$(1/a) \cosh^{-1} (1/pv_0).$$

From the point L on, the wave path proceeds upward and emerges to the surface at the point P.

Obviously, the x-coordinate of P is twice that of L:

(9) $$x_P = 2(1 - p^2 v_0^2)^{1/2}/ap$$

and the total travel-time from O to P is

(10) $$t_P = (2/a) \cosh^{-1} (1/pv_0).$$

Now, as α_0 runs from $90°$ down to $0°$, p runs through its range of values from $p = 1/v_0$ (since $|pv| \leq 1$) to $p = 0$. The point of emergence of the wave at the surface then moves from O indefinitely outward, since its x-coordinate is

(11) $$x = 2(1 - p^2v_o^2)^{1/2}/ap.$$

For each of these waves, the travel-time is

(12) $$t = (2/a) \cosh^{-1} (1/pv_o).$$

The combination of these two yields, parametrically, the equation of the *time-distance* curve of the refracted "kick" over our medium. That is to say, the equation of the refraction *time-distance* curve for our medium can be obtained thus:

From the second, we have

(13) $$\cosh (at/2) = 1/pv_o,$$

and from the first

(14)
$$
\begin{aligned}
x &= 2(1/p^2v_o^2 - 1)^{1/2}/(a/v_o), \\
&= (2v_o/a)(\cosh^2 (at/2) - 1)^{1/2}, \\
&= (2v_o/a) \sinh (at/2).*
\end{aligned}
$$

This may be more conveniently written

$$t = (2/a) \sinh^{-1} (ax/2v_o).\dagger$$

Ex. 173: Construct the refraction time-distance curve for the "rule-of-thumb" medium: $v_0 = 6,000$ ft/sec and $a = 0.6$. In Figure 101 and its table, this is done out to a horizontal distance of $x = 10,000$ ft. Continue it to $x = 30,000$ ft.

FOR TABLES OF HYPERBOLIC FUNCTIONS EXCELLENT FOR OUR PURPOSE, THE READER IS REFERRED TO THE SMITHSONIAN MATHEMATICAL TABLES OF HYPERBOLIC FUNCTIONS WHICH MAY BE OBTAINED FROM THE SMITHSONIAN INSTITUTION AT WASHINGTON, D. C.

Ex. 174: Construct the refraction *time-distance* curve for the linear distribution of velocity

$$v_O = 5,600 + 0.45h.$$

---

* By definition,

$$\sinh x = (e^x - e^{-x})/2.$$

Thus, we have the identity

$$\cosh^2 x - \sinh^2 x = 1.$$

† If $y = \sinh x$, then $x = \sinh^{-1} y$. Here, the -1 is symbolic and *not* an exponent.

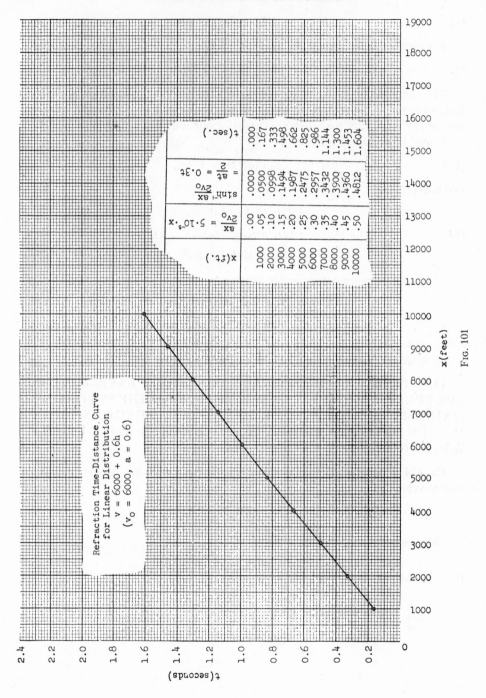

x(ft.)	$\frac{ax}{2v_0} = 5 \cdot 10^{-5} \cdot x$	$\sinh^{-1}\frac{ax}{2v_0}$	$= \frac{at}{2} = 0.3t$	t(sec.)
1000	.00	.0000	.000
2000	.05	.0500	.167
3000	.10	.0998	.333
4000	.15	.1494	.498
5000	.20	.1987	.662
6000	.25	.2475	.825
7000	.30	.2957	.986
8000	.35	.3432	1.144
9000	.40	.3900	1.300
10000	.45	.4360	1.453
	.50	.4812	1.604

Refraction Time–Distance Curve
for Linear Distribution
v = 6000 + 0.6h
(v_0 = 6000, a = 0.6)

x(feet)

FIG. 101

MATHEMATICAL APPENDIX

By definition,

(a) $$y = \cosh x = (e^x + e^{-x})/2.*$$

Note that for x real, $y \geq 1$. Also, if $y = \cosh x$, we write alternatively,

(b) $$x = \cosh^{-1} y.†$$

By squaring (a) we have

(c) $$4y^2 = e^{2x} + 2 + e^{-2x},$$

whence

(d) $$4(y^2 - 1) = e^{2x} - 2 + e^{-2x},$$

and, by extracting the square root of this last expression,

(e) $$(y^2 - 1)^{1/2} = (e^x - e^{-x})/2.$$

Adding (a) and (e) we have:

(f) $$e^x = y + (y^2 - 1)^{1/2},$$

whence

(g) $$x = \log\left[y + (y^2 - 1)^{1/2}\right].$$

Now set

(h) $$y = 1/z.$$

Since $y \geq 1$, $0 < z \leq 1$. Then (g) becomes

(i) $$x = \log\left\{(1/z)\left[1 + (1 - z^2)^{1/2}\right]\right\}.$$

We now recall the fact that in (b)

$$x = \cosh^{-1} y = \cosh^{-1} (1/z),$$

from which we conclude the identity:

(j) $$\cosh^{-1} (1/z) = \log\left\{(1/z)\left[1 + (1 - z^2)^{1/2}\right]\right\}.$$

---

* Cosh x is the abbreviated notation for the hyperbolic cosine of x and is usually read "cosh of x."

† The -1 is symbolic only and is not to be construed as an exponent. The phase is usually read "x equals anti-cosh of y."

Lesson No. 39

LINEAR DISTRIBUTION OF VELOCITY—III.
THE REFRACTION PROBLEM (*Continued*)

We have seen that in the medium being considered, the wave paths emanating from a shot-point O at the surface are arcs of the circles passing through O whose centers lie at a distance v_0/a above the surface.

A typical wave path in the section shown in Figure 102 emerges at pickup point P at distance x from O, the emergence angle there being indicated by α_0.

Considering α_0 as the parameter for the present and noting that the angle made by a wave path at O with the vertical is the same as the emergence angle of that wave path at P, we see that as α_0 varies from $0°$ to $90°$, the point P moves *inward* from infinite distance toward O.

This typical wave path, defined by a value of the parameter α_0, then, is the arc OLP of the circle whose center is

$$(1) \qquad\qquad C: \left[(v_0/a) \cot \alpha_0, \ -v_0/a\right]$$

and whose radius is

$$(2) \qquad\qquad R = v_0/a \sin \alpha_0.$$

The "lowest" point of the wave path, that is, the "depth of penetration," is at L, "directly below" C, at a depth of

$$(3) \qquad \begin{aligned} h_{max} &= R - v_0/a, \\ &= (v_0/a)\left[(1 - \sin \alpha_0)/\sin \alpha_0\right] = R(1 - \sin \alpha_0). \end{aligned}$$

The wave emerges at the point P whose distance from O is twice the abscissa of C; *i.e.*,

$$(4) \qquad\qquad x_P = (2v_0/a) \cot \alpha_0.$$

The travel-time of the wave from O to P is [see page 215, Equation (13)]:

$$(5) \qquad\qquad t_{OP} = (2/a) \cosh^{-1} (1/\sin \alpha_0);$$

or, better, in terms of the x-coordinate of P (see equation (14), *loc. cit.*),

$$(6) \qquad\qquad t = (2/a) \sinh^{-1} (ax/2v_0).$$

This last equation (6), then, defines the *time-distance* curve for the refracted wave in our medium. This curve is shown in the upper part of Figure 102.

As we have seen, the parameter p, instead of the parameter α_0, defined by the relation

$$(7) \qquad\qquad (\sin \alpha_0 = pv_0,)$$

is a far better one to use. Accordingly, some of the preceding results assume the

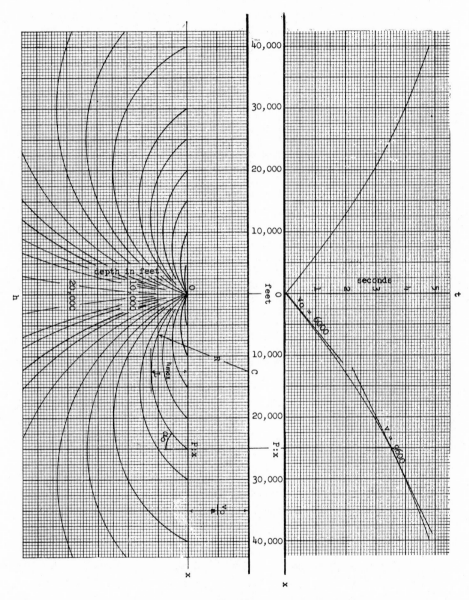

Fɪɢ. 102

following respective forms:

(1)′ $\qquad\qquad\qquad C: [(1 - p^2 v_o{}^2)^{1/2}/ap, - v_o a],$

(2)′ $\qquad\qquad\qquad\qquad R = 1/ap,$

(3′) $\qquad\qquad\qquad\qquad h_{\max} = (1 - pv_o)/ap,$

(4)′ $\qquad\qquad\qquad\qquad x_P = (2/ap)(1 - p^2 v_o{}^2)^{1/2}$

and

(5)′ $\qquad\qquad\qquad\qquad t_{OP} = (2/a) \cosh^{-1}(1/pv_o).$

The equation of the refraction *time-distance* curve is (6); and we have seen that it may be expressed parametrically in α_0 as

I. $\qquad\qquad\qquad \begin{cases} x = (2v_o/a) \cot \alpha_0, \\ t = (2/a) \cosh^{-1}(1/\sin \alpha_0); \end{cases}$

or, parametrically in p as

II. $\qquad\qquad\qquad \begin{cases} x = (2/ap)(1 - p^2 v_o{}^2)^{1/2}, \\ t = (2/a) \cosh^{-1}(1/pv_o) \end{cases}$

or, finally, as (6), namely,

III. $\qquad\qquad\qquad t = (2/a) \sinh^{-1}(ax/2v_o).$

We shall now indulge in a few mathematical manipulations and discuss the consequences thereof:

First, rewrite III,

(a) $\qquad\qquad\qquad\qquad \sinh(at/2) = ax/2v_o.$

Secondly, differentiate both sides of this result with respect to x:

(b) $\qquad\qquad\qquad\qquad (a/2) \cosh(at/2)\, dt/dx = a/2v_o;$

whence,

(c) $\qquad\qquad\qquad\qquad dt/dx = 1/v_0 \cosh(at/2).$

From the second equation of I, above,

(d) $\qquad\qquad\qquad\qquad \cosh(at/2) = 1/\sin \alpha_o.$

Thus, with the use of (d) in (c), we conclude that

(8) $\qquad\qquad\qquad\qquad dt/dx = \sin \alpha_0/v_o,$

or

(9) $\qquad\qquad\qquad\qquad \sin \alpha_o = v_o\, dt/dx.$

But [*cf.* equation (7)] $\sin \alpha_o = p v_o$. Thus,

(10) $$dt/dx = p.$$

Equation (9), above, is none other than the relationship between the emergence angle (α_0) of a wave at the surface and the slope (dt/dx) of the *time-distance* curve at that point which we have discussed in the Lessons 1 and 2.

Equation (10) gives us anew the additional significance of the parameter p. Originally, it will be recalled, p was introduced as the constant of proportionality between the sines of the angles a wave path makes with the interfaces and the velocities of the media between those interfaces. The parameter p now takes on the added—and not unexpected—significance of being equal to the slope of the time-distance curve at the point of emergence of the wave path defined by the value of p.

Ex. 175: Prove that

$$dt/dx = p$$

from equations I [by using the fact that $dt/dx = (dt/d\alpha_0)/(dx/d\alpha_0)$] and from equations II [by using the fact that $dt/dx = (dt/dp)/(dx/dp)$].

Now, consider again a particular wave path—the corresponding particular value of the parameter p, emerging at the point P. The slope of the *time-distance* curve there is

(11) $$dt/dx = p.$$

The angle α between the vertical and the direction of the wave path at any point at depth h has been shown to be

(12) $$\sin \alpha = p(v_o + ah).$$

This *angle* at the point L of deepest penetration is 90°. Thus,

$$1 = p(v_o + ah_{max}),$$

whence

(13) $$p = 1/(v_o + ah_{max}).$$

We now have the result that the value of the parameter p pertaining to a particular wave-path is equal to the reciprocal of the velocity in the medium at the deepest point of penetration.

But, because of (11), this last result is of greater import when stated thus:

The slope of the refraction time-distance curve at a point is equal to the reciprocal of the velocity at the point of deepest penetration of the wave emerging at that point.

In particular,

Ex. 176: *The reciprocal of the slope of the refraction time-distance curve at the shot-point O is equal to v_0.*

The reader is now urged to make a figure similar to Figure 102, using values of v_0 and a with which he is concerned. Figure 102 is based on the "rule-of-thumb" values

$$v_o = 6{,}000 \text{ ft}, \qquad a = 0.6.$$

In Figure 102, the refraction *time-distance* curve is drawn along a profile extending in a line through O, each half of which is 40,000 ft long.

We have chosen the point P, 25,000 ft from O, as a typical pickup point. The travel-time from O to P is seen to be 3.493 sec. (Check this.)

The emergence angle, α_0, at P is seen to be obtained from equation (4):

$$25{,}000 = 2 \ (6{,}000/0.6) \cot \alpha_0,$$

whence

$$a_0 \sim 39°. \text{ (Check this result.)}$$

From this, recalling that

$$\sin \alpha_0/v_o = p,$$

we have

$$p = 0.625/6{,}000 = 0.104 \times 10^{-3} \text{ sec/ft}.$$

This value of p is the one that singles out the wave path to P from all the wave paths.

It is also the value of the slope dt/dx of the *time-distance* curve at P.

Now, the reciprocal of this value of p, namely

$$1/p = 6{,}000/0.625 = 9{,}600 \text{ ft/sec},$$

is the velocity of the medium at the deepest point of penetration of the wave path to P, namely, it is the velocity at L.

We shall check this by a different approach.

According to (3), this depth of penetration is,

$$h_{\max} = 6{,}000/0.6[(1 - 0.625)/0.625],$$

$$= 6{,}000 \text{ ft}.$$

At this depth, the velocity, of course, is

$$v = 6{,}000 + (0.6) \ (6{,}000),$$

$$= 9{,}600 \text{ ft/sec}.$$

which is in agreement with the preceding result.

Finally, note that the reciprocal of the slope of the *time-distance* curve at O is 6,000 ft/sec.

Let us repeat the suggestion that the reader make his own figure for a medium with linear increase of velocity in much the same way as we have done here. It will be a task with eminently satisfying consequences.

Lesson No. 40

LINEAR DISTRIBUTION OF VELOCITY—IV. THE REFRACTION PROBLEM (*Continued*)

In a seismic exploration program, the problem of converting travel-times to subsurface depths is of fundamental importance. The necessary computational procedures for this conversion are considerably simplified if the assumption of a linear distribution of velocity with depth can be used. Consequently, one of the first problems to be solved in such a program is to determine whether an assumption of this type should be adopted; and, if so, what values of v_0 and a are to be used.

Whether or not the hypothesis of a linear variation of velocity with depth may be a good approximation to the actual situation in any region can often be surmised from the lithology. One of the first items on the agenda of a seismic crew should be the "shooting" of a sufficient number of refraction profiles, laid out as ideally as possible on a flat surface and, it is hoped, over a "normal" subsurface.* This latter requirement can be attained by laying out a number of profiles. If the *time-distance* curves for two or more profiles in the area are substantially alike, the conclusion that the subsurface sections are "normal" and "flat" is almost certain to be a valid one.

The next step is to note whether these refraction *time-distance* curves along the profiles are, in appearance, similar to an "anti-hyperbolic sine function" of distance, *i.e.*, the *time-distance* curve shown in Figure 102. If, indeed, the resemblance is sufficiently strong from a qualitative standpoint, we proceed to find the corresponding values of v_0 and a from the data, and then "check back" the rest of the data to see what kind of "fit" has actually been achieved. On the other hand, if the *time-distance* curve is a series of clear cut broken-line segments suggesting a "layered" subsurface, our hypothesis is invalid and we resort back to the methods of average velocities already discussed.

We proceed to show, by a numerical example, how a determination of v_0 and a can be obtained from refraction data.

Consider, then, the data tabulated in Table I which *are assumed already to*

TABLE I

x (feet)	t (seconds)	x (feet)	t (seconds)
2,000	0.347	16,000	2.605
4,000	0.692	18,000	2.887
6,000	1.030	20,000	3.160
8,000	1.364	22,000	3.420
10,000	1.690	24,000	3.675
12,000	2.005	26,000	3.913
14,000	2.308		

* An alternative is the "shooting" of a well, if one exists, for a velocity survey. This method will be discussed in later lessons.

have been corrected for shot-depth and elevation. The resulting *time-distance* curve is plotted in Figure 103.

The first reaction of a computer to the refraction profile data as plotted in Figure 103 is to try to draw the "best fit" line segments. We have tried to do this in the Figure in the manner indicated by the three dashed line segments. Over each of these line segments, too, we show the corresponding apparent velocities (the reciprocals of the slopes); namely, 5,750, 6,700 and 7,850 ft/sec. We assume these data to be reasonably normal for the area (in the sense that a reverse profile, perhaps, or other profiles exhibit close agreement with this one).

Further visual examination of the sequence of points in Figure 103 indicates that a "smooth" curve of the anti-hyperbolic sine type may fit every bit as well as does this one consisting of the three line segments. Let us see, in fact, whether a curve defined analytically by a relationship of the form

(1) $t = (2/a) \sinh^{-1} (ax/2v_o),$

or, equivalently,

(2) $\sinh (at/2) = ax/2v_o,$

can be found to fit the data of Table I as well as the three line segments of Figure 103. Our definition of a "good fit" for the purposes required shall be qualitative. If all the given data can be found to lie within a few thousandths of a second from an analytic curve we shall be satisfied that the analytic curve fits the data. Other more objective tests can be set up to make this concept of a "good fit" more precise, but it is not worthwhile to do so except as a mathematical exercise (one not without interest).

Looked at from the mathematical standpoint, there are two unknowns to be determined: v_0 and a. Two conditions are therefore required. We shall indicate three methods that may be used, although we recommend the last of these as being more general and satisfying. The reason will become apparent.

METHOD A

It has been pointed out (Exercise No. 176) that the reciprocal of the slope of the refraction *time-distance* curve at the origin is v_o. We may therefore assume, as Figure 103 indicates, that

$$v_o = 5,750 \text{ ft}$$

is probably an excellent value.

Thus, in equation (2), above, we have

(3) $\sinh (at/2) = ax/2 (5,750.)$

To determine a we need only use one set of our data. For this purpose we go out some distance from O and use, from Table I:

$$x = 16,000 \text{ ft}, \qquad t = 2.605 \text{ sec.}$$

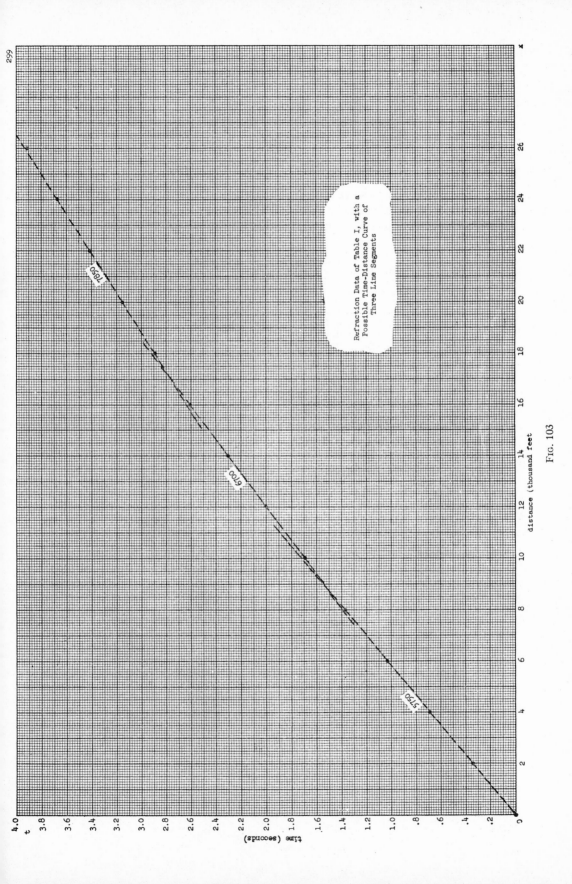

Refraction Data of Table I, with a
Possible Time-Distance Curve of
Three Line Segments

7890

6700

5750

t

4.0
3.8
3.6
3.4
3.2
3.0
2.8
2.6
2.4
2.2
2.0
1.8
1.6
1.4
1.2
1.0
.8
.6
.4
.2
0

time (seconds)

2   4   6   8   10   12   14   16   18   20   22   24   26

distance (thousand feet)

Fig. 103

Then, in (3) we have

$$\sinh{(a\,2.605/2)} = a\,16{,}000/2\,(5{,}750),$$

i.e.,

(4) $$\sinh{(1.3025a)} = 8a/5.75 = 1.391a.$$

The easiest way to solve this equation for a is a "trial and error" one. Assign values to a in the range to be expected, as shown in Table II, and find the corresponding values of both sides of equation (4).

TABLE II

1	2	3	4
a	$1.391\,a$	$1.3025\,a$	$\sinh{(1.3025a)}$
0.30	0.4173	0.3908	0.4009
0.35	0.4868	0.4559	0.4719
0.40	0.5564	0.5210	0.5449
0.45	0.6260	0.5861	0.6202
0.50	0.6955	0.6512	0.6982
0.55	0.7650	0.7164	0.7793
0.60	0.8346	0.7815	0.8635

In the first column we have listed values for a in a range (0.30 to 0.60) in which the solution might be expected to fall. Columns 2 and 3 are obtained by multiplication as indicated by the headings of those columns, motivated, of course, by equation (4). Column 4 is obtained from column 3 and the use of tables of hyperbolic sines. We seek the place where columns 2 and 4 have equal values for the same value of a. A study of Table II indicates that this occurs between $a=0.45$ and $a=0.50$. It is best to reduce this problem now to a graphic solution as is done in Figure 104 in which columns 2 and 4 are plotted as functions of a and the intersection sought.* Linear interpolation is generally good enough for our purposes, but this graphic method has been introduced since we shall make use of it quite generally in the future.

Figure 104 indicates that the solution seems to be

$$a = 0.485.$$

Thus, this method indicates that we should *try*

$$v_o = 5{,}750\ \text{ft/sec}, \quad a = 0.485.$$

Accordingly, in Figure 105 we have indicated points on the curve

(5) $$t = (2/0.485)\ \sinh^{-1}{[(0.485x)/2(5{,}750)]},$$

by $\odot$, computed as shown in Table III.

---

* The curves in Figure 104 are numbered to correspond to the columns in Table II.

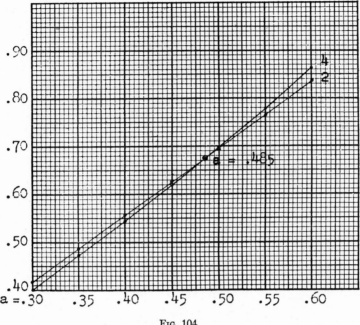

Fig. 104

Also shown on this Figure by heavy points are the data points of Table I. The degree of agreement between a curve through the data points in Table I and the analytic curve represented by (5) can be visually seen in Figure 105.

TABLE III

1	2	3	4
0	0.00000	0.0000	0.000
5	0.21085	0.2093	0.863
10	0.42170	0.4101	1.691
15	0.63255	0.5965	2.460
20	0.84340	0.7661	3.159
25	1.05425	0.9192	3.791

In Table III columns 1, 2, 3 and 4 are the numerical values of the functions respectively represented by:

1. $x/1,000$,

2. $0.485x/2(5.750) = 0.04217x/1,000$,

3. $\sinh^{-1}\left[(0.485x)/2\,(5,750)\right] = \sinh^{-1}(0.04217x/1,000)$,

4. $t = (2/0.485)\sinh^{-1}\left[(0.485x)/2\,(5,750)\right]$,

    $= 4.124\sinh^{-1}(0.04217x/1,000)$.

Ex. 177: Again choosing $v_o = 5,750$, ft/sec, use $x = 26,000$, $t = 3.913$ from Table I to determine a and compare the results with the curve of Figure 105, corresponding to (5).

METHOD B

In this method, we choose from two sets of data from Table I to determine our two unknowns a and v_o. For our example, let these be:

$$x = 8,000 \qquad t = 1.364$$
$$x = 16,000 \qquad t = 2.605$$

Then we have to solve [substituting in equation (2)]

$$\sinh (1.364a/2) = 8,000a/2v_o$$

and

$$\sinh (2.605a/2) = 16,000a/2v_o;$$

i.e., respectively,

(6) $$\sinh (0.6820a) = 4,000a/v_0$$

and

(7) $$\sinh (1.3025a) = 8,000a/v_o.$$

Dividing the second by the first has the effect of eliminating v_0 and we have:

(8) $$\sinh (1.3025a) = 2 \sinh (0.6820a).$$

Again we proceed to compute both sides of this equation as functions of a, exhibited tabularly in Table IV.

TABLE IV

1	2	3	4	5	6
a	$1.3025a$	$\sinh 1.3025a$	$0.6820a$	$\sinh 0.6820a$	$2 \sinh 0.6820a$
0.30	0.3908	0.4009	0.2046	0.2060	0.4120
0.35	0.4559	0.4719	0.2387	0.2410	0.4820
0.40	0.5210	0.5449	0.2728	0.2762	0.5524
0.45	0.5861	0.6202	0.3069	0.3117	0.6234
0.50	0.6512	0.6982	0.3410	0.3476	0.6952
0.55	0.7164	0.7793	0.3751	0.3840	0.7680
0.60	0.7815	0.8635	0.4092	0.4207	0.8418

Our solution is to be found where columns 3 and 6 would have equal values for the same value of a; and, although linear interpolation would serve our purpose, we again use the graphic method (for pedagogical reasons) of Figure 106. Each curve here is numbered to correspond with the column number in Table IV.

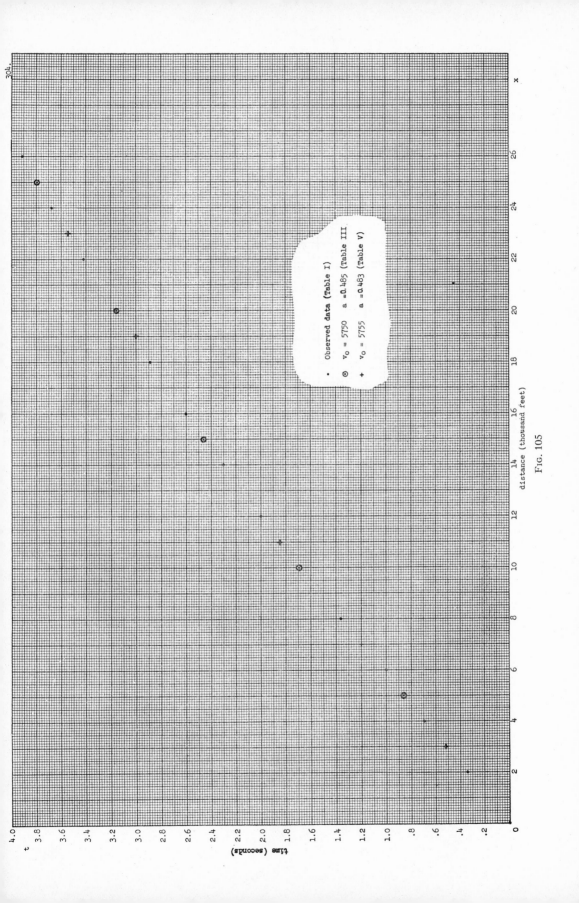

Fig. 105

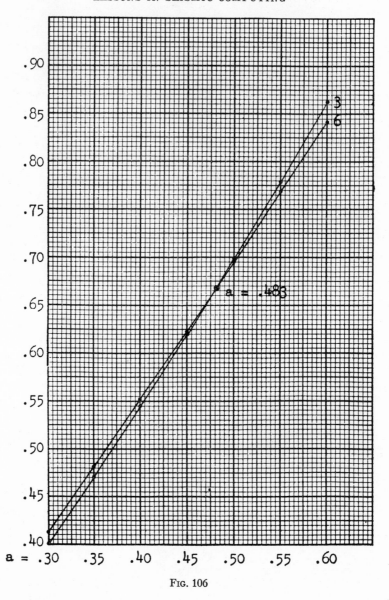

Fig. 106

This graph indicates that

$$a = 0.483$$

is about right.

Using this result in (6) and (7), we have, respectively,

$$v_o = (4{,}000)(0.483)/\sinh\,[(0.6820)(0.483)],$$
$$= 1{,}932/\sinh 0.3294,$$

$$= 1{,}932/0.3352 = 5{,}760;$$

and

$$v_o = (8{,}000)(0.483)/\sinh\left[(1.3025)(0.483)\right],$$
$$= 3{,}864/\sinh 0.6292,$$
$$= 3{,}864/0.6715 = 5{,}750.$$

We thus have a check on our arithmetic (to three-place accuracy) and feel that the average $v_o = 5{,}755$ ft/sec and $a = 0.483$ are good values.

Ex. 178: Use two other sets of data of Table I and follow through Method B.

We now compute points on the curve in Figure 105 to see how well the use of these last values will fit our data of Table I.

Points on the curve for which $v_o = 5{,}755$ ft/sec and $a = 0.483$; *i.e.*, on the curve

$$t = (2/0.483)\sinh^{-1}\left[(0.483x)/2(5{,}755)\right],$$
$$= 4.141\sinh^{-1}(0.042x/1{,}000);$$

are computed in Table V and are indicated by $+$ on Figure 105. The values of x chosen are such as to set off these computed points from the others in the Figure.

TABLE V

1	2	3	4
$x/1{,}000$	$0.042x/1{,}000$	$\sinh^{-1}(0.042x/1{,}000)$	t
3	0.126	0.1256	0.520
7	0.294	0.2899	1.200
11	0.462	0.4470	1.851
15	0.630	0.5944	2.461
19	0.798	0.7311	3.027
23	0.966	0.8571	3.549

METHOD C

This, the best of the three methods, is based on using Method B three times. That is to say, by using each of *three* pairs of data points, obtained from using three sets of data points two at a time, and operating on these three pairs by Method B, we obtain three values for v_0 and three for a. If the "scatter" of these values is not too great the arithmetic averages generally constitute a very good fit.

Suppose, in fact, that we use these three sets of data values from Table I:

$$\text{(a)} \quad x = 8{,}000, \qquad t = 1.364,$$
$$\text{(b)} \quad x = 16{,}000, \qquad t = 2.605,$$
$$\text{(c)} \quad x = 24{,}000, \qquad t = 3.675.$$

First we apply Method B to the first two sets of data points: (a) and (b). This, in fact, has been done above (*cf.* Table IV).

Secondly, apply Method B to the sets of data points (a) and (c).

Finally, apply Method B to the sets of data points (b) and (c).

Ex. 179: Do the numerical work outlined above and average the v_0's and a's from each pair to get the best v_0 and a.

Ex. 180: With these best values of v_0 and a, compute some points of Figure 105.

Lesson No. 41

LINEAR DISTRIBUTION OF VELOCITY—V.
THE WAVE-FRONTS

We return at this point to further mathematical considerations. The problem we now set before us is that of determining the form of the wave-fronts in a vertical section through a shot-point on the surface below which the medium is one in which the velocity increases linearly with depth.

We must first reconsider the results on pages 207 and 208 in the light of their physical significance for we have manipulated the equations formally without "watching our step" closely enough. In fact, a hint of possible difficulties was expressed in the second footnote on pages 207 and 208.

An examination of the processes involved will indicate that the integrals (12) and (13) on page 207 are meaningful and lead to correct results without difficulties if we restrict the upper limit of integration, namely, pv, to be numerically at most equal to unity:

$$| pv | \leq 1.$$

The physical significance of this restriction is that the formal results (16) and (17) are valid only so long as the wave is moving "downward" toward its greatest depth of penetration.

Let us examine this matter in another way.

We have seen that the wave paths are the circles through the shot-point O whose centers lie on the line $h = -v_o/a$. Consider a particular wave-path defined by a particular value of the parameter p. The wave-path will be at a depth h at two points if h is less than the maximum depth of penetration h_{max}. The first of these points, P_d, (see Figure 107) is encountered on its way downward, and the second, P_u, on its way upward to the surface. Consequently, the x-coordinate of a point on the wave path defined by the parameter p, expressed as a function of depth h, should be double-valued. For the same reasons, the *travel-time* from O to the depth h on this wave path should also be double-valued when expressed as a function of p, Accordingly, equations (18) and (19) on pages 207 and 208 must be altered to indicate these facts. Mathematically, it is a matter of allowing— and discussing—the proper option in signs of the roots implied in equations (14) and (15) on page 207.

In fact, let us start from these last equations which we rewrite (using, by the way, the results on page 217):

$$(1) \qquad x = -1/ap \left[(1 - S^2)^{1/2} \right]_{S = pv_o}^{S = p(v_o + ah)}$$

$$(2) \qquad t = -1/a \left[\cosh^{-1} (1/S) \right]_{S = pv_o}^{S = p(v_o + ah)*}.$$

* Note that an option in sign is implied here (*cf.* page 217).

233

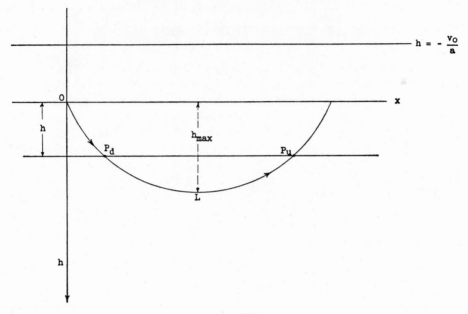

$$h = -\frac{v_0}{a}$$

FIG. 107

The results for the point P_d are straightforward, as we have noted:

(3) $x(P_d) = (1/ap)\left\{[1 - p^2v_o^2]^{1/2} - [1 - p^2(v_o + ah)^2]^{1/2}\right\},$

(4) $t(P_d) = (1/a)\left[\cosh^{-1}(1/pv_o) - \cosh^{-1}1/p(v_o + ah)\right].$

The results for the point of maximum penetration L, also, are straightforward as we have seen on pages 213 and 214 (see Figure 100), namely,

(5) $x(L) = (1/ap)(1 - p^2v_o^2)^{1/2},$

(6) $t(L) = (1/a)\cosh^{-1}1/pv_o.$

Note that these two expressions are the first terms of (3) and (4) respectively, since, for L, $p(v_0 + ah_{max}) = 1$.

From the symmetry of the path with respect to the vertical through L, both in geometry and in travel-time, for corresponding portions of the two-halves of the path, we note that the results for the point P_u are:

(7) $x(P_u) = (1/ap)\left\{[1 - p^2v_o^2]^{1/2} + [1 - p^2(v_o + ah)^2]^{1/2}\right\},$

(8) $t(P_u) = (1/a)\left[\cosh^{-1}1/pv_o + \cosh^{-1}1/p(v_o + ah)\right].$

For purposes of further development, then, we can now say that the equations for the wave-path defined by p and the travel-time connected therewith are:

(9) $x = (1/ap)\left\{[1 - p^2v_o^2]^{1/2} \mp [1 - p^2(v_0 + ah)^2]^{1/2}\right\}$

and

(10) $\qquad t = (1/a) \left[\cosh^{-1} (1/pv_o) \mp \cosh^{-1} 1/p(v_o + ah)\right],$

with the upper signs pertaining to the "first" half of the wave path and the lower to the second half.

Ex. 181: Show how the ambiguity in sign in (9) disappears when it is written as the equation of the circular wave path in the form of equation (20), page 208.

The next question we raise is this:

Given a point $\overline{P}:(\bar{x}, \bar{h})$ in our medium, what is the value of the parameter p defining the unique wave path joining O to $\overline{P}$?

Suppose we answer this question "synthetically" and leave the analytic attack as an exercise. In Figure 108, the midpoint Q of $O\overline{P}$ has the coordinates: $(\bar{x}/2, \bar{h}/2)$. The slope of $O\overline{P}$ is $\bar{h}/\bar{x}$. Accordingly, the slope of QC, the perpendicular bisector of $O\overline{P}$, is $-\bar{x}/\bar{h}$. The equation of QC is, therefore,

$$\bar{x}x + \bar{h}h - (\bar{x}^2 + \bar{h}^2)/2 = 0.$$

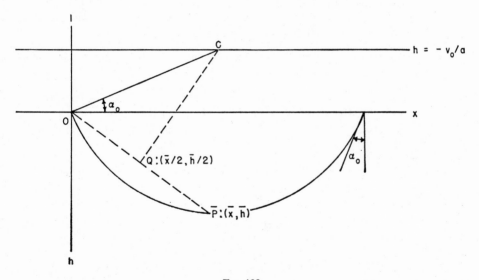

FIG. 108

The point C lies on this line and on $h = -v_0/a$. Accordingly, its x-coordinate is

$$x_C = (1/\bar{x}) \left[(\bar{x}^2 + \bar{h}^2)/2 + \bar{h}v_0/a\right],$$

and

$$h_C = -v_0/a.$$

The point C is the center of the wave path circle between O and $\overline{P}$. Its radius is

$$\overline{OC} = (x_C{}^2 + h_C{}^2)^{1/2} = \left\{ \left[(\bar{x}^2 + \bar{h}^2)/2\bar{x} + \bar{h}v_o/a\bar{x} \right]^2 + [v_o/a]^2 \right\}^{1/2},$$
$$= \left[a^2(\bar{x}^2 + \bar{h}^2)^2 + 4v_o(v_o + a\bar{h})(\bar{x}^2 + \bar{h}^2) \right]^{1/2}/2a\bar{x}.$$

We recall that

$$pv_o = \sin \alpha_0,$$

since α_0 is the angle of emergence, and note that

$$\sin \alpha_0 = (v_o/a)/\overline{OC}.$$

Accordingly,

$$pv_o = 2v_o\bar{x}/\left[a^2(\bar{x}^2 + \bar{h}^2)^2 + 4v_o(v_o + a\bar{h})(\bar{x}^2 + \bar{h}^2) \right]^{1/2}.$$

The bars over the coordinates having served their purpose, we may now state the results in this way:

The value of the parameter p corresponding to the wave path from O through the point $P:(x, h)$ is:

(11) $$p = 2x/\left[a^2(x^2 + h^2)^2 + 4v_o(v_o + ah)(x^2 + h^2) \right]^{1/2}.$$

(Only non-negative values of p are used since we restrict ourselves to the "right-hand" side of the vertical plane through O. Negative values of p yield the symmetrical situation in the left half of the plane.)

Ex. 182: Obtain this last result (11) from equation (9) by algebraic manipulation.

Now, to obtain the travel-time from O to $P:(x, h)$, we first find the value of p which defines the desired wave path, using (11), and then insert that value of p in (10). We proceed to do this analytically in a relatively simple, though indirect, manner. We shall then have the travel-time of a wave from O to $P:(x, h)$ expressed explicitly in terms of the coordinates of P.

Equation (10) is first to be rewritten:

(12)　$$\cosh at = \left\{ 1 \mp [1 - p^2v_0{}^2]^{1/2}[1 - p^2(v_0 + ah)^2]^{1/2} \right\}/p^2v_0(v_0 + ah)*.$$

This expression is then transformed into

(13)
$$\frac{\cosh at - 1}{} = [1 - p^2v_0(v_0 + ah) \mp \left\{ [1 - p^2v_0{}^2][1 - p^2(v_0 + ah)^2] \right\}^{1/2}]/p^2v_0(v_0 + ah).$$

On the other hand, Equation (9), by transposing and squaring, becomes

(14) $$a^2x^2 = [2 - p^2v_0{}^2 - p^2(v_0 + ah)^2 \mp 2\left\{ [1 - p^2v_0{}^2][1 - p^2(v_0 + ah)^2] \right\}^{1/2}]/p^2.$$

To both sides of this last result we add a^2h^2:

---

* This result is obtained by recalling that

$$\cosh (A \pm B) = \cosh A \cosh B \pm \sinh A \sinh B$$

and that

$$\cosh^2 A - \sinh^2 A = 1.$$

$$a^2(x^2 + h^2)$$

(15)
$$= [2 - p^2v_0^2 - p^2(v_0 + ah)^2 \mp 2\{[1 - p^2v_0^2][1 - p^2(v_0 + ah)^2]\}^{1/2} + p^2a^2h^2]/p^2,$$
$$= [2 - 2p^2v_0^2 - 2p^2v_0ah \mp 2\{[1 - p^2v_0^2][1 - p^2(v_0 + ah)^2]\}^{1/2}]/p^2,$$
$$= 2[1 - p^2v_0(v_0 + ah) \mp \{[1 - p^2v_0^2][1 - p^2(v_0 + ah)^2]\}^{1/2}]/p^2.$$

Reconciling (13) with (15) we note our result:

(16)
$$\cosh at - 1 = a^2(x^2 + h^2)/2v_0(v_0 + ah);$$

or, as it may also be written,

(17)
$$t = (1/a) \cosh^{-1}[1 + a^2(x^2 + h^2)/2v_0(v_0 + ah)].$$

Let us summarize the result: *The travel-time from the shot-point O to the point P: (x, h) in our medium is given by relation (17).*

The equations of the *wave fronts* are now immediately apparent. They are defined as being the loci of the points for which the travel-time is the same. Accordingly, in (17) if the travel-time t is assigned a specific value, T, this locus is obtained by setting $t = T$. By rearranging the terms, we have:

(18)
$$2v_o(v_o + ah)(\cosh aT - 1) = a^2(x^2 + h^2);$$

i.e.,

(19)
$$x^2 + [h - (v_0/a)(\cosh aT - 1)]^2 = (v_0^2/a^2)\sinh^2 aT.$$

Ex. 183: Derive this last expression (19) from (18).

Interpreting (19) geometrically: *The wave fronts are circles whose centers are along the h-axis at the points*

$$[0, (v_0/a)(\cosh aT - 1)]$$

and whose radii are

$$(v_0/a) \sinh aT,$$

where T is the travel-time corresponding to each wave front.

For mathematicians only:

Ex. 184: Obtain the differential equation defining the *wave-fronts*.

Ex. 185: Obtain the differential equation defining the *wave-paths*.

Ex. 186: Show that the wave-fronts and the wave-paths are mutually orthog‥onal.*

---

* A solution of this problem using elementary methods only is appended to this Lesson beginning with page 239.

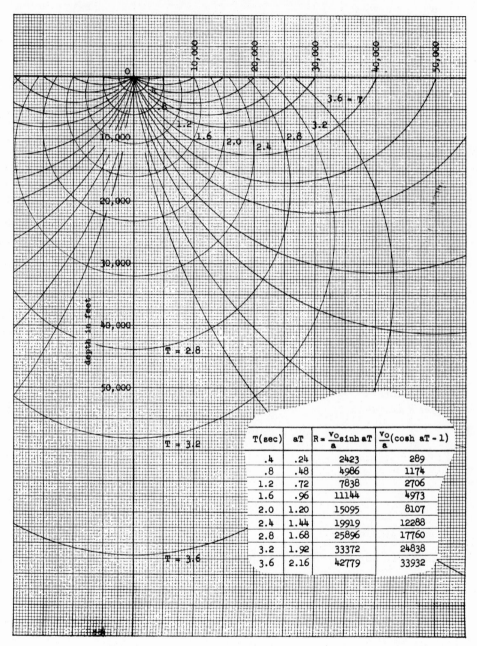

T(sec)	aT	$R = \frac{v_0}{a}\sinh aT$	$\frac{v_0}{a}(\cosh aT - 1)$
.4	.24	2423	289
.8	.48	4986	1174
1.2	.72	7838	2706
1.6	.96	11144	4973
2.0	1.20	15095	8107
2.4	1.44	19919	12288
2.8	1.68	25896	17760
3.2	1.92	33372	24838
3.6	2.16	42779	33932

Fɪɢ. 109

As the last exercise indicates, the wave path circles and the wave front circles cut each other at right angles. That is to say, through every point in a vertical section in our medium, the wave path circle and the wave front circle cut at right angles. Physically, of course, this might have been suspected.

In Figure 109 we indicate a few of the wave paths as shown in Figure 102 and some of the wave-fronts for which $T = 0.4, 0.8, \cdots, 3.6$. We recall that the curves are based on assuming

$$v_o = 6,000 \text{ ft} \quad \text{and} \quad a = 0.6.$$

Ex. 187: Draw a few of the wave-fronts for the case mentioned in Exercise 174.

APPENDIX

Here is an *elementary* solution to Exercise 186.

The slope of the wave front circle (19) is obtained by differentiating that expression, obtaining

(a) $$x + [h - (v_0/a)(\cosh aT - 1)]dh/dx = 0.$$

Accordingly, at the point (x_0, h_0) on the *wave front* for which the travel-time is T, the slope is

(b) $$dh/dx \big|_0 = - x_0/[h_0 - (v_0/a)(\cosh aT - 1)].$$

The *wave path* through this point has the equation

(c) $$(x - k)^2 + (h + v_o/a)^2 = k^2 + (v_o/a)^2,$$

for which k is such that

(d) $$(x_0 - k)^2 + (h_0 + v_o/a)^2 = k^2 + (v_o/a)^2.$$

This result follows simply from the fact that the wave path is the circle through O and (x_0, h_0) whose center is on the line $h = -v_o/a$.

The slope of the wave path circle (c), also, is obtained by differentiation:

$$(x - k) + (h + v_o/a)dh/dx = 0,$$

so that at (x_0, h_0), the slope is

(e) $$dh/dx \big|_0 = - (x_0 - k)/(h_0 + v_0/a).$$

To show that the two slopes (b) and (e) are mutually perpendicular at the point (x_0, h_0) we need only show their product to be -1.

Consider this product

(f) $$x_0(x_0 - k)/(h_0 + v_0/a)[h_0 - (v_0/a)(\cosh aT - 1)],$$

for which, of course, k is obtained from (d)

(g) $$k = (x_0^2 + h_0^2 + 2h_0v_0/a)/2x_0,$$

and also

(h) $x_0{}^2 + [h_0 - (v_0/a)(\cosh aT - 1)]^2 = (v_0{}^2/a^2)\sinh^2 aT,$

since (x_0, h_0) lies on both circles. Using (g) and (h) in (f) will render (f) equal to $-1, Q.E.D.$

Lesson No. 42

LINEAR DISTRIBUTION OF VELOCITY—VI.
WELL SHOOTING THEORY AND PRACTICE

As was mentioned on page 223, the "shooting" of a well, by which we mean a survey of the variation of seismic velocity with depth using the travel-times of seismic waves from the surface to a pickup at points down a bore hole, is an excellent means of determining whether our hypothesis of linear variation of velocity with depth may be used in the area. At the same time we determine what values of v_o and a are most suitable for that area.

Consider (Figure 110) a well into which a pickup is lowered. We shall consider the well-head W as being at a distance d from a shot-point O. The pickup P is at a variable depth h in the well. Assuming the linear distribution of velocity, $v = v_o + ah$, the travel-time of a seismic wave from O to the pickup P is then obtained by the relation (17) on page 237; namely,

(1) $$t = (1/a) \cosh^{-1} \left[1 + a^2(d^2 + h^2)/2v_0(v_0 + ah) \right].$$

We have replaced the coordinate x by d; and, as the pickup P varies in depth (h) in the well, the travel-time (t) of the wave from O to P will be represented by considering (1) as representing t as a function of h.

Ex. 188: If $d=0$, *i.e.*, if the shot-point is at the well-head, equation (1) becomes

$$t = (1/a) \log_e (1 + ah/v_o).$$

Show this by using the definition of cosh x (see page 217) in terms of the exponential and by direct integration from first considerations.

On the right side of Figure 110 we have a coordinate system with (h, t)-axes, on which we have sketched a typical time-depth curve represented by (1).

Starting from the well-head ($h=0$), the travel-time *decreases* for some distance down the hole. There will then be a point in the well to which the travel-time will be a minimum. To find this minimum time and the depth at which it occurs, we rewrite (1)

(2) $$\cosh at = 1 + a^2(d^2 + h^2)/2v_o(v_o + ah)$$

and evaluate dt/dh, the rate of change of t with h; *i.e.*,

$$(a \sinh at)dt/dh = (a^2/2v_o) \left[2h(v_o + ah) - a(d^2 + h^2) \right]/(v_o + ah)^2,$$

$$= (a^2/2v_o) \left[2hv_o + a(h^2 - d^2) \right]/(v_o + ah)^2.$$

The minimum travel-time will occur when

$$dt/dh = 0;$$

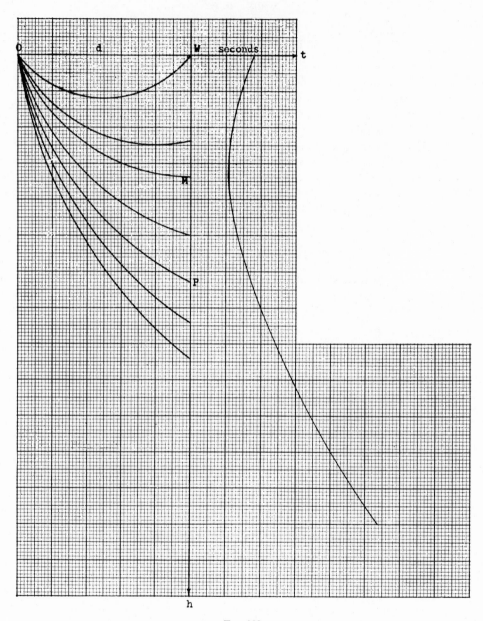

Fig. 110

i.e.,

$$ah^2 + 2hv_o - ad^2 = 0.$$

The solution for this is:

(3) $$h = [(v_0{}^2 + a^2d^2)^{1/2} - v_0]/a.$$

Ex. 189: Show that this is the depth at which the wave from O strikes the well at right angles. (In Figure 110, it is at the depth of M.) Above this point, then, the pickup will get a "kick" from below; and when the pickup is below this point it gets the "kick" from above. It will be the point of least response for a "vertically" mounted pickup.

We proceed to apply this result to the actual data of a well shot in the Texas Gulf Coast in 1938. Two shot-points, A and B, in line with the well and each one thousand feet from it, were used in the manner shown in Figure 111. The data so obtained are tabulated on the next page (Table I).

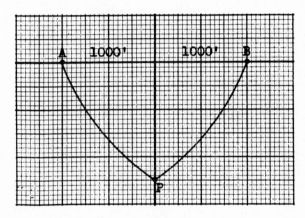

Fig. 111

The method of using two shot-points in line with the well and equally distant therefrom is an excellent one, and one which is at present in common use. In general, it is advisable to have the direction of the line of the two shot-points parallel to the strike of the subsurface beds. A record from each shot-point for each position of the pickup is obtained. Experience has shown that this seeming duplication of data by the use of two shot-points more than doubles their value. The choice of depths in the well for the pickup is governed by the local situation and by the amount of data considered desirable. Usually it is advisable to have the pickup at the various geologic markers in the well and at points suitably distributed between these markers.

On the accompanying graph (Figure 112), we have plotted the average of the travel-times to the pickup from each of the two shot-points against the depth of the pickup below the shot-points, these points being marked by x's.

The "smoothness" of the curve drawn through these points and its typical appearance suggest that the hypothesis of a linear increase of velocity with depth might be justifiable. This we proceed to investigate.

TABLE I

Depth of PU from rotary table (ft)	Depth of PU from surface (ft)	Depth of PU below shot-point h (ft)	Travel-time from shot-point A (scc)	Travel-time from shot-point B (sec)	Average of travel-times t (sec)
2,600	2,588	2,528	0.397	0.398	0.398
3,000	2,988	2,928	0.441	0.441	0.441
3,400	3,388	3,328	0.485	0.485	0.485
3,800	3,788	3,728	0.529	0.527	0.528
4,200	4,188	4,128	0.573	0.573	0.573
4,600	4,588	4,528	0.612	0.616	0.614
5,080	5,068	5,008	0.665	0.664	0.665
5,170	5,158	5,098	0.675	0.673	0.674
5,380	5,368	5,308	0.692	0.692	0.692
5,500	5,488	5,428	0.707	0.703	0.705
5,603	5,591	5,531	0.714	0.715	0.715
6,003	5,991	5,931	0.749	0.750	0.750
6,135	6,123	6,063	0.761	0.763	0.762
6,270	6,258	6,198	0.775	0.775	0.775
6,388	6,376	6,316	0.784	0.784	0.784
6,698	6,686	6,626	0.813	—	0.813
6,869	6,857	6,797	0.829	0.828	0.829
7,025	7,013	6,953	—	0.841	0.841
7,065	7,053	6,993	0.846	0.844	0.845
7,308	7,296	7,236	0.869	0.869	0.869
7,491	7,479	7,419	0.884	0.883	0.884

Let us assume, in fact, that the velocity v at a depth h is given by $v = v_0 + ah$. If this assumption is valid, the travel-time t from the shot-point to the pickup at depth h is given by the relation (1) above, which we now write in the form

$$(4) \qquad \cosh at = 1 + a^2(d^2 + h^2)/2v_o(v_o + ah).$$

Our problem is to discover suitable values for v_0 and a, if they exist, to fit the data. Since we have two unknowns, v_0 and a, we must have two equations of the form above in which the values of the other terms are obtained from the data. Actually, we use three (or more, if desirable) equations of this type in the manner to be outlined and for reasons that will become apparent.

After examining the points of the curve of Figure 112 from the point of view of "smoothness," we choose the following sets from the data to obtain our equations:

$$1.\ d = 1,000, \qquad h = 3,328, \qquad t = 0.485,$$

$$2.\ d = 1,000, \qquad h = 4,528, \qquad t = 0.614,$$

$$3.\ d = 1,000, \qquad h = 6,626, \qquad t = 0.813.$$

For purposes of computation we solve the preceding equation for v_o:

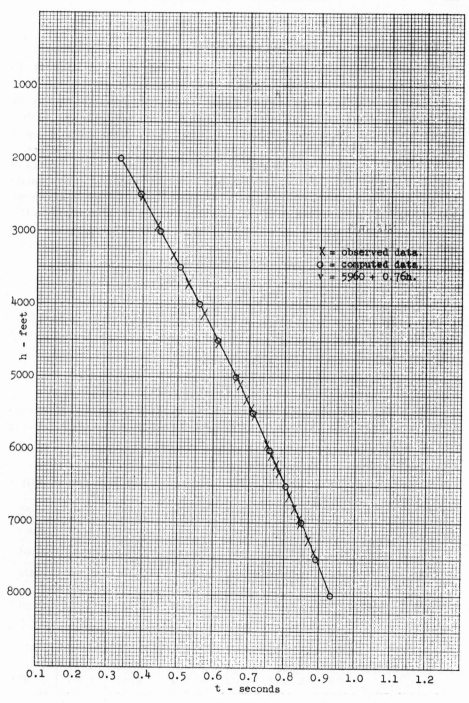

FIG. 112

(5) $\qquad v_0 = (ah/2)\,[\{1 + 2\,[(d/h)^2 + 1]/(\cosh at - 1)\}^{1/2} - 1].$

Ex. 190: Obtain this result from equation (1).

We then arrange our computation in tabular form shown in Table II. In column I are the observed data being used. In column II, arbitrary values for a are chosen covering the range in which its final computed value will probably lie. In column III these values are multiplied by $h/2$ to give $ah/2$. Column IV is a listing of the values of a multiplied by t, the time, and column V is a listing of the values of $\cosh at - 1$, which are obtained from a table of *hyperbolic* cosines.

Column VI contains the quotients of $2\,[(d/h)^2 + 1]$ divided by the values of $\cosh at - 1$ listed in the preceding column, to which 1 has been added. The square roots of these terms, reduced by 1, form column VII, and the terms in column VII multiplied by the values of $ah/2$ as found in column III give column VIII, the values of v_0 corresponding, by virtue of the set of data chosen, to the corresponding values of a.

To summarize this arrangement in another form:

Column	Values
I	Data
II	a
III	$ah/2$
IV	at
V	$\cosh at - 1$
VI	$\{2[(d/h)^2+1]/(\cosh at-1)\}+1$
VII	$\{2[(d/h)^2+1]/(\cosh at-1)+1\}^{1/2}-1$
VIII	$v_0=(ah/2)[\{2[(d/h)^2+1]/(\cosh at-1)+1\}^{1/2}-1]$

In this way, for each set of data chosen, we find how v_0 varies with the corresponding values of a. That is to say, each set of data gives us a curve showing

TABLE II

I	II	III $\times 10^3$	IV	V	VI	VII	VIII
$d=1.000\times10^3$	0.5	0.8320	0.2425	0.02955	74.794	7.648	6,365
$h=3.328\times10^3$	0.6	0.9984	0.2910	0.04264	52.140	6.221	6,210
$t=0.4850$	0.7	1.1648	0.3395	0.05818	38.480	5.203	6,060
$2[(d/h)^2+1]=2.1806$	0.8	1.3312	0.3880	0.07622	29.609	4.442	5,915
	0.9	1.4976	0.4365	0.09678	23.532	3.851	5,765
$d=1.000\times10^3$	0.5	1.1320	0.3070	0.04750	45.156	5.720	6,475
$h=4.528\times10^3$	0.6	1.3584	0.3684	0.06863	31.561	4.618	6,270
$t=0.6140$	0.7	1.5848	0.4298	0.09379	23.363	3.834	6,075
$2[(d/h)^2+1]=2.0974$	0.8	1.8112	0.4912	0.12308	18.041	3.248	5,880
	0.9	2.0376	0.5526	0.15661	14.393	2.794	5,690
$d=1.000\times10^3$	0.5	1.6565	0.4065	0.08377	25.419	4.042	6,695
$h=6.626\times10^3$	0.6	1.9878	0.4878	0.12135	17.857	3.226	6,410
$t=0.8130$	0.7	2.3191	0.5691	0.16636	13.296	2.646	6,135
$2[(d/h)^2+1]=2.0456$	0.8	2.6504	0.6504	0.21907	10.338	2.214	5,870
	0.9	2.9817	0.7317	0.27984	8.310	1.883	5,615

v_o as a function of a. The three curves corresponding to the three sets of data chosen are shown in Figure 113. If the observed data were perfectly suited to our hypothesis, these three curves would, of course, all pass through a common point, the coordinates of which would be the desired values of v_o and of a. In practice this rarely happens. Instead, we get three points of intersection; namely, those of each curve with the other two.

If these three points are reasonably close together, we feel certain that the linear hypothesis is justifiable, and the closeness of these three points to one another serves in some degree as a measure of the accuracy of subsequent work based on this hypothesis. It usually is the best procedure to use for v_o and a the arithmetic mean of the three pairs of values at the three intersections.

On Figure 113 we find that the three intersections for the three sets of data yield the following pairs of values for v_o and a respectively:

$$(5,910, 0.785), \quad (5,970, 0.763), \quad (6,015, 0.731).$$

The averages of these three pairs, to the accuracy we need are, therefore, $v_o = 5,960$ ft/sec and $a = 0.76$.

Accordingly, it seems highly possible that the hypothesis that $v = 5,960 + 0.76h$ is a good one. We proceed, therefore, to compute what the travel-times for our well would be if this were the actual velocity distribution.

Again we use the first formula above, in which, however, v_0 and a are assigned the values determined, d is again taken as 1,000 ft, and h is assigned values corresponding to various depths of the pickup as shown in the following tabulated form (Table III). In this computation we use the same equation in the form

$$t = (1/a) \cosh^{-1} \left[1 + a^2(d^2 + h^2)/2v_0(v_0 + ah) \right]$$

in which, then, $a = 0.76$, $v_o = 5.960$ ft/sec, $d = 1,000$, and h has the values 2,000, 2,500, $\cdots$, 7,500, 8,000.

In the table we have listed in column I the various values of h we are to use, column II contains the values of h^2, and in column III we have the values of $(d^2 + h^2)$ in which $d^2 = 1.000 \cdot 10^6$ since $d = 1000$ ft. Column IV has the values $a^2(d^2 + h^2)$ in which $a^2 = 0.5776$ since $a = 0.76$. Column V lists the values of ah for

TABLE III

I	II	III	IV	V	VI	VII	VIII	IX	X
2.0×10^3	4.00×10^6	5.00×10^6	2.888×10^6	1.520×10^3	7.480×10^3	89.16×10^6	1.0324	0.254	0.334
2.5	6.25	7.25	4.188	1.900	7.860	93.69	1.0447	0.298	0.392
3.0	9.00	10.00	5.776	2.280	8.240	98.22	1.0588	0.341	0.448
3.5	12.25	13.25	7.653	2.660	8.620	102.75	1.0745	0.384	0.505
4.0	16.00	17.00	9.819	3.040	9.000	107.28	1.0915	0.425	0.559
4.5	20.25	21.25	12.274	3.420	9.380	111.81	1.1098	0.465	0.611
5.0	25.00	26.00	15.018	3.800	9.760	116.34	1.1291	0.503	0.661
5.5	30.25	31.25	18.050	4.180	10.140	120.87	1.1493	0.540	0.710
6.0	36.00	37.00	21.371	4.560	10.520	125.40	1.1704	0.576	0.757
6.5	42.25	43.25	24.981	4.940	10.900	129.93	1.1923	0.611	0.803
7.0	49.00	50.00	28.880	5.320	11.280	134.46	1.2148	0.644	0.847
7.5	56.25	57.25	33.068	5.700	11.660	138.99	1.2379	0.677	0.890
8.0	64.00	65.00	37.544	6.080	12.040	143.52	1.2615	0.708	0.931

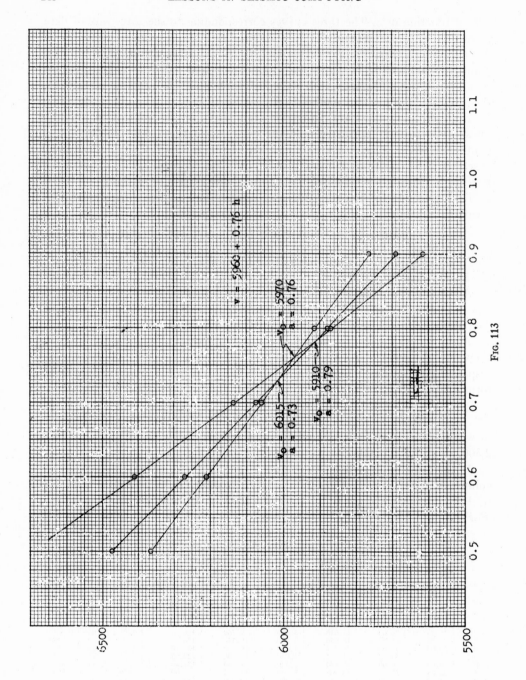

FIG. 113

this value of a and corresponding values of h. To these values of column V we add $v_o = 5.960 \cdot 10^3$ to obtain $v_0 + ah$ in column VI. To obtain the values in column VII we multiply those of VI by $2v_0 = 11.92 \cdot 10^3$, thus giving us the values $2v_0(v_0 + ah)$. We now divide the values in IV by those in VII and add 1.0 to the result so that column VIII contains the values of

$$1 + a^2(d^2 + h^2)/2v_o(v_o + ah).$$

From the tables of the *hyperbolic* cosines we determine the values of the

$$\cosh^{-1}\left[1 + a^2(d^2 + h^2)/2v_o(v_o + ah)\right]$$

which are listed in column IX. These values are finally multiplied by $1/a = 1/0.76 = 1.316$ to obtain the values of t in column X.

Column	Values
I	h
II	h^2
III	$(d^2 + h^2)$
IV	$a^2(d^2 + h^2)$
V	ah
VI	$v_o + ah$
VII	$2v_o(v_o + ah)$
VIII	$1 + a^2(d^2 + h^2)/2v_o(v_o + ah)$
IX	$\cosh^{-1}\left[1 + a^2(d^2 + h^2)/2v_o(v_o + ah)\right]$
X	$t = (1/a)\cosh^{-1}\left[1 + a^2(d^2 + h^2)/2v_0(v_0 + ah)\right]$

The values of t so obtained for the various values of h are plotted as small circles in Figure 112 and the degree of "fit" of the observed data with the corresponding computed values based on our hypothesis can then be visually noted. In this particular case, it is apparent that our law of $v = 5,960 + 0.76h$ forms an excellent basis for further use.

Ex. 191: Using three other sets of data, suitably spaced, from Table I, determine v_o and a in a similar method and compare the results with those obtained above.

Lesson No. 43

LINEAR DISTRIBUTION OF VELOCITY—VII. THE REFLECTION PROBLEM

To apply the results of the several preceding Lessons to the reflection problem is now a relatively simple matter.

As a first step, let the medium (in which the velocity is of the form $v = v_o + ah$) be bounded above by the horizontal plane of the surface of the earth and below, at depth H, by the parallel plane interface $h = H$.

On the upper side of this interface, the velocity is

$$v_o + aH;$$

we shall assume that below this interface the velocity is V, and that, at least for the present,

$$v_o + aH < V.$$

That is to say, the velocity in the lower medium is assumed constant and greater than the value of the velocity in the upper medium at the interface.

The interface is now considered to be a reflecting horizon. In a plane vertical section through the shot-point O, we draw, as usual, the x-axis along the surface

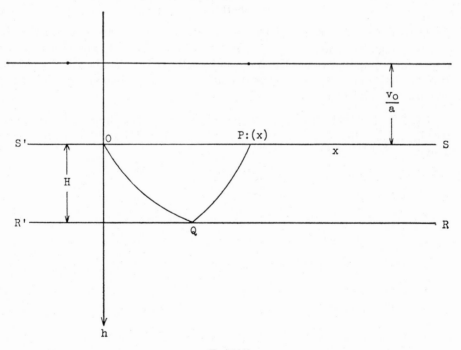

FIG. 114

250

$S'S$ of the ground and vertically, through O, we construct an h-axis. In this vertical plane, the trace of the reflecting interface, $R'R$, is the horizontal straight line whose equation is

$$h = H.$$

The reflected wave path from O to the point P on $S'S$ at distance x from O will consist of the two parts OQ and QP, which are arcs of circles with centers on the line $h = -v_0/a$.

The reflecting point Q is that point on $R'R$ for which the travel-time along OQ and QP is a minimum. It is usually assumed without proof, that Q is the point with coordinates $(x/2, H)$, which, in fact, is quite true. Nonetheless, the statement needs proof. We leave the proof, however, to those who are mathematically curious, as an exercise.

Ex. 192: Show that of all the travel-times for paths OQP, reflected at depth H, the minimum is that for which Q is at $(x/2, H)$. The two parts OQ and QP are then symmetrically situated with respect to the vertical line midway between O and P; each part corresponds to one-half the total travel-time of the reflected path, and the angle of incidence at Q is equal to the angle of reflection.

The situation is sketched in Figure 115. This exercise can be solved by direct analysis or by ingenious arguments, which we leave to the readers who might be interested. We repeat that the result is not one that can be assumed without proof. [If the method of proof chosen is analytical, equation (17) of page 237 should be invoked.]

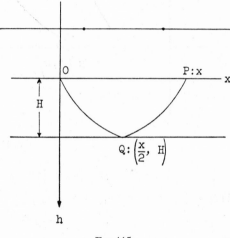

Fɪɢ 115

The next step is to find the equation of the *time-distance* curve for the reflected waves.

The travel-time from O to P along OQP can be obtained in two different ways which we proceed to discuss:

Going back to fundamentals, we note that, if P is on the surface at a distance x from O and if the travel-time of the reflected wave to it is t, then the reflecting point Q is at distance $x/2$ from the vertical through O and the travel-time from O to Q is $t/2$.

If, then, the parameter defining the reflected wave arriving at P has the value p, we may then write, using equation (16) and (17) of page 207:

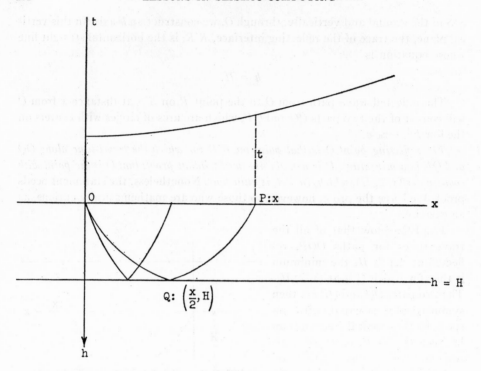

FIG. 116

$$x = (2/ap) \left\{ [1 - p^2 v_o{}^2]^{1/2} - [1 - p^2(v_o + aH)^2]^{1/2} \right\},$$

(1) $\quad t = (2/a) \log \left[\left\{ 1 + [1 - p^2 v_o{}^2]^{1/2} \right\} \right.$

$$\left. p(v_0 + aH) / \left\{ 1 + [1 - p^2(v_0 + aH)^2]^{1/2} \right\} p v_0 \right].$$

These two, then, define the *time-distance* curve parametrically.

Ex. 193: Show, from above, that

$$dt/dx = p,$$

and explain the significance of this result.

From the preceding, we can now eliminate the parameter p. We should then arrive at the equation of the desired reflection *time-distance* curve in a preferable form. The result of this elimination, it will become evident, is the same as replacing t and x in equation (17) of page 237 respectively by $t/2$ and $x/2$. We will then have

(2) $\qquad t = (2/a) \cosh^{-1} [1 + a^2(x^2 + 4H^2)/8v_o(v_o + aH)],$

or, perhaps, better,

(3) $\qquad \cosh (at/2) = [(ax/2v_0)^2 + 1 + (1 + aH/v_0)^2/2(1 + aH/v_0).$

At this stage it may be of some interest to consider the seismic "events" which are expected from the medium we are describing.

In Figure 117* the curve R represents the *time-distance* curve of the reflections from the interface $R'R$ above which it is assumed that $v=v_0+ah$ and below which the velocity is constant, V. We also assume that $V>v_0+aH$, where the depth of $R'R$ is H. The curve D represents the *time-distance* curve of the direct wave, which is valid until the (pickup) point corresponding to the depth of penetration, H, (for the direct wave) is reached, when it must clearly merge into the curve R, and beyond this point both curves cease to exist. The line L, represents the *time-distance* curve of the wave refracted along $R'R$. This obviously must be the extension of the tangent line to R, beyond the curve D, whose slope is $1/V$ [corresponding to the wave striking $R'R$ at the critical angle $\alpha=\sin^{-1}\left(\overline{v_0+aH}/V\right)$.]

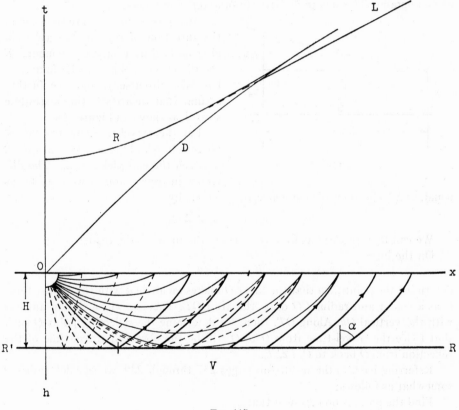

Fig. 117

* This figure and the following paragraph we paraphrased from a paper appearing in *Geophysics*, Volume I, Number 1, January, 1936, page 13.

The waves whose travel-times are represented by D are shown in solid paths. The waves which are reflected and correspond to the curve R are shown in dotted paths. The refracted waves corresponding to L are shown in heavy paths.

In actual practice, the use of the linear increase of velocity with depth is widespread and varies in the routine applications. Usually the custom is to reduce reflection travel-times to charts or nomograms, or the equivalent. For the present we shall not go into applicable numerical methods which may be used, since the reader can supply his own if he understands what we have discussed. In any case he has probably been equipped with such tables or "curves" in profusion, if his duties demand that he use the velocity information available to convert travel-times to depths.

There is one point, on this score, that ought to be mentioned in a little more detail since it is the basis of a number of different types of slide rules or charts or nomograms. This has to do with dipping reflecting beds.

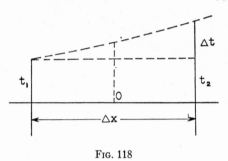

FIG. 118

Again we assume we are shooting in the direction of dip (a "4-way" will give us two necessary components, if the direction of dip is to be found, as has been discussed); and, we further assume that we are shooting a straddle spread, as shown in Figure 118.

Let the travel-times to the "end" pickups be t_1 and t_2, and the total spread between the end pickups, Δx. The difference in time t_1 and t_2, we refer to, as usual, as Δt. The angle of emergence, α, is defined by

$$\sin \alpha = v_o(\Delta t/\Delta x).$$

We can then proceed as follows (leaving the proof to the reader):
On the line

$$h = -v_o/a$$

determine the point C so that the line CO makes an angle α with the x-axis. With C as a center and radius CO draw the arc OQT. This arc will make an angle α with the vertical Oh. Along OT, then, we determine the reflecting point Q such that twice the travel-time from O to Q will be the observed travel-time of the reflection from O back to O, i.e., t_o.

Referring back to the results on pages 237 through 239, we can determine Q somewhat as follows:
Find the point S on Oh, such that

$$OS = (v_o/a)\left[\cosh(at_o/2) - 1\right].$$

With S as a center and radius

$$r = (v_o/a)\sinh(at_o/2)$$

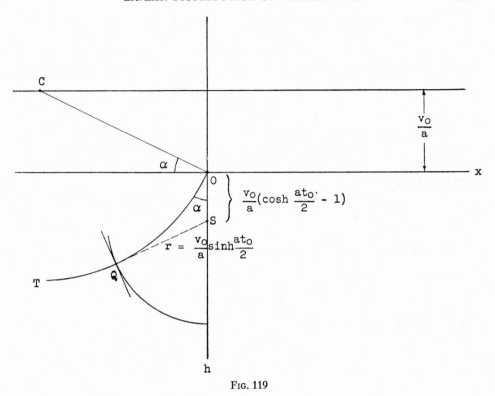

$$\frac{v_0}{a}\left(\cosh \frac{at_0}{2} - 1\right)$$

$$r = \frac{v_0}{a}\sinh\frac{at_0}{2}$$

Fɪɢ. 119

draw an arc of a circle, which determines Q as its intersection with OT.

The tangent line to this circle, at Q, is the desired dip information.

The proofs of all these statements are not difficult, since they all depend on the mathematical considerations already developed.

It should, in fact, be apparent that dip charts can readily be made with parametric curves involving the two essential parameters: travel-time t and the Δt. Such dip charts will be very similar to Figure 109 on page 238.

APPENDIX TO LESSON NO. 43

OUTLINE OF DIRECT ANALYTIC PROOF OF EXERCISE 192

In Figure 114, using equation (17) of page 237; and assigning the coordinates (X, H) to Q, the travel-time for OQ is

$$t_{OQ} = (1/a) \cosh^{-1}[1 + a^2(X^2 + H^2)/2v_0(v_0 + aH)].$$

The travel-time for QP, similarly, is

$$t_{QP} = (1/a) \cosh^{-1} [1 + a^2[(x - X)^2 + H^2]/2v_0(v_0 + aH)],$$

in which x is the coordinate of P.

Thus the total travel-time for OQP is

$$t = t_{OQ} + t_{QP},$$

and to get the value of X for which t is a minimum, one need only find its value when

$$dt/dX = 0.$$

We might suggest that the manipulation will be easier if, first the vertical axis be moved at distance $x/2$ towards P. In that way, advantages of "symmetry" may be gained. If, now, Q is taken at a distance, say u, from this new vertical axis, we write

$$t_{OQ} = (1/a) \cosh^{-1} \left[1 + a^2[(x/2 + u)^2 + H^2]/2v_o(v_o + aH)\right]$$

and

$$t_{QP} = (1/a) \cosh^{-1} \left[1 + a^2[(x/2 - u)^2 + H^2]/2v_o(v_o + aH)\right].$$

It will follow that

$$t = t_{OQ} + t_{QP}$$

is a minimum for $u=0$, Q.E.D.

THE RELATION BETWEEN OFFSET AND Δ*t* IN
REFLECTION SHOOTING

The term "offset" in reflection shooting technique is defined as the distance between the shot-point O and the line L of the pick ups. In Figure I, the offset is the distance

$$\overline{OP} = a,$$

the point $\overline{P}$ being the foot of the perpendicular from O to L. For ordinary "profile" shooting, L passes through O, and thus ordinary profile shooting may be considered as a special case for which the offset is zero.

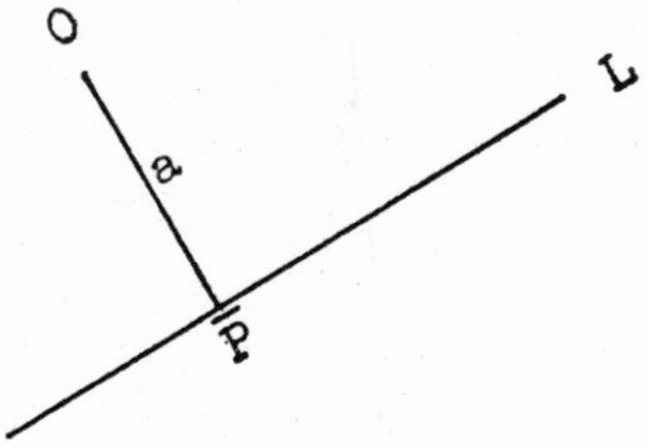

As one might expect, the pickups along L are usually spaced symmetrically with respect to $\overline{P}$. Designating the end pickups by P_1 and P_2, and the half-spread by s, (Figure II),

$$P_1\overline{P} = \overline{P}P_2 = s.$$

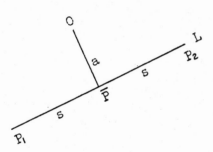

Fig. I

Let us assume a medium in which the seismic velocity v is constant and which is bounded above by the horizontal plane of the earth and below by a dipping plane, p. Consider the waves originating at O and reflected by the dipping plane. Let P be a typical pickup position on L whose distance from $\overline{P}$, the center of the spread, is x. The travel-times of the reflected wave to P, P_1, and P_2 will be indicated by t, t_1, and t_2 respectively.

Fig. II

As is customary we define

$$\Delta t = \left| t_1 - t_2 \right|$$

and

$$\Delta x = \overline{P_1P_2} = 2s.$$

It is our problem to study the relations existing between $\Delta t/\Delta x$ and the offset a. For purposes of analysis, we first set up a convenient coordinate system.

With the shot-point O for an origin, the x-axis is chosen as the line through O parallel to the line L of pickups. The line $\overline{OP}$ will then be the y-axis. The orientation of these axes is as shown in Figure III. The vertical through O, oriented positively downward, is the z-axis.

In the general case, the dipping reflecting plane p is disposed randomly, so to speak, with respect to O and L.

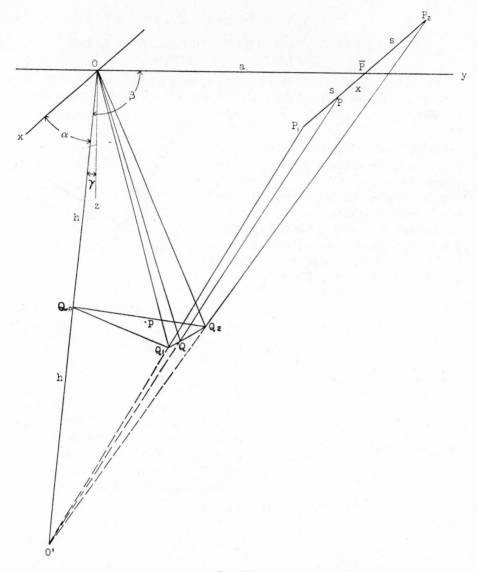

Fɪɢ. III

Let O' be the image point of O with respect to the dipping plane p. This means, it will be recalled, that the line OO' is perpendicular to and pierces the dipping plane p at a point Q_o midway between O add O'. In fact, we write

$$OQ_o = Q_oO' = h,$$

and

$$OO' = 2h,$$

where h is the distance from the shot-point O perpendicular to the dipping plane p.

The plane p must be characterized by the direction and amount of dip in addition to the value of h. For mathematical purposes, as we shall see, this is best done by specifying the (direction) angles α, β and γ which $\overrightarrow{OO'}$, the normal to p, makes with the x-, y-, and z-axes, respectively.

The coordinates of the point Q_o are

$$(h \cos \alpha,\ h \cos \beta,\ h \cos \gamma).$$

These coordinates, in fact, are the projections of OQ_0 on the three coordinate axes; and if, with these projections as sides, we construct a rectangular parallelepiped, $\overline{OQ}_0$ will be its main diagonal. Thus, by the Pythagorean theorem:

$$(h \cos \alpha)^2 + (h \cos \beta)^2 + (h \cos \gamma)^2 = \overline{OQ}_o{}^2 = h^2,$$

from which follows the fundamental relation between the direction angles,

$$\cos^2 \alpha + \cos^2 \beta + \cos^2 \gamma = 1.$$

The coordinates of the image point O' are

$$O':\ (2h \cos \alpha,\ 2h \cos \beta,\ 2h \cos \gamma).$$

The typical point P on the line of pickups L at a distance x from $\overline{P}$ has as its coordinates

$$P:\ (x,\ a,\ 0).$$

Now, as we have seen, the length of the reflected path $\overline{OQP}$ is that of $\overline{O'QP}$, and is equal to vt. Accordingly,

$$v^2t^2 = (x - 2h \cos \alpha)^2 + (a - 2h \cos \beta)^2 + (0 - 2h \cos \gamma)^2,$$
$$= x^2 + a^2 - 4hx \cos \alpha - 4ha \cos \beta + 4h^2(\cos^2 \alpha + \cos^2 \beta + \cos^2 \gamma);$$

i.e.,

$$v^2t^2 = x^2 + a^2 + 4h^2 - 4hx \cos \alpha - 4ha \cos \beta.$$

This last equation, then, is the *time-distance* curve for the reflection along the line of pickups L.

By differentiation,

$$v^2t\,dt/dx = x - 2h \cos \alpha;$$

i.e.,

$$dt/dx = (x - 2h \cos \alpha)/v^2t.$$

As we have stated, we are interested in $\Delta t/\Delta x$ along L, which we approximate by the value of the derivative dt/dx at the midpoint $\overline{P}$ of the spread, where $x=0$. At $\overline{P}$, too, the travel-time t will be that for which $x=0$:

$$v^2 t^2 = a^2 + 4h^2 - 4ha \cos \beta;$$

i.e.,

$$t = (a^2 + 4h^2 - 4ha \cos \beta)^{1/2}/v.$$

Accordingly, we write, for our line L,

$$\Delta t/\Delta x = -2h \cos \alpha/v(a^2 + 4h^2 - 4ha \cos \beta).^{1/2}$$

Let us now discuss the practical implications of this result.

CASE I. *THE REFLECTING PLANE p IS HORIZONTAL*

This means that the normal OO' to the reflecting plane p is the z-axis. Accordingly,

$$\alpha = \beta = 90°, \qquad \gamma = 0°;$$

i.e.,

$$\cos \alpha = \cos \beta = 0, \qquad \cos \gamma = 1.$$

For this case, then,

$$\Delta t/\Delta x \equiv 0,$$

a result which, of course, is obvious since it says that the travel-times of the reflections to P_1 and P_2 are equal, regardless of the amount of offset a.

CASE II: *THE DIRECTION OF STRIKE OF THE REFLECTING PLANE p IS THAT OF THE X-AXIS*

This means that $\overline{OO'}$ is perpendicular to the x-axis; *i.e.,* $\alpha=90°$. The angle of dip is then γ and

$$\beta = 90° - \gamma.$$

Accordingly,

$$\cos \alpha = 0,$$

and, again,

$$\Delta t/\Delta x = 0,$$

regardless of the amount of offset a.

This, again, is an obvious result.

It indicates the further obvious conclusion that if

$$\Delta t/\Delta x = 0$$

one can conclude only that either p is horizontal or dipping in a direction at right angles to P_1P_2.

CASE III: *THE DIRECTION OF STRIKE OF THE REFLECTING PLANE P IS THE Y-AXIS*

In this case,

$$\beta = 90°, \qquad \cos \beta = 0,$$

the angle of dip is γ, and

$$\alpha = 90° - \gamma, \qquad \cos \alpha = \sin \gamma.$$

In this case

$$\Delta t/\Delta x = - 2h \sin \gamma/v(a^2 + 4h^2)^{1/2}.$$

We see, now, that in this case $\Delta t/\Delta x$ drops off to zero inversely with a, beginning with a value of $-\sin \gamma/v$ for $a=0$. It is to be noted that $\Delta t/\Delta x$ attains *half* this initial value at an offset distance of

$$a = 2(3)^{1/2}h,$$

$$\cong 3.5h.$$

For an offset a equal to h, $\Delta t/\Delta x$ drops only to about 90 per cent of its value for $a=0$.

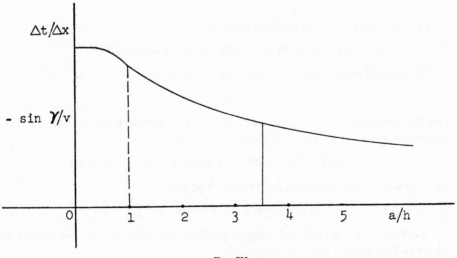

Fɪɢ. IV

The initial value of $\Delta t/\Delta x$, that is, its value for zero offset, depends only on the dip (γ) and velocity (v). However, its rate of decrease with increasing offset (a) diminishes with the increasing depth (h) to the reflecting bed.

CASE IV: *THE GENERAL CASE*

The angle of dip of the reflecting plane is, in this case also, equal to γ. It can be shown that the strike of the dipping plane is parallel to the line λ of Figure V where

$$\tan \theta = - \cos \alpha / \cos \beta.$$

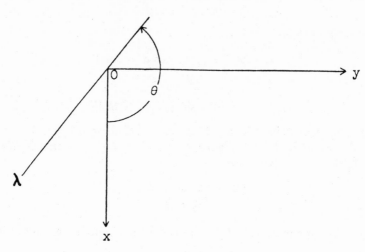

Fɪɢ. V

In this general case, as we have seen,

$$\Delta t / \Delta x = - 2h \cos \alpha / v (a^2 + 4h^2 - 4ha \cos \beta)^{1/2}.$$

For zero offset $(a=0)$, the value of $\Delta t / \Delta x$ is seen to be

$$- \cos \alpha / v$$

and this drops off, with increasing offset a, asymptotically to zero. It attains half its value for zero offset for the value of a determined by

$$-2h \cos \alpha / v (a^2 + 4h^2 - 4ha \cos \beta)^{1/2} = - \cos \alpha / 2v;$$

i.e., when the offset distance, in terms of h and β, is

$$a = 2h [\cos \beta + (3 + \cos^2 \beta)^{1/2}].$$

We have thus established simple relationships with which the values of $\Delta t / \Delta x$ to be expected may be computed.

To the Readers of the Lessons:

In the proof reading of this last Lesson (No. 43) it was suggested that a direct analytic proof of Exercise 192 would tend to round out the completeness of the developments in the Lesson. Accordingly, I am appending an outline of such a proof herewith and I leave it to the reader to fill in the details.

At the same time I should like to take this opportunity to say a few words which perhaps have long been overdue. In the first place, for well over a year, the publication of these Lessons has been placed in the capable hands of Miss Betty Stone. The physical appearance of the Lessons attests to her ability. For her good-natured patience with the many preliminary drafts, the necessary rewriting and other onerous chores, I am truly grateful. She and Mr. H. W. Merritt formed an excellent proofreading team, with the latter always willing to wade through and check mathematical manipulations and grammatical constructions. For such errors as still persist in spite of this, whether of omission or commission, I alone am responsible; and there are spots in the Lessons where this responsibility rests heavily upon me. Perhaps in a future edition some of these more glaring errors will be rectified.

It is also now opportune to restate the purpose of the Lessons since misunderstandings have arisen. The purpose of the Lessons has been to furnish the seismic computer with a broad understanding of seismic paths, the properties of which form the basis of most of the necessary numerical calculations. Important as it is to be able to read seismic records, to pick reflections, to pick first kicks, to separate unwanted events from the rest of the seismic data, these Lessons were based on the assumption that the data had already been cleansed of all their "impurities" and were ready to be dealt with. Consequently, very little, if anything, has been said about the numerous gadgets and other paraphernalia which help in the routine chores.

It is to be firmly hoped that in the future others may want to go on and write detailed considerations of the important problems of the computer in studying seismic events. The more recent work tending to develop mechanical "seismic-record reading" is gaining a great deal of interest, and the necessary developments may be hastened by a good series of lessons of this sort.

With this Lesson, I am bringing the series to a close, at least temporarily. If other topics in the general development should suggest themselves from time to time, I shall be only too happy to put them into the form of additional Lessons and distribute them to the list which we are retaining (and which, by the way, consists of about 320 names). There may, in fact, be ideas that the various readers have in mind for such topics, and I shall be glad to consider them.

Meanwhile, I am toying with the idea of writing a series of perhaps ten short chapters or so on the Elementary Concepts of the Gravity Method in Exploration for Oil,* written in somewhat the same style as used in these Lessons. Is there a need for such a series? Please let me know your desires.

* Editor's Note: Unfortunately, this series although begun was never completed.

I hope that all these Lessons have been of some use; in particular, I am grateful to the many readers who have from time to time sent in corrections, suggestions, and criticisms. I hope that these do not cease.

Yours very truly,

M. M. SLOTNICK

ALPHABETICAL INDEX